The Project Physics Course

Reader

UNIT **3** The Triumph of Mechanics

A Component of the
Project Physics Course

Published by
HOLT, RINEHART and WINSTON, Inc.
New York, Toronto

This publication is one of the many instructional materials developed for the Project Physics Course. These materials include Texts, Handbooks, Teacher Resource Books, Readers, Programmed Instruction Booklets, Film Loops, Transparencies, 16mm films and laboratory equipment. Development of the course has profited from the help of many colleagues listed in the text units.

Directors of Harvard Project Physics

Gerald Holton, Department of Physics, Harvard University

F. James Rutherford, Chairman of the Department of Science Education, New York University, New York

Fletcher G. Watson, Harvard Graduate School of Education

Picture Credits

Cover picture: "Deluge." Drawing by Leonardo da Vinci. Royal Collection, Windsor Castle.

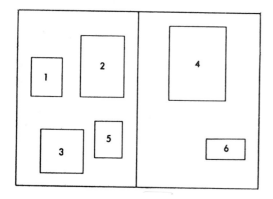

Double-page spread on following pages:
(1) Photo by Glen J. Pearcy.
(2) *Jeune fille au corsage rouge lisant* by Jean Baptiste Camille Corot. Painting. Collection Bührle, Zurich.
(3) Harvard Project Physics staff photo.
(4) *Femme lisant* by Georges Seurat. Conté crayon drawing. Collection C. F. Stoop, London.

(5) *Portrait of Pierre Reverdy* by Pablo Picasso. Etching. Museum of Modern Art, N.Y.C.
(6) *Lecture au lit* by Paul Klee. Drawing. Paul Klee Foundation, Museum of Fine Arts, Berne.

Sources and Acknowledgments
Project Physics Reader 3

1. *Silence, Please* from *Tales From the White Hart* by Arthur C. Clarke. Reprinted with permission of the author and his agents Scott Meredith Literary Agency, and David Higham Associates, Ltd.
2. *The Steam Engine Comes of Age* from *A History of Science and Technology* by R. J. Forbes and E. Dijksterhuis, copyright © 1963 by Penguin Books, Ltd. Reprinted with permission.
3. *The Great Conservation Principles* from *The Character of Physical Law* by Richard P. Feynman, copyright © 1965 by Richard P. Feynman. Published by the British Broadcasting Corporation and The M.I.T. Press. Reprinted with permission.
4. *The Barometer Story* by Alexander Calandra from *Current Science, Teacher's Edition,* Section 1, Vol. XLIX, Number 14, January 1964. Reprinted with special permission of *Current Science, Teacher's Edition,* published by American Education Publications, copyright © 1964 by Xerox Corp.
5. *The Great Molecular Theory of Gases* from *Physics for the Inquiring Mind: The Methods, Nature, and Philosophy of Physical Science* by Eric M. Rogers, copyright © 1960 by Princeton University Press. Reprinted with permission.
6. *Entropy and the Second Law of Thermodynamics* from *Basic Physics* by Kenneth W. Ford, copyright © 1968 by Ginn and Company. Reprinted with permission.
7. *The Law of Disorder* from *One, Two, Three ... Infinity* by George Gamow, copyright 1947 by George Gamow. Reprinted with permission of The Viking Press, Inc., and Macmillan & Co. Ltd.
8. *The Law* by Robert M. Coates, copyright 1947 by The New Yorker Magazine, Inc. Reprinted with permission.
9. *The Arrow of Time* from *Insight* by Dr. J. Bronowski, copyright © 1964 by Dr. J. Bronowski. Reprinted with permission of Harper & Row, Publishers, and Macdonald & Co. (Publishers) Ltd., London.
10. *James Clerk Maxwell* (Part 1) by James R. Newman from *Scientific American,* June 1955, copyright © 1955 by Scientific American, Inc. Reprinted with permission. All rights reserved.
11. *Frontiers of Physics Today—Acoustics* from *Physics Today* by Leo L. Beranek, copyright © 1969. Reprinted with permission.

12. *Randomness and the Twentieth Century* by Alfred M. Bork. Reprinted from *The Antioch Review,* volume XXVII, No. 1 with permission of the editors.

13. *Waves* from *Theory of Physics* by Richard Stevenson and R. B. Moore, copyright © 1967 by Richard Stevenson and R. B. Moore. Published by W. B. Saunders Company. Reprinted with permission.

14. *What Is a Wave?* by Albert Einstein and Leopold Infeld from *The Evolution of Physics,* copyright © 1961 by Estate of Albert Einstein. Published by Simon and Schuster. Reprinted with permission.

15. *Musical Instruments and Scales* from *Classical and Modern Physics* by Harvey E. White, Ph.D., copyright 1940 by Litton Educational Publishing, Inc. Reprinted with permission of Van Nostrand Reinhold Company.

16. *Founding a Family of Fiddles* by Carleen M. Hutchins from *Physics Today,* copyright © 1967 by the American Institute of Physics, New York. Reprinted with permission.

17. *The Seven Images of Science* from *Modern Science and the Intellectual Tradition* by Gerald Holton from *Science,* Vol. 131, pp. 1187-1193, April 22, 1960. Copyright © 1960 by the American Association of Science. Reprinted with permission.

18. *Scientific Cranks* from *Fads and Fallacies in the Name of Science* by Martin Gardner, copyright © 1957 by Martin Gardner. Published by Dover Publications, Inc. Reprinted with permission.

19. *Physics and the Vertical Jump* from the *American Journal of Physics,* Vol. 38, Number 7, July 1970, by Elmer L. Offenbacher, copyright © 1970. Reprinted with permission.

This is not a physics textbook. Rather, it is a physics reader, a collection of some of the best articles and book passages on physics. A few are on historic events in science, others contain some particularly memorable description of what physicists do; still others deal with philosophy of science, or with the impact of scientific thought on the imagination of the artist.

There are old and new classics, and also some little-known publications; many have been suggested for inclusion because some teacher or physicist remembered an article with particular fondness. The majority of articles is not drawn from scientific papers of historic importance themselves, because material from many of these is readily available, either as quotations in the Project Physics text or in special collections.

This collection is meant for your browsing. If you follow your own reading interests, chances are good that you will find here many pages that convey the joy these authors have in their work and the excitement of their ideas. If you want to follow up on interesting excerpts, the source list at the end of the reader will guide you for further reading.

Reader 3

Table of Contents

1 **Silence, Please**   1
Arthur C. Clarke

2 **The Steam Engine Comes of Age**   12
R. J. Forbes and E. J. Dijksterhuis

3 **The Great Conservation Principle**   20
Richard Feynman

4 **The Barometer Story**   45
Alexander Calandra

5 **The Great Molecular Theory of Gases**   46
Eric M. Rogers

6 **Entropy and the Second Law of Thermodynamics**   59
Kenneth W. Ford

7 **The Law of Disorder**   87
George Gamow

8 **The Law**   125
Robert M. Coates

9 **The Arrow of Time**   127
Jacob Bronowski

10 **James Clerk Maxwell**   133
James R. Newman

11 **Frontiers of Physics Today: Acoustics**   155
Leo L. Beranek

12 **Randomness and The Twentieth Century**   167
Alfred M. Bork

13 **Waves**   188
Richard Stevenson and R. B. Moore

14 **What is a Wave?** 208
Albert Einstein and Leopold Infeld

15 **Musical Instruments and Scales** 213
Harvey E. White

16 **Founding a Family of Fiddles** 233
Carleen M. Hutchins

17 **The Seven Images of Science** 245
Gerald Holton

18 **Scientific Cranks** 248
Martin Gardner

19 **Physics and the Vertical Jump** 254
Elmer L. Offenbacher

A fictional scientist tells of an apparatus for producing silence. Although the proposed scheme is improbable, the story has a charming plausibility.

---

1 Silence, Please

Arthur C. Clarke

An excerpt from his *Tales from the White Hart,* 1954.

YOU COME upon the "White Hart" quite unexpectedly in
one of these anonymous little lanes leading down from
Fleet Street to the Embankment. It's no use *telling* you
where it is: very few people who have set out in a determined effort to get there have ever actually arrived. For
the first dozen visits a guide is essential: after that you'll
probably be all right if you close your eyes and rely on
instinct. Also—to be perfectly frank—we don't want any
more customers, at least on *our* night. The place is already
uncomfortably crowded. All that I'll say about its location is that it shakes occasionally with the vibration of
newspaper presses, and that if you crane out of the window of the gent's room you can just see the Thames.

From the outside, is looks like any other pub—as indeed it is for five days of the week. The public and saloon
bars are on the ground floor: there are the usual vistas of
brown oak panelling and frosted glass, the bottles behind
the bar, the handles of the beer engines . . . nothing out
of the ordinary at all. Indeed, the only concession to the
twentieth century is the juke box in the public bar. It was
installed during the war in a laughable attempt to make
G.I.'s feel at home, and one of the first things we did was
to make sure there was no danger of its ever working
again.

At this point I had better explain who "we" are. That
is not as easy as I thought it was going to be when I
started, for a complete catalogue of the "White Hart's"
clients would probably be impossible and would certainly
be excruciatingly tedious. So all I'll say at this point is
that "we" fall into three main classes. First there are the
journalists, writers and editors. The journalists, of course,
gravitated here from Fleet Street. Those who couldn't
make the grade fled elsewhere: the tougher ones remained.
As for the writers, most of them heard about us from
other writers, came here for copy, and got trapped.

Where there are writers, of course, there are sooner or later editors. If Drew, our landlord, got a percentage on the literary business done in his bar, he'd be a rich man. (We suspect he is a rich man, anyway.) One of our wits once remarked that it was a common sight to see half a dozen indignant authors arguing with a hard-faced editor in one corner of the "White Hart", while in another, half a dozen indignant editors argued with a hard-faced author.

So much for the literary side: you will have, I'd better warn you, ample opportunities for close-ups later. Now let us glance briefly at the scientists. How did *they* get in here?

Well, Birkbeck College is only across the road, and King's is just a few hundred yards along the Strand. That's doubtless part of the explanation, and again personal recommendation had a lot to do with it. Also, many of our scientists are writers, and not a few of our writers are scientists. Confusing, but we like it that way.

The third portion of our little microcosm consists of what may be loosely termed "interested laymen". They were attracted to the "White Hart" by the general brouhaha, and enjoyed the conversation and company so much that they now come along regularly every Wednesday—which is the day when we all get together. Sometimes they can't stand the pace and fall by the wayside, but there's always a fresh supply.

With such potent ingredients, it is hardly surprising that Wednesday at the "White Hart" is seldom dull. Not only have some remarkable stories been told there, but remarkable things have *happened* there. For example, there was the time when Professor ———, passing through on his way to Harwell, left behind a brief-case containing—well, we'd better not go into that, even though we did so at the time. And most interesting it was, too. . . . Any Russian agents will find me in the corner under the dartboard. I come high, but easy terms can be arranged.

Now that I've finally thought of the idea, it seems astonishing to me that none of my colleagues has ever got round to writing up these stories. Is it a question of being so close to the wood that they can't see the trees? Or is it lack of incentive? No, the last explanation can hardly hold: several of them are quite as hard up as I am, and have complained with equal bitterness about Drew's "NO CREDIT" rule. My only fear, as I type these words on my old Remington Noiseless, is that John Christopher or George Whitley or John Beynon are already hard at work using up the best material. Such as, for instance, the story of the Fenton Silencer. . . .

I don't know when it began: one Wednesday is much like another and it's hard to tag dates on to them. Besides, people may spend a couple of months lost in the "White Hart" crowd before you first notice their existence. That had probably happened to Harry Purvis, because when I first came aware of him he already knew the names of most of the people in our crowd. Which is more than I do these days, now that I come to think of it.

But though I don't know *when,* I know exactly *how* it all started. Bert Huggins was the catalyst, or, to be more accurate, his voice was. Bert's voice would catalyse anything. When he indulges in a confidential whisper, it sounds like a sergeant major drilling an entire regiment. And when he lets himself go, conversation languishes elsewhere while we all wait for those cute little bones in the inner ear to resume their accustomed places.

He had just lost his temper with John Christopher (we all do this at some time or other) and the resulting detonation had disturbed the chess game in progress at the back of the saloon bar. As usual, the two players were surrounded by backseat drivers, and we all looked up with a start as Bert's blast whammed overhead. When the echoes died away, someone said: "I wish there was a way of shutting him up."

It was then that Harry Purvis replied: "There is, you know."

Not recognising the voice, I looked round. I saw a small, neatly-dressed man in the late thirties. He was smoking one of those carved German pipes that always makes me think of cuckoo clocks and the Black Forest. That was the only unconventional thing about him: otherwise he might have been a minor Treasury official all dressed up to go to a meeting of the Public Accounts Committee.

"I beg your pardon?" I said.

He took no notice, but made some delicate adjustments to his pipe. It was then that I noticed that it wasn't, as I'd thought at first glance, an elaborate piece of wood carving. It was something much more sophisticated—a contraption of metal and plastic like a small chemical engineering plant. There were even a couple of minute valves. My God, it *was* a chemical engineering plant. . . .

I don't goggle any more easily than the next man, but I made no attempt to hide my curiosity. He gave me a superior smile.

"All for the cause of science. It's an idea of the Biophysics Lab. They want to find out exactly what there is in tobacco smoke—hence these filters. You know the old argument—*does* smoking cause cancer of the tongue, and if so, how? The trouble is that it takes an awful lot of—er—distillate to identify some of the obscurer bye-products. So we have to do a lot of smoking."

"Doesn't it spoil the pleasure to have all this plumbing in the way?"

"I don't know. You see, I'm just a volunteer. I don't smoke."

"Oh," I said. For the moment, that seemed the only reply. Then I remembered how the conversation had started.

"You were saying," I continued with some feeling, for there was still a slight tintinus in my left ear, "that there was some way of shutting up Bert. We'd all like to hear it—if that isn't mixing metaphors somewhat."

"I was thinking," he replied, after a couple of experimental sucks and blows, "of the ill-fated Fenton Silencer. A sad story—yet, I feel, one with an interesting lesson for us all. And one day—who knows?—someone *may* perfect it and earn the blessings of the world."

Suck, bubble, bubble, *plop*. . . .

"Well, let's hear the story. When did it happen?"

He sighed.

"I'm almost sorry I mentioned it. Still, since you insist —and, of course, on the understanding that it doesn't go beyond these walls."

"Er—of course."

"Well, Rupert Fenton was one of our lab assistants. A very bright youngster, with a good mechanical background, but, naturally, not very well up in theory. He was always making gadgets in his spare time. Usually the idea was good, but as he was shaky on fundamentals the things

4

hardly ever worked. That didn't seem to discourage him: I think he fancied himself as a latter-day Edison, and imagined he could make his fortune from the radio tubes and other oddments lying around the lab. As his tinkering didn't interfere with his work, no-one objected: indeed, the physics demonstrators did their best to encourage him, because, after all, there is something refreshing about any form of enthusiasm. But no-one expected he'd ever get very far, because I don't suppose he could even integrate e to the x."

"Is such ignorance *possible?*" gasped someone.

"Maybe I exaggerate. Let's say $x\ e$ to the x. Anyway, all his knowledge was entirely practical—rule of thumb, you know. Give him a wiring diagram, however complicated, and he could make the apparatus for you. But unless it was something *really* simple, like a television set, he wouldn't understand how it worked. The trouble was, he didn't realise his limitations. And that, as you'll see, was most unfortunate.

"I think he must have got the idea while watching the Honours Physics students doing some experiments in acoustics. I take it, of course, that you all understand the phenomenon of interference?"

"Naturally," I replied.

"Hey!" said one of the chess-players, who had given up trying to concentrate on the game (probably because he was losing.) *"I don't."*

Purvis looked at him as though seeing something that had no right to be around in a world that had invented penicillin.

"In that case," he said coldly, "I suppose I had better do some explaining." He waved aside our indignant protests. "No, I insist. It's precisely those who don't understand these things who need to be told about them. If someone had only explained the theory to poor Fenton while there was still time. . . ."

He looked down at the now thoroughly abashed chess-player.

"I do not know," he began, "if you have ever considered the nature of *sound*. Suffice to say that it consists of a series of waves moving through the air. Not, however, waves like those on the surface of the sea—oh dear no! *Those* waves are up and down movements. Sound waves consist of alternate compressions and rarefactions."

"Rare-what?"

"Rarefactions."

"Don't you mean 'rarefications'?"

"I do not. I doubt if such a word exists, and if it does, it shouldn't," retorted Purvis, with the *aplomb* of Sir Alan Herbert dropping a particularly revolting neologism into his killing-bottle. "Where was I? Explaining sound, of course. When we make any sort of noise, from the faintest whisper to that concussion that went past just now, a series of pressure changes moves through the air. Have you ever watched shunting engines at work on a siding? You see a perfect example of the same kind of thing. There's a long line of goods-wagons, all coupled together. One end gets a bang, the first two trucks move together—and then you can see the compression wave moving right along the line. Behind it the reverse thing happens—the rarefaction —I repeat, *rarefaction*—as the trucks separate again.

"Things are simple enough when there is only one source of sound—only one set of waves. But suppose you have two wave-patterns, moving in the same direction? That's when interference arises, and there are lots of pretty experiments in elementary physics to demonstrate it. All we need worry about here is the fact—which I think you will all agree is perfectly obvious—that if one could get two sets of waves *exactly* out of step, the total result would be precisely zero. The compression pulse of one sound wave would be on top of the rarefaction of another—net result—no change and hence no sound. To go back to my analogy of the line of wagons, it's as if you gave the last truck a jerk and a push simultaneously. Nothing at all would happen.

"Doubtless some of you will already see what I am driving at, and will appreciate the basic principle of the Fenton Silencer. Young Fenton, I imagine, argued in this manner. 'This world of ours,' he said to himself, 'is too full of noise. There would be a fortune for anyone who could invent a really perfect silencer. Now, what would that imply . . . ?'

"It didn't take him long to work out the answer: I told you he was a bright lad. There was really very little in his pilot model. It consisted of a microphone, a special amplifier, and a pair of loudspeakers. Any sound that happened to be about was picked up by the mike, amplified and *inverted* so that it was exactly out of phase with the original noise. Then it was pumped out of the speakers, the original wave and the new one cancelled out, and the net result was silence.

"Of course, there was rather more to it than that. There had to be an arrangement to make sure that the cancelling wave was just the right intensity—otherwise you might be worse off than when you started. But these are technical details that I won't bore you with. As many of you will recognise, it's a simple application of negative feed-back."

"Just a moment!" interrupted Eric Maine. Eric, I should mention, is an electronics expert and edits some television paper or other. He's also written a radio play about space-flight, but that's another story. "Just a moment! There's something wrong here. You *couldn't* get silence that way. It would be impossible to arrange the phase . . ."

Purvis jammed the pipe back in his mouth. For a moment there was an ominous bubbling and I thought of the first act of "Macbeth". Then he fixed Eric with a glare.

"Are you suggesting," he said frigidly, "that this story is untrue?"

"Ah—well, I won't go as far as that, but . . ." Eric's voice trailed away as if he had been silenced himself. He pulled an old envelope out of his pocket, together with an assortment of resistors and condensers that seemed to have got entangled in his handkerchief, and began to do some figuring. That was the last we heard from him for some time.

"As I was saying," continued Purvis calmly, *"that's* the way Fenton's Silencer worked. His first model wasn't very powerful, and it couldn't deal with very high or very low notes. The result was rather odd. When it was switched on, and someone tried to talk, you'd hear the two ends of the spectrum—a faint bat's squeak, and a kind of low rumble. But he soon got over that by using a more linear circuit (dammit, I can't help using *some* technicalities!) and in the later model he was able to produce complete silence over quite a large area. Not merely an ordinary room, but a full-sized hall. Yes. . . .

"Now Fenton was not one of these secretive inventors who won't tell anyone what they are trying to do, in case their ideas are stolen. He was all too willing to talk. He discussed his ideas with the staff and with the students, whenever he could get anyone to listen. It so happened that one of the first people to whom he demonstrated his improved Silencer was a young Arts student called—I think—Kendall, who was taking Physics as a subsidiary subject. Kendall was much impressed by the Silencer, as well he might be. But he was not thinking, as you may have imagined, about its commercial possibilities, or the boon it would bring to the outraged ears of suffering humanity. Oh dear no! He had quite other ideas.

"Please permit me a slight digression. At College we have a flourishing Musical Society, which in recent years has grown in numbers to such an extent that it can now tackle the less monumental symphonies. In the year of which I speak, it was embarking on a very ambitious enterprise. It was going to produce a new opera, a work by a talented young composer whose name it would not be fair to mention, since it is now well-known to you all. Let us call him Edward England. I've forgotten the title of the work, but it was one of these stark dramas of tragic love which, for some reason I've never been able to understand, are supposed to be less ridiculous with a musical accompaniment than without. No doubt a good deal depends on the music.

"I can still remember reading the synopsis while waiting for the curtain to go up, and to this day have never been able to decide whether the libretto was meant seriously or not. Let's see—the period was the late Victorian era, and the main characters were Sarah Stampe, the passionate postmistress, Walter Partridge, the saturnine gamekeeper, and the squire's son, whose name I forget. It's the old story of the eternal triangle, complicated by the villager's resentment of change—in this case, the new telegraph system, which the local crones predict will Do Things to the cows' milk and cause trouble at lambing time.

"Ignoring the frills, it's the usual drama of operatic jealousy. The squire's son doesn't want to marry into the Post Office, and the gamekeeper, maddened by his rejection, plots revenge. The tragedy rises to its dreadful climax when poor Sarah, strangled with parcel tape, is found hidden in a mail-bag in the Dead Letter Department. The villagers hang Partridge from the nearest telegraph pole, much to the annoyance of the linesmen. He was supposed to sing an aria while he was being hung: *that* is one thing

I regret missing. The squire's son takes to drink, or the Colonies, or both: and that's that.

"I'm sure you're wondering where all this is leading: please bear with me for a moment longer. The fact is that while this synthetic jealousy was being rehearsed, the real thing was going on back-stage. Fenton's friend Kendall had been spurned by the young lady who was to play Sarah Stampe. I don't think he was a particularly vindictive person, but he saw an opportunity for a unique revenge. Let us be frank and admit that college life *does* breed a certain irresponsibility—and in identical circumstances, how many of *us* would have rejected the same chance?

"I see the dawning comprehension on your faces. But we, the audience, had no suspicion when the overture started on that memorable day. It was a most distinguished gathering: everyone was there, from the Chancellor downwards. Deans and professors were two a penny: I never did discover how so many people had been bullied into coming. Now that I come to think of it, I can't remember what I was doing there myself.

"The overture died away amid cheers, and, I must admit, occasional cat-calls from the more boisterous members of the audience. Perhaps I do them an injustice: they may have been the more musical ones.

"Then the curtain went up. The scene was the village square at Doddering Sloughleigh, *circa* 1860. Enter the heroine, reading the postcards in the morning's mail. She comes across a letter addressed to the young squire and promptly bursts into song.

"Sarah's opening aria wasn't quite as bad as the overture, but it was grim enough. Luckily, we were to hear only the first few bars. . . .

"Precisely. We need not worry about such details as how Kendall had talked the ingenuous Fenton into it— if, indeed, the inventor realised the use to which his device was being applied. All I need say is that it was a most convincing demonstration. There was a sudden, deadening blanket of silence, and Sarah Stampe just faded out like a TV programme when the sound is turned off. Everyone was frozen in their seats, while the singer's lips went on moving silently. Then she too realised what had happened. Her mouth opened in what would have been a piercing scream in any other circumstances, and she fled into the wings amid a shower of postcards.

"Thereafter, the chaos was unbelievable. For a few minutes everyone must have thought they had lost the sense of hearing, but soon they were able to tell from the behaviour of their companions that they were not alone in their deprivation. Someone in the Physics Department must have realised the truth fairly promptly, for soon little slips of paper were circulating among the V.I.P.'s in the front row. The Vice-Chancellor was rash enough to try and restore order by sign-language, waving frantically to the audience from the stage. By this time I was too sick with laughter to appreciate such fine details.

"There was nothing for it but to get out of the hall, which we all did as quickly as we could. I think Kendall had fled—he was so overcome by the effect of the gadget that he didn't stop to switch it off. He was afraid of staying around in case he was caught and lynched. As for Fenton—alas, we shall never know *his* side of the story. We can only reconstruct the subsequent events from the evidence that was left.

"As I picture it, he must have waited until the hall was empty, and then crept in to disconnect his apparatus. We heard the explosion all over the college."

"The *explosion?*" someone gasped.

"Of course. I shudder to think what a narrow escape we all had. Another dozen decibels, a few more phons—and it might have happened while the theatre was still packed. Regard it, if you like, as an example of the inscrutable workings of providence that only the inventor was caught in the explosion. Perhaps it was as well: at least he perished in the moment of achievement, and before the Dean could get at him."

"Stop moralising, man. What happened?"

"Well, I told you that Fenton was very weak on theory. If he'd gone into the mathematics of the Silencer he'd have found his mistake. The trouble is, you see, that one can't *destroy* energy. Not even when you cancel out one train of waves by another. All that happens then is that the energy you've neutralized accumulates *somewhere else*. It's rather like sweeping up all the dirt in a room—at the cost of an unsightly pile under the carpet.

"When you look into the theory of the thing, you'll find that Fenton's gadget wasn't a silencer so much as a *collector* of sound. All the time it was switched on, it was really absorbing sound energy. And at that concert, it was certainly going flat out. You'll understand what I mean if you've ever looked at one of Edward England's scores. On top of that, of course, there was all the noise the audience was making—or I should say was *trying* to make—during the resultant panic. The total amount of energy must have been terrific, and the poor Silencer had to keep on sucking it up. Where did it go? Well, I don't know the circuit details—probably into the condensers of the power pack. By the time Fenton started to tinker with it again, it was like a loaded bomb. The sound of his approaching footsteps was the last straw, and the overloaded apparatus could stand no more. It blew up."

For a moment no-one said a word, perhaps as a token of respect for the late Mr. Fenton. Then Eric Maine, who for the last ten minutes had been muttering in the corner over his calculations, pushed his way through the ring of listeners. He held a sheet of paper thrust aggressively in front of him.

"Hey!" he said. "I was right all the time. The thing couldn't work. The phase and amplitude relations. . . ."

Purvis waved him away.

"That's just what I've explained," he said patiently. "You should have been listening. Too bad that Fenton found out the hard way."

He glanced at his watch. For some reason, he now seemed in a hurry to leave.

"My goodness! Time's getting on. One of these days, remind me to tell you about the extraordinary thing we saw through the new proton microscope. That's an even more remarkable story."

He was half way through the door before anyone else could challenge him. Then George Whitley recovered his breath.

"Look here," he said in a perplexed voice. "How is it that we never heard about this business?"

Purvis paused on the threshold, his pipe now burbling briskly as it got into its stride once more. He glanced back over his shoulder.

"There was only one thing to do," he replied. "We didn't want a scandal—*de mortuis nil nisi bonum,* you know. Besides, in the circumstances, don't you think it was highly appropriate to—ah—*hush* the whole business up? And a very good night to you all."

The invention of the steam engine was a major factor in the early stages of the Industrial Revolution.

2   The Steam Engine Comes of Age

R. J. Forbes and E. J. Dijksterhuis

A chapter from their book *A History of Science and Technology*, 1963.

THE steam engine, coke, iron, and steel are the four principal factors contributing to the acceleration of technology called the Industrial Revolution, which some claim to have begun about 1750 but which did not really gain momentum until about 1830. It started in Great Britain but the movement gradually spread to the Continent and to North America during the nineteenth century.

SCIENCE INSPIRES THE ENGINEER

During the Age of Projects the engineer had little help from the scientists, who were building the mathematical-mechanical picture of the Newtonian world and discussing the laws of nature. However, during the eighteenth century, the Age of Reason, when the principles of this new science had been formulated, the scientists turned to the study of problems of detail many of which were of direct help to the engineer. The latter was perhaps less interested in the new ideals of 'progress' and 'citizenship of the world' than in the new theory of heat, in applied mechanics and the strength of materials, or in new mathematical tools for their calculations. The older universities like Oxford and Cambridge contributed little to this collaboration. The pace was set by the younger ones such as the universities of Edinburgh and Glasgow, which produced such men as Hume, Roebuck, Kerr, and Black, who stimulated the new technology. The Royal Society, and also new centres like the Lunar Society and the Manchester Philosophical Society and the many similar societies on the Continent, contributed much to this new technology by studying and discussing the latest scientific theories and the arts. Here noblemen, bankers, and merchants met to hear the scientist, the inventor, and the engineer and to help to realize many of the projects which the latter put forward. They devoted much money to scientific investigations, to demonstrations and stimulated inventions by offering prizes for practical solutions of burning problems. They had the capital to promote the 'progress' which made Dr Johnson cry out: 'This age is running mad after innovation. All business of the world is to be done in a new way, men are to be hanged in a new way; Tyburn itself is not safe from the fury of innovation!' New institutions such as the Conservatoire des Arts et Métiers and the Royal Institution of Great Britain were founded to spread the new science and technology by lectures and demonstrations and the number of laymen attending these lectures was overwhelming.

ENGINEERS AND SKILLED LABOUR

The new professional engineers which the École des Ponts et Chaussées began to turn out were the descendants of the sappers and military engineers. However, the new technology also needed other types of engineers for which new schools such as the École Polytechnique and the École des Mines were founded. In Great Britain the State was less concerned with the education of the new master craftsmen. They were trained in practice: such famous workshops as that of Boulton and Watt in Soho, Birmingham, or those of Dobson and Barlow, Asa Lees, and Richard Roberts. Their success depended not only on good instruction but also on appropriate instruments and skilled labour.

The scientists of the eighteenth century had turned out many new instruments which were of great value to the engineer. They were no longer made individually by the research scientist, but by professional instrument makers in Cassel, Nuremberg, or London, and such university towns as Leiden, Paris, and Edinburgh. Their instruments became more efficient and precise as better materials became available such as good glass for lenses and more accurate methods for working metals.

Skilled labour was more difficult to create. The older generation of Boulton and Watt had to work with craftsmen such as smiths and carpenters, they had to re-educate them and create a new type of craftsmen, 'skilled labour'. The design of early machinery often reveals that it was built by the older type of craftsmen that belonged to the last days of the guild system. The new industrialists tried out several systems of apprenticeship in their machine shops during the eighteenth century until they finally solved this educational problem during the next century and created schools and courses for workmen for the new industries, qualified to design and to make well-specified engines and machine parts.

A factor that contributed greatly to this development was the rise of the science of applied mechanics and the methods of testing materials. The theories and laws which such men as Palladio, Derand, Hooke, Bernoulli, Euler, Coulomb, and Perronet formulated may have been imperfect but they showed the way to estimate the strength of materials so important in the construction of machinery. 's Gravesande and Van Musschenbroek were the first to design and demonstrate various machines for measuring tensile, breaking, and bending strengths of various materials early in the eighteenth century. Such instruments were gradually improved by Gauthey, Rondelet, and others. The elastic behaviour of beams, the strength of arches, and many other problems depended on such tests. Some scientists developed tests for certain types of materials, for instance for timber (Buffon), stone (Gauthey), or metals (Réaumur). Such knowledge was of prime importance to the development of the steam engine and other machinery which came from the machine shops.

MACHINE SHOPS

The engineers who led this Industrial Revolution had to create both the tools and the new workmen. Watt, himself a trained instrument maker, had to invent several new tools and machines and to train his workmen in foundries and machine shops. Hence his notebooks are full of new ideas and machines. He invented the copying press. His ingenious contemporaries Maudsley and Bramah were equally productive. Joseph Bramah was responsible for our modern water closet (1778) and the first successful patent lock (1784) which no one succeeded in opening with a skeleton key before Hobbs (1851), who spent fifty-one hours of labour on it.

The difficulty in finding suitable labour arose from the fact that the new machines were no longer single pieces created by one smith, but that series of such machines were built from standard parts which demanded much greater precision in manufacturing such parts. The steam engine parts had to be finished accurately to prevent the steam escaping between metal surfaces which slid over each other, especially as steam pressures were gradually increased to make these machines more efficient. Hence the importance of the new tools and finishing processes, such as the lathe and drilling, cutting and finishing machinery.

In 1797 Henry Maudsley invented the screw-cutting lathe. Lathes originally belonged to the carpenter's shop. Even before the eighteenth century they had been used to turn soft metals such as tin and lead. These lathes were now moved by means of treadles instead of a bow, though Leonardo da Vinci had already designed lathes with interchangeable sets of gear wheels to regulate the speed of the lathe. Maudsley applied similar ideas and introduced the slide rest. Brunel, Roberts, Fox, Witworth, and others perfected the modern lathe, which permitted moving the object horizontally and vertically, adjustment by screws, and automatic switching off when the operation was completed. The older machine lathes were first moved by hand, then by a steam engine, and finally by electric motors. Now the mass production of screws, bolts, nuts, and other standard parts became possible and machines were no longer separate pieces of work. They were assembled from mass-produced parts.

The tools of the machine shop were greatly improved during the nineteenth century, pulleys, axles, and handles being perfected. The new turret or capstan lathe had a round or hexagonal block rotating about its axis and holding in a hole in each side the cutting or planing tool needed. These tools could then at will be brought into contact with the metal to be finished, thus performing the work of six separate lathes in a much shorter time. The turret block was made to turn automatically (1857) and finally Hartness invented the flat turret lathe, replacing the block by a horizontal face plate which gave the lathe greater flexibility and allowed work at higher speeds. Such lathes ranged from the small types used by the watchmaker to those for processing large guns. This development was completed by the introduction of high-speed tool steels by Taylor and White about the beginning of our century, making the machine lathe a universal tool for the mass production of machine parts.

FACTORIES AND INDUSTRIAL REVOLUTION

This brought about a great change in the manufacturing process itself. No longer were most commodities now made in the private shops of craftsmen, but in larger workshops in which a water wheel or a steam engine moved an axle from which smaller machinery derived its power by means of gear wheels or belts, each machine only partly processing the metal or material. Hence the manufacturing process was split up into a series of operations, each of which was performed by a special piece of machinery instead of being worked by hand by one craftsman who mastered all the operations.

The modern factory arose only slowly. Even in 1800 the word 'factory' still denoted a shop, a warehouse, or a depot; the eighteenth century always spoke of 'mills' in many of which the prime mover still was a horse mill or tread mill. The textile factory law of 1844 was the first to speak of 'factories'.

It is obvious that the new factories demanded a large outlay of capital. The incessant local wars had impoverished central Europe and Italy and industry did not flourish there, so many German inventors left their country to seek their fortune in western Europe. State control of the 'manufactures' in France had not been a success. The French government had not created a new class of skilled labour along with the new engineers, and Napoleon's 'self-supporting French industry' was doomed to be a failure when overseas trade was re-established after his fall. Neither the Low Countries nor Scandinavia had the necessary capital and raw materials needed for the Industrial Revolution. Only in eighteenth-century England did such a fortunate combination of factors exist, a flourishing overseas trade, a well-developed banking system, raw materials in the form of coal and iron ores, free trade and an industry-minded middle class willing to undertake the risks of introducing new machinery and recruiting the new skilled labour from the ranks of the farmers and immigrants from Ireland and Scotland.

Hence we find the first signs of the Industrial Revolution in Great Britain rather than in France, which, however, soon followed suit. Competition from Germany did not start until the middle of the nineteenth century, and from the United States not until the beginning of our century.

THE BEAM ENGINES

The prime mover of this new industry was the steam engine. The primitive machine that pumped water was transformed into a prime mover by the efforts of Newcomen and Watt. Thomas Newcomen (1663–1729) and John Calley built a machine in which steam of 100° C moved a piston in its cylinder by condensation (1705). This piston was connected with the end of a beam, the other end of which was attached to the rod of the pump or any other machine. Most of these engines were used to drain mines. John Smeaton (1724–92) studied the Newcomen engine and perfected it by measurement and calculation, changing its boiler and valves and turning it into the most popular steam engine up to 1800.

James Watt (1736–1819), trained as an instrument maker, heard the lectures of John Robison and Joseph Black at Edinburgh, where the new theory of heat was expounded and methods were discussed to measure the degree and the amount of heat, as well as the phenomena of evaporation and condensation. He perceived that a large amount of heat was wasted in the cylinder of the Newcomen engine, heating it by injection of steam and cooling it by injecting cold water to condense the steam. Hence he designed an engine in which the condensation took place in a separate condenser, which was connected with the cylinder by opening a valve at the correct moment, when the steam had forced the piston up (1763).

Watt tried to have his engine built at John Roebuck's Carron Iron Works in Scotland but did not find the skilled workmen there to make the parts. So he moved southwards and started work at the works of Matthew Boulton, who built Roebuck's share in Watt's patents (1774). At the nearby Bradley foundry of John Wilkinson, cylinders could be bored accurately and thus Watt produced his first large-scale engine in 1781. The power output of the Watt engine proved to be four times that of a Newcomen engine. It was soon used extensively to pump water in brine works, breweries, and distilleries. Boulton and Murdock helped to advertise and apply Watt's engines.

THE DOUBLE-ACTING ROTATIVE ENGINE

However, Watt was not yet satisfied with these results. His Patent of 1781 turned the steam engine into a universally efficient prime mover. The rod on the other arm of the beam was made to turn the up-and-down movement of the beam into a rotative one, by means of the 'sun and planet movement' of a set of gear wheels connecting the rod attached to the end of the beam with the axle on which the driving wheels and belts were fixed which moved the machines deriving their energy from this axle.

A further patent of 1782 made his earlier engine into a double-acting one, that is a steam engine in which steam was admitted alternately on each side of the piston. This succeeded only when Boulton and Watt had mastered the difficult task of casting and finishing larger and more accurate cylinders. Watt also had to improve the connexion of the beam and the piston rod by means of his extended three-bar system (1784) which he called the 'parallel movement'. He was also able to introduce a regulator which cut off the steam supply to the cylinder at the right moment and leaving the rest of the stroke to the expansion of the steam made better use of its energy.

In 1788 he designed his centrifugal governor which regulated the steam supply according to the load keeping constant the number of strokes of the piston per minute. Six years later he added the steam gauge or indicator to his engine, a miniature cylinder and piston, connected with the main cylinder. The small piston of this indicator was attached to a pen which could be made to indicate on a piece of paper the movements of the little piston and thus provide a control on the movements of the steam engine proper. William Murdock (1754–1839), by inventing the sliding valves and the means of preparing a paste to seal off the seams between the cast iron surface of the machine parts, contributed much to the success of these engines as proper packing was not yet available.

By 1800 some 500 Boulton and Watt engines were in operation, 160 of which pumped water back on to water wheels moving machinery. The others were mostly rotative engines moving other machinery and twenty-four produced blast air for iron furnaces, their average strength being 15–16 h.p.

THE MODERN HIGH-PRESSURE STEAM ENGINE

The period 1800–50 saw the evolution of the steam engine to the front rank of prime movers. This was achieved by building steam engines which could be moved by high-pressure steam of high temperature containing much more energy per pound than the steam of 100° C which moved the earlier Watt engines. This was only possible by perfecting the manufacture of the parts of the steam engine, by better designing, and by the more accurate finishing and fit of such parts.

Jabez Carter Hornblower built the first 'compound engine', in which the steam released from the first cylinder was left to expand further in a second one. These compound engines did away with the Watt condenser, but could not yet compete seriously until high pressure steam was applied. Richard Trevithick and Oliver Evans were the pioneers of the high-pressure engine, which meant more horse power per unit of weight of the steam engine. This again meant lighter engines and the possibility of using them for road and water traffic.

Nor were properly designed steam engines possible until the theory of heat had been further elaborated and the science of thermodynamics formulated, the theory of gases studied, and more evidence produced for the strength of metals and materials at high temperatures. Another important problem was the construction of boilers to produce the high-pressure steam. The ancient beehive-shaped boilers of Watt's generation could not withstand such pressures. Trevithick created the Cornish boiler (1812), a horizontal cylinder heated by an inner tube carrying the combustion gases through the boiler into the flue and adding to the fuel efficiency of the boilers. The Lancashire boiler, designed by William Fairbairn (1844), had two tubes and became a serious competitor of the Cornish boiler. Better grates for burning the coal fuel were designed such as the 'travelling grate stoker' of John Bodmer (1841), and more fuel was economized by heating the cold feed water of the boiler with flue gases in Green's economizer (1845). Then multitubular boilers were built in the course of the nineteenth century, most of which were vertical boilers, the best known of which was the Babcock and Wilcox tubular boiler (1876).

Further factors helping to improve the design of high-pressure steam engines were the invention of the direct-action steam pump by Henry Worthington (1841), the steam hoist (1830), and James Nasmyth's steam hammer (1839). In the meantime Cartwright (1797) and Barton (1797) had perfected metallic packing which ensure tight joints and prevented serious leakage.

Thus steam pressures rose from 3·5 atm in 1810 to about 5 or 6 atm in 1830, but these early high-pressure engines were still of the beam type. Then came the much more efficient rotation engines in which the piston rod was connected with the driving wheel by means of a crank. Though even the early American Corliss engine (1849) still clung to the beam design, John M'Naught (1845) and E. Cowper (1857) introduced modern rotative forms, which came to stay. Three-cylinder engines of this type were introduced by Brotherhood (1871) and Kirk (1874) and became very popular prime movers for steamships (1881).

Not until 1850 was the average output of the steam engines some 40 h.p., that is significantly more than the 15 h.p. windmill or water-wheel of the period. Again the steam engine was not bound to sites where water or wind were constantly available, it was a mobile prime mover which could be installed where needed, for instance in iron works situated near coal fields and iron ores. In 1700 Great Britain consumed some 3,000,000 tons of coal, mostly to heat its inhabitants. This amount had doubled by 1800 because of the introduction of the steam engine, and by 1850 it has risen to 60,000,000 tons owing to the steam engine and the use of coke in metallurgy. . .

A survey of the most fundamental principles that underlie all of physics—and what they have in common.

3 The Great Conservation Principles

Richard Feynman

An excerpt from his book *The Character of Physical Law,* 1965.

When learning about the laws of physics you find that there are a large number of complicated and detailed laws, laws of gravitation, of electricity and magnetism, nuclear interactions, and so on, but across the variety of these detailed laws there sweep great general principles which all the laws seem to follow. Examples of these are the principles of conservation, certain qualities of symmetry, the general form of quantum mechanical principles, and unhappily, or happily, as we considered last time, the fact that all the laws are mathematical. In this lecture I want to talk about the conservation principles.

The physicist uses ordinary words in a peculiar manner. To him a conservation law means that there is a number which you can calculate at one moment, then as nature undergoes its multitude of changes, if you calculate this quantity again at a later time it will be the same as it was before, the number does not change. An example is the conservation of energy. There is a quantity that you can calculate according to a certain rule, and it comes out the same answer always, no matter what happens.

Now you can see that such a thing is possibly useful. Suppose that physics, or rather nature, is considered analogous to a great chess game with millions of pieces in it, and we are trying to discover the laws by which the pieces move. The great gods who play this chess play it very rapidly, and it is hard to watch and difficult to see. However, we are catching on to some of the rules, and there are some rules which we can work out which do not require that we watch every move. For instance, suppose there is one bishop only, a red bishop, on the board, then since the bishop moves diagonally and therefore never changes the colour of its square, if we look away for a moment while the gods play and then look back again, we can expect that there will be still a red bishop on the board, maybe in a different place, but on the same colour square. This is in the nature of a conservation law. We do not need to watch the insides to know at least something about the game.

It is true that in chess this particular law is not necessarily perfectly valid. If we looked away long enough it could happen that the bishop was captured, a pawn went down to queen, and the god decided that it was better to hold a bishop instead of a queen in the place of that pawn, which happened to be on a black square. Unfortunately it may well turn out that some of the laws which we see today may not be exactly perfect, but I will tell you about them as we see them at present.

I have said that we use ordinary words in a technical fashion, and another word in the title of this lecture is 'great', 'The Great Conservation Principles'. This is not a technical word: it was merely put in to make the title sound more dramatic, and I could just as well have called it 'The Conservation Laws'. There are a few conservation laws that do not work; they are only approximately right, but are sometimes useful, and we might call those the 'little' conservation laws. I will mention later one or two of those that do not work, but the principal ones that I am going to discuss are, as far as we can tell today, absolutely accurate.

I will start with the easiest one to understand, and that is the conservation of electric charge. There is a number, the total electric charge in the world, which, no matter what happens, does not change. If you lose it in one place you will find it in another. The conservation is of the total of all electric charge. This was discovered experimentally by Faraday.* The experiment consisted of getting inside a great globe of metal, on the outside of which was a very delicate galvanometer, to look for the charge on the globe,

*Michael Faraday, 1791–1867, English physicist.

because a small amount of charge would make a big effect. Inside the globe Faraday built all kinds of weird electrical equipment. He made charges by rubbing glass rods with cat's fur, and he made big electrostatic machines so that the inside of this globe looked like those horror movie laboratories. But during all these experiments no charge developed on the surface; there was no net charge made. Although the glass rod may have been positive after it was charged up by rubbing on the cat's fur, then the fur would be the same amount negative, and the total charge was always nothing, because if there were any charge developed on the inside of the globe it would have appeared as an effect in the galvanometer on the outside. So the total charge is conserved.

This is easy to understand, because a very simple model, which is not mathematical at all, will explain it. Suppose the world is made of only two kinds of particles, electrons and protons – there was a time when it looked as if it was going to be as easy as that – and suppose that the electrons carry a negative charge and the protons a positive charge, so that we can separate them. We can take a piece of matter and put on more electrons, or take some off; but supposing that electrons are permanent and never disintegrate or disappear – that is a simple proposition, not even mathematical – then the total number of protons, less the total number of electrons, will not change. In fact in this particular model the total number of protons will not change, nor the number of electrons. But we are concentrating now on the charge. The contribution of the protons is positive and that of the electrons negative, and if these objects are never created or destroyed alone then the total charge will be conserved. I want to list as I go on the number of properties that conserve quantities, and I will start with charge (fig. 14). Against the question whether charge is conserved I write 'yes'.

This theoretical interpretation is very simple, but it was later discovered that electrons and protons are not permanent; for example, a particle called the neutron can disintegrate into a proton and an electron – plus something else

	Charge	Baryon No.	Strangeness	Energy	Angular Momentum
Conserved (locally)	Yes	Yes	Nearly	Yes	Yes
Comes in Units	Yes	Yes	Yes	No	Yes
Source of a field	Yes	?	?	Yes	

NB This is the completed table which Professor Feynman added to throughout his lecture.

Figure 14

which we will come to. But the neutron, it turns out, is electrically neutral. So although protons are not permanent, nor are electrons permanent, in the sense that they can be created from a neutron, the charge still checks out; starting before, we had zero charge, and afterwards we had plus one and minus one which when added together become zero charge.

An example of a similar fact is that there exists another particle, besides the proton, which is positively charged. It is called a positron, which is a kind of image of an electron. It is just like the electron in most respects, except that it has the opposite sign of charge, and, more important, it is called an anti-particle because when it meets with an electron the two of them can annihilate each other and disintegrate, and nothing but light comes out. So electrons are not permanent even by themselves. An electron plus a positron will just make light. Actually the 'light' is invisible to the eye; it is gamma rays; but this is the same thing for a physicist, only the wavelength is different. So a particle and its anti-particle can annihilate. The light has no electric charge, but we remove one positive and one negative charge, so we have not changed the total charge. The theory of conservation of charge is therefore slightly more complicated but still very unmathematical. You simply add together the number of positrons you have and the number of protons, take away the number of electrons – there are additional particles you have to check, for example antiprotons which contribute negatively, pi-plus mesons which are positive, in fact each fundamental particle in nature has a charge (possibly zero). All we have to do is add up the total number, and whatever happens in any reaction the total amount of charge on one side has to balance with the amount on the other side.

That is one aspect of the conservation of charge. Now comes an interesting question. Is it sufficient to say only that charge is conserved, or do we have to say more? If charge were conserved because it was a real particle which moved around it would have a very special property. The total amount of charge in a box might stay the same in two ways. It may be that the charge moves from one place to another within the box. But another possibility is that the charge in one place disappears, and simultaneously charge arises in another place, instantaneously related, and in such a manner that the total charge is never changing. This second possibility for the conservation is of a different kind from the first, in which if a charge disappears in one place and turns up in another something has to travel through the space in between. The second form of charge conservation is called local charge conservation, and is far more detailed than the simple remark that the total charge does not change. So you see we are improving our law, if it is true that charge is locally conserved. In fact it is true. I have tried to show you from time to time some of the possibilities of reasoning, of interconnecting one idea with another, and I would now like to describe to you an argument, fundamentally due to Einstein, which indicates that if anything is conserved – and in this case I apply it to charge – it must be conserved locally. This argument relies on one thing, that if two fellows are passing each other in space ships, the question of which guy is doing the moving and which one standing still cannot be resolved by any experiment. That is called the principle of relativity, that uniform motion in a straight line is relative, and that we can look at any phenomenon from either point of view and cannot say which one is standing still and which one is moving.

Suppose I have two space ships, A and B (fig. 15). I am

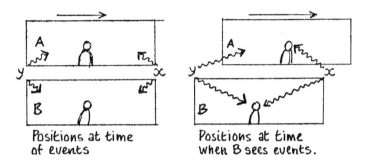

Positions at time of events

Positions at time when B sees events.

Figure 15

going to take the point of view that A is the one that is moving past B. Remember that is just an opinion, you can also look it at the other way and you will get the same phenomena of nature. Now suppose that the man who is standing still wants to argue whether or not he has seen a charge at one end of his ship disappear and a charge at the other end appear at the same time. In order to make sure it is the same time he cannot sit in the front of the ship, because he will see one before he sees the other because of the travel time of light; so let us suppose that he is very careful and sits dead centre in the middle of the ship. We have another man doing the same kind of observation in the other ship. Now a lightning bolt strikes, and charge is created at point x, and at the same instant at point y at the other end of the ship the charge is annihilated, it disappears. At the same instant, note, and perfectly consistent with our idea that charge is conserved. If we lose one electron in one place we get another elsewhere, but nothing passes in between. Let us suppose that when the charge disappears there is a flash, and when it is created there is a flash, so that we can see what happens. B says they both happen at the same time, since he knows he is in the middle of the ship and the light from the bolt which creates x reaches him at the same time as the light from the flash of disappearance at y. Then B will say, 'Yes, when one disappeared the other was created'. But what happens to our friend in the other ship? He says, 'No, you are wrong my friend. I saw x created before y'. This is because he is moving towards x, so the light from x will have a shorter distance to travel than the light from y, since he is moving away from y. He could say, 'No, x was created first and then y disappeared, so for a short time after x was created and before y disappeared I got some charge. That is not the conservation of charge. It is against the law'. But the first fellow says, 'Yes, but you are moving'. Then he says, 'How do you know? I think you are moving', and so on. If we are unable, by any experiment, to see a difference in the physical laws whether we are moving or not, then if the conservation of charge were not local only a certain kind of man would see it work right, namely the guy who is standing still, in an absolute sense. But such a thing is impossible according to Einstein's relativity principle, and therefore it is impossible to have non-local conservation of charge. The locality of the conservation of charge is consonant with the theory of relativity, and it turns out that this is true of all the conservation laws. You can appreciate that if anything is conserved the same principle applies.

There is another interesting thing about charge, a very strange thing for which we have no real explanation today. It has nothing to do with the conservation law and is independent of it. Charge always comes in units. When we have a charged particle it has one charge or two charges, or minus one or minus two. Returning to our table, although this has nothing to do with the conservation of charge, I must write down that the thing that is conserved comes in units. It is very nice that it comes in units, because that makes the theory of conservation of charge very easy to understand. It is just a *thing* we can count, which goes from place to place. Finally it turns out technically that the total charge of a thing is easy to determine electrically because the charge has a very important characteristic; it is the source of the electric and magnetic field. Charge is a measure of the interaction of an object with electricity, with an electric field. So another item which we should add to the list is that charge is the source of a field; in other words, electricity is related to charge. Thus the particular quantity which is conserved here has two other aspects which are not connected with the conservation directly, but are interesting anyway. One is that it comes in units, and the other that it is the source of a field.

There are many conservation laws, and I will give some more examples of laws of the same type as the conservation of charge, in the sense that it is merely a matter of counting. There is a conservation law called the conservation of baryons. A neutron can go into a proton. If we count each of these as one unit, or baryon, then we do not lose the number of baryons. The neutron carries one baryonic charge unit, or represents one baryon, a proton represents one baryon – all we are doing is counting and making big words! – so if the reaction I am speaking of occurs, in which a neutron decays into a proton, an electron and an anti-neutrino, the total number of baryons does not change. However there are other reactions in nature. A proton plus a proton can produce a great variety of strange objects, for example a lambda, a proton and a K plus. Lambda and K plus are names for peculiar particles.

$$\text{(easy)} \quad P + P \rightarrow \lambda + P + K^+$$

In this reaction we know we put two baryons in, but we see only one come out, so possibly either lambda or K+ has a baryon. If we study the lambda later we discover that very slowly it disintegrates into a proton and a pi, and ultimately the pi disintegrates into electrons and what-not.

$$(\text{slow}) \;\; \lambda \rightarrow P + \pi$$

What we have here is the baryon coming out again in the proton, so we think the lambda has a baryon number of 1, but the K+ does not, the K+ has zero.

On our chart of conservation laws (fig. 14), then, we have charge and now we have a similar situation with baryons, with a special rule that the baryon number is the number of protons, plus the number of neutrons, plus the number of lambdas, minus the number of anti-protons, minus the number of anti-neutrons, and so on; it is just a counting proposition. It is conserved, it comes in units, and nobody knows but everybody wants to think, by analogy, that it is the source of a field. The reason we make these tables is that we are trying to guess at the laws of nuclear interaction, and this is one of the quick ways of guessing at nature. If charge is the source of a field, and baryon does the same things in other respects it ought to be the source of a field too. Too bad that so far it does not seem to be, it is possible, but we do not know enough to be sure.

There are one or two more of these counting propositions, for example Lepton numbers, and so on, but the idea is the same as with baryons. There is one, however, which is slightly different. There are in nature among these strange particles characteristic rates of reaction, some of which are very fast and easy, and others which are very slow and hard. I do not mean easy and hard in a technical sense, in actually doing the experiment. It concerns the rates at which the reactions occur when the particles are present. There is a clear distinction between the two kinds of reaction which I have mentioned above, the decay of a pair of protons, and the much slower decay of the lambda. It turns out that if you take only the fast and easy reactions there is one more counting law, in which the lambda gets a minus 1, and the K plus gets a plus 1, and the proton gets zero. This is called the strangeness number, or hyperon charge, and it appears that the rule that it is conserved is right for every easy reaction, but wrong for the slow reactions. On our chart (fig. 14) we must therefore add the conservation law called the conservation of strangeness, or the conservation of hyperon number, which is nearly right. This is very peculiar; we see why this quantity has been called strangeness. It is nearly true that it is conserved, and true that it comes in units. In trying to understand the strong interactions which are involved in nuclear forces, the fact that in strong interactions the thing is conserved has made people propose that for strong interactions it is also the source of a field, but again we do not know. I bring these matters up to show you how conservation laws can be used to guess new laws.

There are other conservation laws that have been proposed from time to time, of the same nature as counting. For example, chemists once thought that no matter what happened the number of sodium atoms stayed the same. But sodium atoms are not permanent. It is possible to transmute atoms from one element to another so that the original element has completely disappeared. Another law which was for a while believed to be true was that the total mass of an object stays the same. This depends on how you define mass, and whether you get mixed up with energy. The mass conservation law is contained in the next one which I am going to discuss, the law of conservation of energy. Of all the conservation laws, that dealing with energy is the most difficult and abstract, and yet the most useful. It is more difficult to understand than those I have described so far, because in the case of charge, and the others, the mechanism is clear, it is more or less the conservation of objects. This is not absolutely the case, because of the problem that we get new things from old things, but it is really a matter of simply counting.

The conservation of energy is a little more difficult, because this time we have a number which is not changed in time, but this number does not represent any particular thing. I would like to make a kind of silly analogy to explain a little about it.

I want you to imagine that a mother has a child whom she leaves alone in a room with 28 absolutely indestructible blocks. The child plays with the blocks all day, and when the mother comes back she discovers that there are indeed 28 blocks; she checks all the time the conservation of blocks! This goes on for a few days, and then one day when she comes in there are only 27 blocks. However, she finds one block lying outside the window, the child had thrown it out. The first thing you must appreciate about conservation laws is that you must watch that the stuff you are trying to check does not go out through the wall. The same thing could happen the other way, if a boy came in to play with the child, bringing some blocks with him. Obviously these are matters you have to consider when you talk about conservation laws. Suppose one day when the mother comes to count the blocks she finds that there are only 25 blocks, but suspects that the child has hidden the other three blocks in a little toy box. So she says, 'I am going to open the box'. 'No,' he says, 'you cannot open the box.' Being a very clever mother she would say, 'I know that when the box is empty it weighs 16 ounces, and each block weighs 3 ounces, so what I am going to do is to weigh the box'. So, totalling up the number of blocks, she would get –

$$\text{No. of blocks seen} + \frac{\text{Weight of box} - 16\text{oz.}}{3\text{oz.}}$$

and that adds up to 28. This works all right for a while, and then one day the sum does not check up properly. However, she notices that the dirty water in the sink is changing its level. She knows that the water is 6 inches deep when there is no block in it, and that it would rise $\frac{1}{4}$ inch if a block was in the water, so she adds another term, and now she has –

$$\text{No. of blocks seen} + \frac{\text{Weight of box-16oz.}}{\text{3oz.}} + \frac{\text{Ht. of Water} - 6\text{in.}}{\frac{1}{4}\text{in.}}$$

and once again it adds up to 28. As the boy becomes more ingenious, and the mother continues to be equally ingenious, more and more terms must be added, all of which represent blocks, but from the mathematical standpoint are abstract calculations, because the blocks are not seen.

Now I would like to draw my analogy, and tell you what is common between this and the conservation of energy, and what is different. First suppose that in all of the situations you never saw any blocks. The term 'No. of blocks seen' is never included. Then the mother would always be calculating a whole lot of terms like 'blocks in the box', 'blocks in the water', and so on. With energy there is this difference, that there are no blocks, so far as we can tell. Also, unlike the case of the blocks, for energy the numbers that come out are not integers. I suppose it might happen to the poor mother that when she calculates one term it comes out $6 \frac{1}{8}$ blocks, and when she calculates another it comes out $\frac{7}{8}$ of a block, and the others give 21, which still totals 28. That is how it looks with energy.

What we have discovered about energy is that we have a scheme with a sequence of rules. From each different set of rules we can calculate a number for each different kind of energy. When we add all the numbers together, from all the different forms of energy, it always gives the same total. But as far as we know there are no real units, no little ball-bearings. It is abstract, purely mathematical, that there is a number such that whenever you calculate it it does not change. I cannot interpret it any better than that.

This energy has all kinds of forms, analogous to the blocks in the box, blocks in the water, and so on. There is energy due to motion called kinetic energy, energy due to gravitational interaction (gravitational potential energy, it is called), thermal energy, electrical energy, light energy, elastic energy in springs and so on, chemical energy, nuclear energy – and there is also an energy that a particle has from its mere existence, an energy that depends directly on its mass. The last is the contribution of Einstein, as you undoubtedly know. $E = mc^2$ is the famous equation of the law I am talking about.

Although I have mentioned a large number of energies, I would like to explain that we are not completely ignorant about this, and we do understand the relationship of some of them to others. For instance, what we call thermal energy is to a large extent merely the kinetic energy of the motion of the particles inside an object. Elastic energy and chemical energy both have the same origin, namely the forces between the atoms. When the atoms rearrange themselves in a new pattern some energy is changed, and if that quantity changes it means that some other quantity also has to change. For example, if you are burning something the chemical energy changes, and you find heat where you did not have heat before, because it all has to add up right. Elastic energy and chemical energy are both interactions of atoms, and we now understand these interactions to be a combination of two things, one electrical energy and the other kinetic energy again, only this time the formula for it is quantum mechanical. Light energy is nothing but electrical energy, because light has now been interpreted as an electric and magnetic wave. Nuclear energy is not represented in terms of the others; at the moment I cannot say more than that it is the result of nuclear forces. I am not just talking here about the energy released. In the uranium nucleus there is a certain amount of energy, and when the thing disintegrates the amount of energy remaining in the nucleus changes, but the total amount of energy in the world does not change, so a lot of heat and stuff is generated in the process, in order to balance up.

This conservation law is very useful in many technical ways. I will give you some very simple examples to show how, knowing the law of conservation of energy and the formulae for calculating energy, we can understand other laws. In other words many other laws are not independent, but are simply secret ways of talking about the conservation of energy. The simplest is the law of the lever (fig. 16).

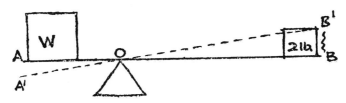

Figure 16

We have a lever on a pivot. The length of one arm is 1 foot and the other 4 feet. First I must give the law for gravity energy, which is that if you have a number of weights, you take the weight of each and multiply it by its height above the ground, add this together for all the weights, and that gives the total of gravity energy. Suppose I have a 2 lb weight on the long arm, and an unknown mystic weight on the other side – X is always the unknown, so let us call it W to make it seem that we have advanced above the usual! Now the question is, how much must W be so that it just balances and swings quietly back and forth without any trouble? If it swings quietly back and forth, that means that the energy is the same whether the balance is parallel to the ground or tilted so that the 2 lb weight is, say, 1 inch above the ground. If the energy is the same then it does not care much which way, and it does not fall over. If the 2 lb weight goes up 1 inch how far down does W go? From the diagram you can see (fig. 3) that if AO is 1 foot and OB is 4 feet, then when BB' is 1 inch AA' will be $\frac{1}{4}$ inch. Now apply the law for gravity energy. Before anything happened all the heights were zero, so the total energy was zero. After the move has happened to get the gravity energy we multiply the weight 2 lb by the height 1 inch and add it to the unknown weight W times the height – $\frac{1}{4}$ inch. The sum of this must give the same energy as before – zero. So –

$$2 - \frac{W}{4} = 0, \text{ so } W \text{ must be } 8$$

This is one way we can understand the easy law, which you already knew of course, the law of the lever. But it is interesting that not only this but hundreds of other physical laws can be closely related to various forms of energy. I showed you this example only to illustrate how useful it is.

The only trouble is, of course, that in practice it does not really work because of friction in the fulcrum. If I have something moving, for example a ball rolling along at a constant height, then it will stop on account of friction. What happened to the kinetic energy of the ball? The answer is that the energy of the motion of the ball has gone into the energy of the jiggling of the atoms in the floor and in the ball. The world that we see on a large scale looks like a nice round ball when we polish it, but it is really quite complicated when looked at on a little scale; billions of tiny atoms, with all kinds of irregular shapes. It is like a very rough boulder when looked at finely enough, because it is made out of these little balls. The floor is the same, a bumpy business made out of balls. When you roll this monster boulder over the magnified floor you can see that the little atoms are going to go snap-jiggle, snap-jiggle. After the thing has rolled across, the ones that are left behind are still shaking a little from the pushing and snapping that they went through; so there is left in the floor a jiggling motion, or thermal energy. At first it appears as if the law of conservation is false, but energy has the tendency to hide from us and we need thermometers and other instruments to make sure that it is still there. We find that energy is conserved no matter how complex the process, even when we do not know the detailed laws.

The first demonstration of the law of conservation of

energy was not by a physicist but by a medical man. He demonstrated with rats. If you burn food you can find out how much heat is generated. If you then feed the same amount of food to rats it is converted, with oxygen, into carbon dioxide, in the same way as in burning. When you measure the energy in each case you find out that living creatures do exactly the same as non-living creatures. The law for conservation of energy is as true for life as for other phenomena. Incidentally, it is interesting that every law or principle that we know for 'dead' things, and that we can test on the great phenomenon of life, works just as well there. There is no evidence yet that what goes on in living creatures is necessarily different, so far as the physical laws are concerned, from what goes on in non-living things, although the living things may be much more complicated.

The amount of energy in food, which will tell you how much heat, mechanical work, etc., it can generate, is measured in calories. When you hear of calories you are not eating something called calories, that is simply the measure of the amount of heat energy that is in the food. Physicists sometimes feel so superior and smart that other people would like to catch them out once on something. I will give you something to get them on. They should be utterly ashamed of the way they take energy and measure it in a host of different ways, with different names. It is absurd that energy can be measured in calories, in ergs, in electron volts, in foot pounds, in B.T.U.s, in horsepower hours, in kilowatt hours – all measuring exactly the same thing. It is like having money in dollars, pounds, and so on; but unlike the economic situation where the ratio can change, these dopey things are in absolutely guaranteed proportion. If anything is analogous, it is like shillings and pounds – there are always 20 shillings to a pound. But one complication that the physicist allows is that instead of having a number like 20 he has irrational ratios like 1·6183178 shillings to a pound. You would think that at least the more modern high-class theoretical physicists would use a common unit, but you find papers with degrees Kelvin for measuring energy, megacycles, and now inverse Fermis, the latest invention. For those who want some proof that physicists are human, the proof is in the idiocy of all the different units which they use for measuring energy.

There are a number of interesting phenomena in nature which present us with curious problems concerning energy. There has been a recent discovery of things called quasars, which are enormously far away, and they radiate so much energy in the form of light and radio waves that the question is where does it come from? If the conservation of energy is right, the condition of the quasar after it has radiated this enormous amount of energy must be different from its condition before. The question is, is it coming from gravitation energy – is the thing collapsed gravitationally, in a different condition gravitationally? Or is this big emission coming from nuclear energy? Nobody knows. You might propose that perhaps the law of conservation of energy is not right. Well, when a thing is investigated as incompletely as the quasar – quasars are so distant that the astronomers cannot see them too easily – then if such a thing seems to conflict with the fundamental laws, it very rarely is that the fundamental laws are wrong, it usually is just that the details are unknown.

Another interesting example of the use of the law of conservation of energy is in the reaction when a neutron disintegrates into a proton, an electron, and an anti-neutrino. It was first thought that a neutron turned into a proton plus an electron. But the energy of all the particles could be measured, and a proton and an electron together did not add up to a neutron. Two possibilities existed. It might have been that the law of energy conservation was not right; in fact it was proposed by Bohr* for a while that perhaps the conservation law worked only statistically, on the average. But it turns out now that the other possibility is the correct one, that the fact that the energy does not check out is because there is something else coming out, something

*Niels Bohr, Danish physicist.

which we now call an anti-neutrino. The anti-neutrino which comes out takes up the energy. You might say that the only reason for the anti-neutrino is to make the conservation of energy right. But it makes a lot of other things right, like the conservation of momentum and other conservation laws, and very recently it has been directly demonstrated that such neutrinos do indeed exist.

This example illustrates a point. How is it possible that we can extend our laws into regions we are not sure about? Why are we so confident that, because we have checked the energy conservation here, when we get a new phenomenon we can say it has to satisfy the law of conservation of energy? Every once in a while you read in the paper that physicists have discovered that one of their favourite laws is wrong. Is it then a mistake to say that a law is true in a region where you have not yet looked? If you will never say that a law is true in a region where you have not already looked you do not know anything. If the only laws that you find are those which you have just finished observing then you can never make any predictions. Yet the only utility of science is to go on and to try to make guesses. So what we always do is to stick our necks out, and in the case of energy the most likely thing is that it is conserved in other places.

Of course this means that science is uncertain; the moment that you make a proposition about a region of experience that you have not directly seen then you must be uncertain. But we always must make statements about the regions that we have not seen, or the whole business is no use. For instance, the mass of an object changes when it moves, because of the conservation of energy. Because of the relation of mass and energy the energy associated with the motion appears as an extra mass, so things get heavier when they move. Newton believed that this was not the case, and that the masses stayed constant. When it was discovered that the Newtonian idea was false everyone kept saying what a terrible thing it was that physicists had found out that they were wrong. Why did they think they were right? The effect is very small, and only shows when you get near the speed of light. If you spin a top it weighs the same as if you do not spin it, to within a very very fine fraction. Should they then have said, 'If you do not move any faster than so-and-so, then the mass does not change'? That would then be certain. No, because if the experiment happened to have been done only with tops of wood, copper and steel, they would have had to say 'Tops made out of copper, wood and steel, when not moving any faster than so and so . . .'. You see, we do not know all the conditions that we need for an experiment. It is not known whether a radioactive top would have a mass that is conserved. So we have to make guesses in order to give any utility at all to science. In order to avoid simply describing experiments that have been done, we have to propose laws beyond their observed range. There is nothing wrong with that, despite the fact that it makes science uncertain. If you thought before that science was certain – well, that is just an error on your part.

To return then, to our list of conservation laws (fig. 14), we can add energy. It is conserved perfectly, as far as we know. It does not come in units. Now the question is, is it the source of a field? The answer is yes. Einstein understood gravitation as being generated by energy. Energy and mass are equivalent, and so Newton's interpretation that the mass is what produces gravity has been modified to the statement that the energy produces the gravity.

There are other laws similar to the conservation of energy, in the sense that they are numbers. One of them is momentum. If you take all the masses of an object, multiply them by the velocities, and add them all together, the sum is the momentum of the particles; and the total amount of momentum is conserved. Energy and momentum are now understood to be very closely related, so I have put them in the same column of our table.

Another example of a conserved quantity is angular momentum, an item which we discussed before. The angular momentum is the area generated per second by objects moving about. For example, if we have a moving object, and we take any centre whatsoever, then the speed at which the area (fig. 17) swept out by a line from centre to object,

Figure 17

increases, multiplied by the mass of the object, and added together for all the objects, is called the angular momentum. And that quantity does not change. So we have conservation of angular momentum. Incidentally, at first sight, if you know too much physics, you might think that the angular momentum is not conserved. Like the energy it appears in different forms. Although most people think it only appears in motion it does appear in other forms, as I will illustrate. If you have a wire, and move a magnet up into it, increasing the magnetic field through the flux through the wire, there will be an electric current – that is how electric generators work. Imagine that instead of a wire I have a disc, on which there are electric charges analogous to the electrons in the wire (fig. 18). Now I bring a magnet dead centre along the

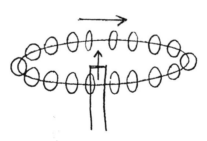

Figure 18

axis from far away, very rapidly up to the disc, so that now there is a flux change. Then, just as in the wire, the charges will start to go around, and if the disc were on a wheel it would be spinning by the time I had brought the magnet up. That does not look like conservation of angular momentum, because when the magnet is away from the disc nothing is turning, and when they are close together it is spinning. We have got turning for nothing, and that is against the rules. 'Oh yes,' you say, 'I know, there must be some other kind of interaction that makes the magnet spin the opposite way.' That is not the case. There is no electrical force on the magnet tending to twist it the opposite way. The explanation is that angular momentum appears in two forms: one of them is angular momentum of motion, and the other is angular momentum in electric and magnetic fields. There is angular momentum in the field around the magnet, although it does not appear as motion, and this has the opposite sign to the spin. If we take the opposite case it is even clearer (fig. 19).

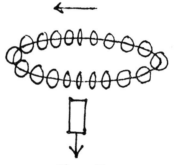

Figure 19

If we have just the particles, and the magnet, close together, and everything is standing still, I say there is angular momentum in the field, a hidden form of angular momentum which does not appear as actual rotation. When you pull the magnet down and take the instrument apart, then all the fields separate and the angular momentum now has to appear and the disc will start to spin. The law that makes it spin is the law of induction of electricity.

Whether angular momentum comes in units is very diffi-cult for me to answer. At first sight it appears that it is absolutely impossible that angular momentum comes in units, because angular momentum depends upon the direc-tion at which you project the picture. You are looking at an area change, and obviously this will be different depending on whether it is looked at from an angle, or straight on. If angular momentum came in units, and say you looked at something and it showed 8 units, then if you looked at it from a very slightly different angle, the number of units would be very slightly different, perhaps a tiny bit less than 8. But 7 is not a little bit less than 8; it is a definite amount less than eight. So it cannot possibly come in units. However this proof is evaded by the subtleties and peculiarities of quantum mechanics, and if we measure the angular momen-tum about any axis, amazingly enough it is always a number of units. It is not the kind of unit, like an electric charge, that you can count. The angular momentum does come in units in the mathematical sense that the number we get in any measurement is a definite integer times a unit. But we cannot interpret this in the same way as with units of electric charge, imaginable units that we can count – one, then another, then another. In the case of angular momen-tum we cannot imagine them as separate units, but it comes out always as an integer . . . which is very peculiar.

There are other conservation laws. They are not as interesting as those I have described, and do not deal exactly

Figure 20

with the conservation of numbers. Suppose we had some kind of device with particles moving with a certain definite symmetry, and suppose their movements were bilaterally symmetrical (fig. 20). Then, following the laws of physics, with all the movements and collisions, you could expect, and rightly, that if you look at the same picture later on it will still be bilaterally symmetrical. So there is a kind of conservation, the conservation of the symmetry character. This should be in the table, but it is not like a number that you measure, and we will discuss it in much more detail in the next lecture. The reason this is not very interesting in classical physics is because the times when there are such nicely symmetrical initial conditions are very rare, and it is therefore a not very important or practical conservation law. But in quantum mechanics, when we deal with very simple systems like atoms, their internal constitution often has a kind of symmetry, like bilateral symmetry, and then the symmetry character is maintained. This is therefore an important law for understanding quantum phenomena.

One interesting question is whether there is a deeper basis for these conservation laws, or whether we have to take them as they are. I will discuss that question in the next lecture, but there is one point I should like to make now. In discussing these ideas on a popular level, there seem to be a lot of unrelated concepts; but with a more profound understanding of the various principles there appear deep interconnections between the concepts, each one implying others in some way. One example is the relation between relativity and the necessity for local conservation. If I had stated this without a demonstration, it might appear to be some kind of miracle that if you cannot tell how fast you are moving this implies that if something is conserved it must be done not by jumping from one place to another.

At this point I would like to indicate how the conservation of angular momentum, the conservation of momentum, and a few other things are to some extent related. The conservation of angular momentum has to do with the area swept by particles moving. If you have a lot of particles (fig. 21), and take your centre (x) very far away, then the distances are almost the same for every object. In this case the only thing that counts in the area sweeping, or in the conservation of angular momentum, is the component of motion, which in figure 21 is vertical. What we discover then

Figure 21

is that the total of the masses, each multiplied by its velocity vertically, must be a constant, because the angular momentum is a constant about any point, and if the chosen point is far enough away only the masses and velocities are relevant. In this way the conservation of angular momentum implies the conservation of momentum. This in turn implies something else, the conservation of another item which is so closely connected that I did not bother to put it in the table. This is a principle about the centre of gravity (fig. 22).

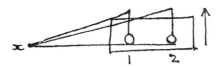

Figure 22

A mass, in a box, cannot just disappear from one position and move over to another position all by itself. That is nothing to do with conservation of the mass; you still have the mass, just moved from one place to another. Charge could do this, but not a mass. Let me explain why. The laws of physics are not affected by motion, so we can suppose that this box is drifting slowly upwards. Now we take the angular momentum from a point not far away, x. As the box is drifting upwards, if the mass is lying quiet in the box, at position 1, it will be producing an area at a given rate. After the mass has moved over to position 2, the area will be increasing at a greater rate, because although the altitude will be the same because the box is still drifting upwards, the distance from x to the mass has increased. By the conservation of angular momentum you cannot change the rate at which the area is changing, and therefore you simply cannot move one mass from one place to another unless you push on something else to balance up the angular momentum. That is the reason why rockets in empty space cannot go . . . but they do go. If you figure it out with a lot of masses, then if you move one forward you must move others back, so that the total motion back and forward of all the masses is nothing. This is how a rocket works. At first it is standing still, say, in empty space, and then it shoots some gas out of the back, and the rocket goes forward. The point is that of all the stuff in the world, the centre of mass, the average of all the mass, is still right where it was before. The interesting part has moved on, and an uninteresting part that we do not care about has moved back. There is no theorem that says that the interesting things in the world are conserved – only the total of everything.

Discovering the laws of physics is like trying to put together the pieces of a jigsaw puzzle. We have all these different pieces, and today they are proliferating rapidly. Many of them are lying about and cannot be fitted with the other ones. How do we know that they belong together? How do we know that they are really all part of one as yet incomplete picture? We are not sure, and it worries us to some extent, but we get encouragement from the common characteristics of several pieces. They all show blue sky, or they are all made out of the same kind of wood. All the various physical laws obey the same conservation principles.

A physicist and educator here tells a parable to illustrate the inadequacies he sees in the present system of teaching.

4   The Barometer Story

Alexander Calandra

An article from *Current Science, Teacher's Edition*, 1964.

SOME time ago, I received a call from a colleague who asked if I would be the referee on the grading of an examination question. It seemed that he was about to give a student a zero for his answer to a physics question, while the student claimed he should receive a perfect score and would do so if the system were not set up against the student. The instructor and the student agreed to submit this to an impartial arbiter, and I was selected.

The Barometer Problem

I went to my colleague's office and read the examination question, which was, "Show how it is possible to determine the height of a tall building with the aid of a barometer."

The student's answer was, "Take the barometer to the top of the building, attach a long rope to it, lower the barometer to the street, and then bring it up, measuring the length of the rope. The length of the rope is the height of the building."

Now, this is a very interesting answer, but should the student get credit for it? I pointed out that the student really had a strong case for full credit, since he had answered the question completely and correctly. On the other hand, if full credit were given, it could well contribute to a high grade for the student in his physics course. A high grade is supposed to certify that the student knows some physics, but the answer to the question did not confirm this. With this in mind, I suggested that the student have another try at answering the question. I was not surprised that my colleague agreed to this, but I was surprised that the student did.

Acting in terms of the agreement, I gave the student six minutes to answer the question, with the warning that the answer should show some knowledge of physics. At the end of five minutes, he had not written anything. I asked if he wished to give up, since I had another class to take care of, but he said no, he was not giving up. He had many answers to this problem; he was just thinking of the best one. I excused myself for interrupting him, and asked him to please go on. In the next minute, he dashed off his answer, which was:

"Take the barometer to the top of the building and lean over the edge of the roof. Drop the barometer, timing its fall with a stopwatch. Then, using the formula $S = \frac{1}{2} at^2$, calculate the height of the building."

At this point, I asked my colleague if he would give up. He conceded and I gave the student almost full credit. In leaving my colleague's office, I recalled that the student had said he had other answers to the problem, so I asked him what they were. "Oh, yes," said the student. "There are many ways of getting the height of a tall building with the aid of a barometer. For example, you could take the barometer out on a sunny day and measure the height of the barometer, the length of its shadow, and the length of the shadow of the building, and by the use of simple proportion, determine the height of the building."

"Fine," I said. "And the others?"

"Yes," said the student. "There is a very basic measurement method that you will like. In this method, you take the barometer and begin to walk up the stairs. As you climb the stairs, you mark off the length of the barometer along the wall. You then count the number of marks, and this will give you the height of the building in barometer units. A very direct method.

"Of course, if you want a more sophisticated method, you can tie the barometer to the end of a string, swing it as a pendulum, and determine the value of 'g' at the street level and at the top of the building. From the difference between the two values of 'g,' the height of the building can, in principle, be calculated."

Finally he concluded, "If you don't limit me to physics solutions to this problem, there are many other answers, such as taking the barometer to the basement and knocking on the superintendent's door. When the superintendent answers, you speak to him as follows: 'Dear Mr. Superintendent, here I have a very fine barometer. If you will tell me the height of this building, I will give you this barometer.'"

At this point, I asked the student if he really didn't know the answer to the problem. He admitted that he did, but that he was so fed up with college instructors trying to teach him how to think and to use critical thinking, instead of showing him the structure of the subject matter, that he decided to take off on what he regarded mostly as a sham.

The kinetic theory of gases is a marvelous structure of interconnecting assumption, prediction, and experiment. This chapter supplements and reinforces the discussion of kinetic theory in the text of Unit 3.

5   The Great Molecular Theory of Gases

Eric M. Rogers

An excerpt from his book *Physics for the Inquiring Mind: The Methods, Nature, and Philosophy of Physical Science*, 1960.

Newton's theory of universal gravitation was a world-wide success. His book, the *Principia,* ran into three editions in his lifetime and popular studies of it were the fashion in the courts of Europe. Voltaire wrote an exposition of the *Principia* for the general reader; books were even published on "Newton's Theory expounded to Ladies." Newton's theory impressed educated people not only as a brilliant ordering of celestial Nature but as a model for other grand explanations yet to come. We consider Newton's theory a *good* one because it is simple and productive and links together many different phenomena, giving a general feeling of understanding. The theory is simple because its basic assumptions are a few clear statements. This simplicity is not spoiled by the fact that some of the deductions need difficult mathematics. The success of Newton's planetary theory led to attempts at more theories similarly based on the laws of motion. For example, gases seem simple in behavior. Could not some theory of gases be constructed, to account for Boyle's Law by "predicting" it, and to make other predictions and increase our general understanding?

Such attempts led to a great molecular theory of gases. As in most great inventions the essential discovery is a single idea which seems simple enough once it is thought of: the idea that gas pressure is due to bombardment by tiny moving particles, the "molecules" of gas. Gases have simple common properties. They always fill their container and exert a uniform pressure all over its top, bottom, and sides, unlike solids and liquids. At constant temperature, PRESSURE · VOLUME remains constant, however the gas is compressed or expanded. Heating a gas increases its pressure or volume or both—and the rate of increase with temperature is the same for all gases ("Charles' Law"). Gases move easily, diffuse among each other and seep through porous walls.

Could these properties be "explained" in terms of some mechanical picture? Newton's contemporaries revived the Greek philosophers' idea of matter being made of "fiery atoms" in constant motion. Now, with a good system of mechanics they could treat such a picture realistically and ask what "atoms" would do. The most striking general property that a theory should explain was Boyle's Law.

Boyle's Law

In 1661 Boyle announced his discovery, "not without delight and satisfaction" that the pressures and volumes of air are "in reciprocal proportions." That was his way of saying: PRESSURE ∝ 1/VOLUME or PRESSURE · VOLUME remains constant, when air is compressed. It was well known that air expands when heated, so the restriction "at constant temperature" was obviously necessary for this simple law. This was Boyle's discovery of the "spring of the air"—a spring of variable strength compared with solid Hooke's Law springs.

In laboratory you should try a "Boyle's-Law experiment" with a sample of dry air, not to "discover" a law that you already know, but as a problem in precision, "your skill against nature." You

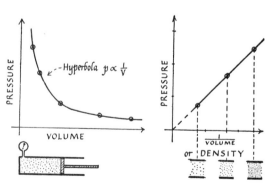

FIG. 25-1. BOYLE'S LAW

will be limited to a small range of pressures (say ½ atmosphere to 2 atm.) and your accuracy may be sabotaged by the room temperature changing or by a slight taper in the glass tube that contains the sample.[1] If you plot your measurements on a graph showing PRESSURE vs. VOLUME you will find they mark a hyperbola—but that is too difficult a curve to recognize for sure and claim as verification of Boyle's Law.[2] Then plot PRESSURE vs. 1/VOLUME and look for a straight line through the origin.

Boyle's measurements were fairly rough and extended only from a fraction of an atmosphere to about 4 atm. If you make precise measurements with air you will find that pV changes by only a few tenths of 1% at most, over that range. Your graph of p vs. $1/V$ will show your experimental points very close to a straight line through the origin. Since MASS/VOLUME is density and MASS is constant, values of $1/V$ represent DENSITY, and Boyle's Law says

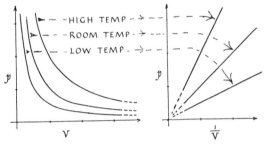

FIG. 25-2. BOYLE'S LAW ISOTHERMALS

PRESSURE ∝ DENSITY. This makes sense on many a simple theory of gas molecules: "put twice as many molecules in a box and you will double the pressure."

All the measurements on a Boyle's-Law graph line are made *at the same temperature*: it is an *isothermal* line. Of course we can draw several isothermals on one diagram, as in Fig. 25-2.

If the range of pressure is increased, larger deviations appear—Boyle's simple law is only an approximate account of real gas behavior. It fits well at low pressures but not at high pressures when the sample is crowded to high density. Fig. 25-3 shows the

[1] Even modern glass tubing is slightly tapered, unless made uniform by an expensive process; so when experiments "to verify Boyle's Law" show deviations from pV = constant they are usually exhibiting tube-taper rather than misbehavior of air. If the air sample is replaced by certain other gases such as CO_2, or by some organic vapor, real deviations from Boyle's Law become obvious and interesting. See Ch. 30.

[2] The only safe shapes of graphs for testing a law, or finding one, are straight lines and circles.

experimental facts for larger pressures, up to 3000 atmospheres. (For graphs of CO_2's behavior, including liquefaction, see Ch. 30.)

Theory

Boyle tried to guess at a mechanism underlying his experimental law. As a good chemist, he pictured tiny atomic particles as the responsible agents. He suggested that gas particles might be springy, like little balls of curly wool piled together, resisting compression. Newton placed gas particles farther apart, and calculated a law of repulsion-force to account for Boyle's Law. D. Bernoulli published a bombardment theory, without special force-laws, that predicted Boyle's Law. He pointed out that *moving* particles would produce pressure by bombarding the container; and he suggested that heating air must make its particles move faster. This was the real beginning of our present theory. He made a brave attempt, but his account was incomplete. A century later, in the 1840's, Joule and others set forth a successful "kinetic theory of gases," on this simple basic view:

> *A gas consists of small elastic particles in rapid motion: and the pressure on the walls is simply the effect of bombardment.*

Joule showed that this would "explain" Boyle's Law, and that it would yield important information about the gas particles themselves. This was soon polished by mathematicians and physicists into a large, powerful theory, capable of enriching our understanding.

In modern theories, we call the moving particles *molecules*, a name borrowed from chemistry, where it means the smallest particle of a substance that exists freely. Split a molecule and you have separate atoms, which may have quite different properties from the original substance. A molecule of water, H_2O, split into atoms yields two hydrogen atoms and one oxygen atom, quite different from the particles or molecules of water. Left alone, these separated atoms gang up in pairs, H_2, O_2—molecules of hydrogen and oxygen gas. In kinetic theory, we deal with the complete molecules, and assume they are not broken up by collisions. And we assume the molecules exert no forces on each other except during collisions; and then, when they are very close, they exert strong repulsive forces for a very short time: in fact that is all a collision *is*.

You yourself have the necessary tools for constructing a molecular theory of gases. Try it. Assume

"BOYLE'S LAW" FOR AIR

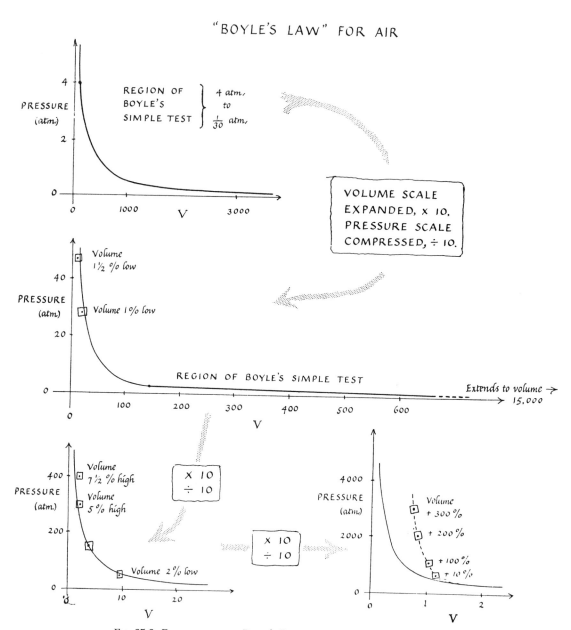

FIG. 25-3. DEVIATIONS FROM BOYLE'S LAW FOR AIR AT ROOM TEMPERATURE
The curve shows the PRESSURE:VOLUME relationship for an ideal gas obeying Boyle's Law.
The points show the behavior of air, indistinguishable from the curve at low pressures.

that gas pressure is due to molecules bouncing elastically on the containing walls. Carry out the first stages by working through Problems 1 and 2. They start with a bouncing ball and graduate to many bouncing molecules, to emerge with a prediction of the behavior of gases. After you have tried the problems, return to the discussion of details.

Difficulties of the Simple Theory

The relation you worked out in Problem 2 seems to predict a steady pressure and Boyle's-Law behavior, from molecular chaos. How can a rain of molecules hitting a wall make a steady pressure? Only if the collisions come in such rapid succession that their bumps seem to smooth out into a constant force. For that the

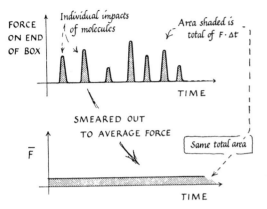

FIG. 25-6. SMOOTHING OUT IMPACTS

molecules of a gas must be exceedingly numerous, and very small. If they are small any solid pressure-gauge or container wall will be enormously massive compared with a single gas molecule, so that, as impacts bring it momentum, it will smooth them out to the steady pressure we observe. (What would you expect if the container wall were as light as a few molecules?)

The problem pretended that molecules travel straight from end to end and never collide with each other en route. They certainly do collide—though we cannot say how often without further information. How will that affect the prediction?

★ PROBLEM 3. COLLISIONS IN SIMPLE THEORY

(a) Show that it does not matter, in the simple derivation of Problems 1 and 2, whether molecules collide or not. (Consider two molecules moving to and fro from end to end, just missing each other as they cross. Then suppose they collide head-on and rebound. Why will their contribution to the pressure be unchanged? Explain with a diagram.)

(b) What special assumption about molecules is required for (a)?

(c) Suppose the molecules swelled up and became very bulky (but kept the same speed, mass, etc.), would the effect of mutual collisions be an increase of pressure (for the same volume etc.) or a decrease or what? (Note: "bulky" means large in size, not necessarily large in mass.)

(d) Give a clear reason for your answer to (c).

Molecular Chaos

Molecules hitting each other, and the walls, at random—some head on, some obliquely, some glancing—cannot all keep the same speed v. One will gain in a collision, and another lose, so that the gas is a chaos of molecules with random motions whose speeds (changing at every collision) cover a wide range. Yet they

must preserve some constancy, because a gas exerts a steady pressure.

In the prediction $p \cdot V = (\frac{1}{3})[N \, m \, \overline{v^2}]$, we do not have all N molecules moving with the same speed, each contributing $m \, \overline{v^2}$ inside the brackets. Instead we have molecule #1 with its speed v_1, molecule #2 with $v_2, \ldots,$ molecule N with speed v_N. Then

$$p \cdot V = (\frac{1}{3}) \, [m \, v_1{}^2 + m \, v_2{}^2 + \ldots + mv_N{}^2]$$
$$= (\frac{1}{3}) \, [m \, (v_1{}^2 + v_2{}^2 + \ldots + v_N{}^2) \,]$$
$$= (\frac{1}{3}) \, [m \, (N \cdot \text{AVERAGE } v^2) \,] \quad \text{See note 3.}$$

The v^2 in our prediction must therefore be an average v^2, so that we write a bar over it to show it is an average value. Our theoretical prediction now runs:

$$\text{PRESSURE} \cdot \text{VOLUME} = \frac{1}{3} N \cdot m \cdot \overline{v^2}.$$

We know that if we keep a gas in a closed bottle its pressure does not jump up and down as time goes on; its pressure and volume stay constant. Therefore in spite of all the changes in collisions, the molecular $\overline{v^2}$ stays constant. Already our theory helps us to picture some order—constant $\overline{v^2}$—among molecular chaos.

A More Elegant Derivation

To most scientists the regimentation that leads to the factor $\frac{1}{3}$ is too artificial a trick. Here is a more elegant method that treats the molecules' random velocities honestly with simple statistics. Suppose molecule #1 is moving in a slanting direction in the box, with velocity v_1. (See Fig. 25-7.) Resolve this vector v_1 into three

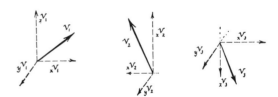

FIG. 25-7. ALTERNATIVE TREATMENT OF GAS MOLECULE MOTION
(More professional, less artificial.)

In this we keep the random velocities, avoiding regimentation, but split each velocity v into three components, $_xv, _yv, _zv$, parallel to the sides of the box. Then we deal with $_xv^2$ in calculating the pressure and arrive at the same result. Sketches show three molecules with velocities split into components.

components along directions x, y, z, parallel to the edges of the box. Then v_1 is the resultant of $_xv_1$ along x and $_yv_1$ along y and $_zv_1$ along z; and since these are mutually perpendicular, we have, by the three-dimensional form

[3] Because AVERAGE $v^2 = $ (sum of all the v^2 values)/(number of v^2 values) $= (v_1{}^2 + v_2{}^2 + \ldots + v_N{}^2)/(N)$
$\therefore \, (v_1{}^2 + v_2{}^2 + \ldots + v_N{}^2) = N \cdot (\text{AVERAGE } v^2)$ or $N \cdot \overline{v^2}$
This $\overline{v^2}$ is called the "mean square velocity." To obtain it, take the speed of each molecule at an instant, square it, add all the squares, and divide by the number of molecules. Or, choose one molecule and average its v^2 over a long time—say a billion collisions.

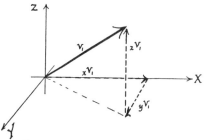

of Pythagoras' theorem: $v_1^2 = {}_xv_1^2 + {}_yv_1^2 + {}_zv_1^2$
And for molecule #2 $v_2^2 = {}_xv_2^2 + {}_yv_2^2 + {}_zv_2^2$
And for molecule #3 $v_3^2 = {}_xv_3^2 + {}_yv_3^2 + {}_zv_3^2$
   and so on   . . . .
And for molecule #N $v_N^2 = {}_xv_N^2 + {}_yv_N^2 + {}_zv_N^2$

Add all these equations:

$$(v_1^2 + v_2^2 + v_3^2 + \ldots + v_N^2)$$
$$= ({}_xv_1^2 + {}_xv_2^2 + {}_xv_3^2 + \ldots + {}_xv_N^2)$$
$$+ ({}_yv_1^2 + {}_yv_2^2 + {}_yv_3^2 + \ldots + {}_yv_N^2)$$
$$+ ({}_zv_1^2 + {}_zv_2^2 + {}_zv_3^2 + \ldots + {}_zv_N^2)$$

Divide by the number of molecules, N, to get *average* values:

$$\therefore \quad \overline{v^2} = \overline{{}_xv^2} + \overline{{}_yv^2} + \overline{{}_zv^2}$$

Appealing to symmetry, and ignoring the small bias given by gravity, we claim that the three averages on the right are equal—the random motions of a statistically large number of molecules should have the same distribution of velocities in any direction.

$$\therefore \quad \overline{{}_xv^2} = \overline{{}_yv^2} = \overline{{}_zv^2}$$
$$\therefore \quad \overline{v^2} = 3\overline{{}_zv^2}$$

To predict the pressure on the end of the box we proceed as in Problem 2, but we use v_x for a molecule's velocity along the length of the box. (That is the velocity we need, because ${}_yv$ and ${}_zv$ do not help the motion from end to end and are not involved in the change of momentum at each end.) Then the contribution of molecule #1 to PRESSURE · VOLUME is $m \cdot {}_xv_1^2$ and the contribution of all N molecules is

$$m \, ({}_xv_1^2 + {}_xv_2^2 + \ldots + {}_xv_N^2) \text{ or } m \cdot N \cdot \overline{{}_xv^2};$$

and by the argument above this is $m \cdot N \cdot (\overline{v^2}/3)$

$$\therefore \quad \text{PRESSURE · VOLUME} = (\tfrac{1}{3}) \, N \cdot m \cdot \overline{v^2}$$

(If you adopt this derivation, you should carry through the algebra of number of hits in t secs, etc., as in Problem 2.)

Molecular Theory's Predictions

Thinking about molecular collisions and using Newton's Laws gave the $(\tfrac{1}{3}) \, N \cdot m \cdot \overline{v^2}$ prediction:

$$\text{PRESSURE · VOLUME} = (\tfrac{1}{3}) \, N \cdot m \cdot \overline{v^2}$$

This looks like a prediction of Boyle's Law. The fraction $(\tfrac{1}{3})$ is a constant number; N, the number of molecules, is constant, unless they leak out or split

up; m, the mass of a molecule, is constant. Then *if the average speed remains unchanged, $(\tfrac{1}{3}) \, N \cdot m \cdot \overline{v^2}$ remains constant and therefore $p \cdot V$ should remain constant, as Boyle found it does. But does the speed of molecules remain fixed?* At this stage, you have no guarantee. For the moment, anticipate later discussion and *assume* that molecular motion is connected with the heat-content of a gas, and that *at constant temperature gas molecules keep a constant average speed*, the same speed however much the gas is compressed or rarefied.[4] Later you will receive clear reasons for believing this. If you accept it now, you have predicted that:

> The product $p \cdot V$ *is constant* for a gas at constant temperature.

You can see the prediction in simplest form by considering changes of DENSITY instead of VOLUME: just put twice as many molecules in the same box, and the pressure will be doubled.

A marvelous prediction of Boyle's Law? Hardly marvelous: we had to pour in many assumptions—with a careful eye on the desired result, we could scarcely help choosing wisely. A theory that gathers assumptions and predicts only one already-known law—and that under a further assumption regarding temperature—would not be worth keeping. But our new theory is just beginning: it is also helpful in "explaining" evaporation, diffusion, gas friction; it predicts effects of sudden compression; it makes vacuum-pumps easier to design and understand. And it leads to measurements that give validity to its own assumptions. Before discussing the development, we ask a basic question, "Are there really any such things as molecules?"

Are there really molecules?

"That's the worst of circumstantial evidence. The prosecuting attorney has at his command all the facilities of organized investigation. He uncovers facts. He selects only those which, in his opinion, are significant. Once he's come to the conclusion the defendant is guilty, the only facts he considers significant are those which point to the guilt of the defendant. That's why circumstantial evidence is such a liar. Facts themselves are meaningless. It's only the interpretation we give those facts which counts."

"Perry Mason"—Erle Stanley Gardner[*]

---

[4] Actually, compressing a gas warms it, but we believe that when it cools back to its original temperature its molecules, though still crowded close, return to the same average speed as before compression.

[*] *The Case of the Perjured Parrot*, Copyright 1939, by Erle Stanley Gardner.

A century ago, molecules seemed useful: a helpful concept that made the regularities of chemical combinations easy to understand and provided a good start for a simple theory of gases. But did they really exist? There was only circumstantial evidence that made the idea plausible. Many scientists were skeptical, and at least one great chemist maintained his right to disbelieve in molecules and atoms even until the beginning of this century. Yet one piece of experimental evidence appeared quite early, about 1827: the Brownian motion.

The Brownian Motion

The Scottish botanist Robert Brown (1773-1858) made an amazing discovery: he practically saw molecular motion. Looking through his microscope at small specks of solid suspended in water, he saw them dancing with an incessant jigging motion. The microscopic dance made the specks look alive, but it never stopped day after day. Heating made the dance more furious, but on cooling it returned to its original scale. We now know that any solid specks in any fluid will show such a dance, the smaller the speck the faster the dance, a random motion with no rhyme or reason. Brown was in fact watching the effects of water molecules jostling the solid specks. The specks were being pushed around like an elephant in the midst of a football game.

Watch this "Brownian motion" for yourself. Look at small specks of soot in water ("India ink") with a high-magnification microscope. More easily, look at smoke in air with a low-power microscope. Fill a small black box with smoke from a cigarette or a dying match, and illuminate it with strong white light from the side. The smoke scatters bluish-white light in all directions, some of it upward into the microscope. The microscope shows the smoke as a crowd of tiny specks of white ash which dance about with an entirely irregular motion.[5] (See Fig. 30-3 for an example)

Watching the ash specks, you can see why Brown at first thought he saw living things moving, but you can well imagine the motion to be due to chance bombardment by air molecules. Nowadays we not only think it may be that; we are sure it is, because we can calculate the effects of such bombardment and check them with observation. If air molecules were infinitely small and infinitely numerous, they would bombard a big speck symmetrically from all sides and there would be no Brownian motion to see. At the other extreme, if there were only a few very big molecules of surrounding air, the ash speck would make great violent jumps when it did get hit. From what we see, we infer something between these extremes; there must be many molecules in the box, hitting the ash speck from all sides, many times a second. In a short time, many hundreds of molecules hit the ash speck from every direction; and occasionally a few hundreds more hit one side of it than the other and drive it noticeably in one direction. A big jump is rare, but several tiny random motions in the same general direction may pile up into a visible shift.[6] Detailed watching and calculation from later knowledge tell us that what we see under the microscope are those gross resultant shifts; but, though the individual movements are too small to see, we can still estimate their speed by cataloguing the gross staggers and analysing them statistically.

You can see for yourself that smaller specks dance faster. Now carry out an imaginary extrapolation to smaller and smaller specks. Then what motion would you expect to see with specks as small as molecules if you could see them? But can we see molecules?

Seeing molecules?

Could we actually see a molecule? That would indeed be convincing—we feel sure that what we *see* is real, despite many an optical illusion. All through the last century's questioning of molecules, scientists agreed that seeing one is hopeless—not just unlikely but impossible, for a sound physical reason. Seeing uses light, which consists of waves of very short wavelength, only a few thousand Ångström Units[7] from crest to crest. We see by using these waves to form an image:

with the naked eye we can see the shape of a pin's head, a millimeter across, or 10,000,000 AU

with a magnifying glass we examine a fine hair, 1,000,000 AU thick

with a low-power microscope we see a speck of smoke ash, 100,000 AU

with a high-power microscope, we see bacteria, from 10,000 down to 1000 AU

but there the sequence stops. It must stop because the wavelength of visible light sets a limit there. Waves can make clear patterns of obstacles that are larger

---

[5] There may also be general drifting motions—convection currents—but these are easily distinguished. An ash speck in focus shows as a small sharp wisp of white, often oblong; but when it drifts or dances away out of focus the microscope shows it as a fuzzy round blob, just as camera pictures show distant street lights out of focus.

[6] Imagine an observer with poor sight tracing the motion of an active guest at a crowded party. He might fail to see the guest's detailed motion of small steps here and there, and yet after a while he would notice that the guest had wandered a considerable distance.

[7] 1 Ångström Unit, 1 AU, is 10^{-10} meter.

than their wavelength, or even about their wavelength in size. For example, ocean waves sweeping past an island show a clear "shadow" of calm beyond. But waves treat smaller obstacles quite differently. Ocean waves meeting a small wooden post show no calm behind. They just lollop around the post and join up beyond it as if there were no post there. A blind man paddling along a stormy seashore could infer the presence of an island nearby, but would never know about a small post just offshore from him.[8] Light waves range in wavelength from 7000 ÅU for red to 4000 for violet. An excursion into the short-wave ultraviolet, with photographic film instead of an eye, is brought to a stop by absorption before wavelength 1000 ÅU: lenses, specimen, even the air itself, are "black" for extreme ultraviolet light. X-rays, with shorter wavelength still, can pass through matter and show grey shadows, but they practically cannot be focused by lenses. So, although X-rays have the much shorter wavelength that could pry into much finer structures, they give us only unmagnified shadow pictures. Therefore the limit imposed by light's wavelength seemed impassable. Bacteria down to 1000 ÅU could be seen, but virus particles, ten times smaller, must remain invisible. And molecules, ten times smaller still, must be far beyond hope. Yet viruses, responsible for many diseases, are of intense medical interest—we now think they may mark the borderline between living organisms and plain chemical molecules. And many basic questions of chemistry might be answered by seeing molecules.

The invisibility of molecules was unwelcome, but seemed inescapable. Then, early in this century, X-rays offered indirect information. The well-ordered atoms and molecules of crystals can scatter X-rays into regular patterns, just as woven cloth can "diffract" light into regular patterns—look at a distant lamp at night through a fine handkerchief or an umbrella. X-ray patterns revealed both the arrangement of atoms in crystals and the spacing of their layers. Such measurements confirmed the oil-film estimates of molecular size. More recently, these X-ray diffraction-splash pictures have sketched the general *shape* of some big molecules— really only details of crystal structure, but still a good hint of molecular shape. Then when physicists still cried "no hope" the electron microscope was invented. Streams of electrons, instead of light-waves, pass through the tiny object under examination, and are focused by electric or magnetic fields to form a greatly magnified image on a photographic film. Electrons are incomparably smaller agents than light-waves,[9] so small that

even "molecules" can be delineated. Then we can "see" virus particles and even big molecules in what seem to be reliable photographs with huge magnifications. These new glimpses of molecular structure agree well with the speculative pictures drawn by chemists arguing very cleverly from chemical behavior.

Recently, still sharper methods have been developed. At the end of this book you will see a picture of the individual atoms of metal in a needle point. Why not show that now? Because, like so much in atomic physics, the method needs a sophisticated knowledge of assumptions as well as techniques before you can decide in what sense the photograph tells the truth. Going still deeper, very-high-energy electrons are now being used to probe the structure of atomic nuclei, yielding indirect shadow pictures of them.

In the last 100 years, molecules have graduated from being tiny uncounted agents in a speculative theory to being so real that we even expect to "see" their shape. Most of the things we know about them—speed, number, mass, size—were obtained a century ago with the help of kinetic theory. *The theory promoted the measurements, then the measurements gave validity to the theory.* We shall now leave dreams of seeing molecules, and study what we can measure by simple experiments.

Measuring the Speed of Molecules

Returning to our prediction that:

$$\text{PRESSURE} \cdot \text{VOLUME} = (\tfrac{1}{3})\, N \cdot m \cdot \overline{v^2}$$

We can use this if we trust it, to estimate the actual speed of the molecules. N is the number of molecules and m is the mass of one molecule so Nm *is the total mass M of all the molecules* in the box of gas. Then we can rewrite our prediction:

$$\text{PRESSURE} \cdot \text{VOLUME} = (\tfrac{1}{3}) \cdot M \cdot \overline{v^2}$$

where M is the total mass of gas. We can weigh a big sample of gas with measured volume at known pressure and substitute our measurements in the relation above to find the value of $\overline{v^2}$ and thus the value of the average speed.

Fig. 25-9 shows the necessary measurements. Using the ordinary air of the room, we measure its pressure by a mercury barometer. (Barometer height and the measured density of mercury and the measured value of the Earth's gravitational field strength, 9.8 newtons per kilogram, will give the pressure in absolute units, newtons per square meter.)[10] We weigh the air which fills a flask. For this, we weigh the flask first full of air at atmospheric pressure and second after a vacuum pump has taken out nearly all the air. Then we open the flask under water and let water enter to replace the air pumped

[8] Tiny obstacles do produce a small scattered ripple, but this tells nothing about their shape. Bluish light scattered by very fine smoke simply indicates there are very tiny specks there, but does not say whether they are round or sharp-pointed or oblong. The still more bluish light of the sky is sunlight scattered by air molecules.

[9] Electrons speeding through the electron microscope behave as if they too have a wavelength, but far shorter than the wavelength of light. So they offer new possibilities of "vision," whether you regard them as minute bullets smaller than atoms, or as ultra-short wave patterns. A technology of "electron optics" has developed, with "lenses" for electron microscopes and for television tubes (which are electron projection-lanterns).

[10] Since we made our kinetic theory prediction with the help of Newton's Law II, the predicted *force* must be in absolute units, newtons; and the predicted *pressure* must be in newtons per square meter.

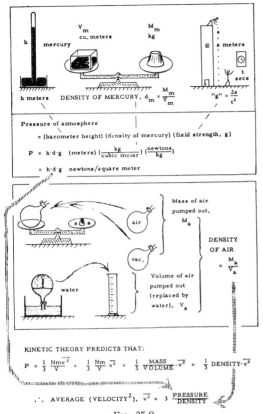

V_m cu. meters M_m kg

h mercury

s meters

t secs

DENSITY OF MERCURY, $d_m = \dfrac{M_m}{V_m}$

$"g" = \dfrac{2s}{t^2}$

Pressure of atmosphere

= (barometer height) (density of mercury) (field strength, g)

$P = h \cdot d \cdot g$ (meters) $(\frac{kg}{cubic\ meter})$ $(\frac{newtons}{kg})$

= $h \cdot d \cdot g$ newtons/square meter

Mass of air pumped out, M_a

air

DENSITY OF AIR = $\dfrac{M_a}{V_a}$

vac.

water

Volume of air pumped out (replaced by water), V_a

KINETIC THEORY PREDICTS THAT:

$$P = \frac{1}{3}\frac{Nmv^2}{V} = \frac{1}{3}\frac{Nm}{V}\overline{v^2} = \frac{1}{3}\frac{MASS}{VOLUME}\cdot\overline{v^2} = \frac{1}{3}DENSITY\cdot\overline{v^2}$$

$$\therefore\ AVERAGE\ (VELOCITY^2),\ \overline{v^2} = 3\ \frac{PRESSURE}{DENSITY}$$

Fig. 25-9.
Measuring Molecule Velocities Indirectly, but Simply, Assuming Kinetic Theory.

out. Measuring the volume of water that enters the flask tells us the volume of air which has a known mass. Inserting these measurements in the predicted relation we calculate $\overline{v^2}$ and thence its square root $\sqrt{(\overline{v^2})}$ which we may call the "average speed," $\overline{v}$ (or more strictly the "root mean square," or R.M.S. speed). You should see these measurements made and calculate the velocity, as in the following problem.

★ PROBLEM 4. SPEED OF OXYGEN MOLECULES

Experiment shows that 32 kg of oxygen occupy 24 cubic meters at atmospheric pressure, at room temperature.
(a) Calculate the density, MASS/VOLUME, of oxygen.
(b) Using the relation given by kinetic theory, calculate the mean square velocity, $\overline{v^2}$, of the molecules.
(c) Take the square root and find an "average" velocity, in meters/sec.
(d) Also express this very roughly in miles/hour.
(Take 1 kilometer to be 5/8 mile)

Air molecules moving ¼ mile a second! Here is theory being fruitful and validating its own assumption, as theory should. We assumed that gases con-

sist of molecules that are moving, probably moving fast; and our theory now tells us how fast, with the help of simple gross measurements. Yet theory cannot prove its own prediction is true—the result can only be true to the assumptions that went in. So we need experimental tests. If the theory passes one or two tests, we may trust its further predictions.

Speed of Molecules: experimental evidence

We have rough hints from the speed of sound and from the Brownian motion.

PROBLEM 5. SPEED OF SOUND

We believe that sound is carried by waves of compression and rarefaction, with the changes of crowding and motion handed on from molecule to molecule at collisions. If air does consist of moving molecules far apart, what can you say about molecular speed, given that the measured speed of sound in air is 340 meters/sec ($\approx$ 1100 ft/sec)?

PROBLEM 6. BROWNIAN MOTION

Looking at smoke under a microscope you will see large specks of ash jigging quite fast; small specks jig faster still.
(a) There may be specks too small to see. What motion would you expect them to have?
(b) Regarding a single air molecule as an even smaller "ash speck," what can you state about its motion?

The two problems above merely suggest general guesses. Here is a demonstration that shows that gas molecules move very fast. Liquid bromine is released at the bottom of a tall glass tube.[*] The

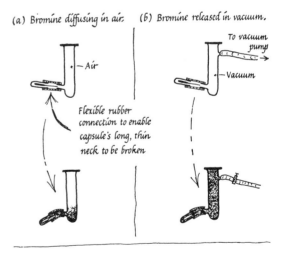

(a) Bromine diffusing in air. (b) Bromine released in vacuum.

To vacuum pump

Air

Vacuum

Flexible rubber connection to enable capsule's long, thin neck to be broken

(c) Sketch of capsule, about half life-size

Fig. 25-10. Motion of Bromine Molecules: Demonstration of Molecular Speed.

[*] The bromine is inserted as liquid bromine in a small glass capsule with a long nose that can be broken easily.

liquid evaporates immediately to a brown vapor or "gas," which slowly spreads throughout the tube. The experiment is repeated in a tube from which all air has been pumped out. Now the brown gas moves very fast when released. (In air, its molecules still move fast, but their net progress is slow because of many collisions with air molecules.)

Direct Measurement

The real test must be a direct measurement. Molecular speeds have been measured by several experimenters. Here is a typical experiment, done by Zartman. He let a stream of molecules shoot through a slit in the side of a cylindrical drum that could be spun rapidly. The molecules were of bismuth metal, boiled off molten liquid in a tiny oven in a vacuum. A series of barriers with slits selected a narrow stream to hit the drum. Then each time the slit in the drum came around, it admitted a small flock of moving molecules. With the drum at rest, the molecules travelled across to the opposite wall inside the drum and made a mark on a receiving film opposite the slit. With the drum spinning, the film was carried around an appreciable distance while the molecules were travelling across to it, and the mark on it was shifted to a new position. The molecules' velocity could be calculated from the shift of the mark and the drum's diameter and spin-speed. When the recording film was taken out of the drum it showed a sharp central mark of deposited metal but the mark made while it spun was smeared out into a blur showing that the molecular velocities had not all been the same but were spread over a considerable range. Gas molecules have random motion with frequent collisions and we must expect to find a great variety of velocities at any instant. It is the *average* velocity, or rather the root-mean-square average, $\sqrt{(\overline{v^2})}$, that is involved in kinetic theory prediction. The probable distribution of velocities, clustering round that average, can be predicted by extending simple kinetic theory with the help of the mathematical statistics of chance. In Zartman's experiment, we expect the beam of hot vapor molecules to have the same chance distribution of velocities with its peak at an average value characteristic of the temperature. Measurements of the actual darkening of the recording film showed just such a distribution and gave an average that

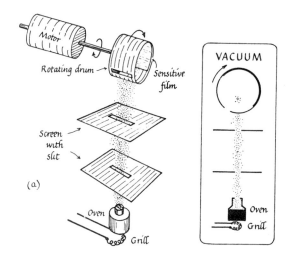

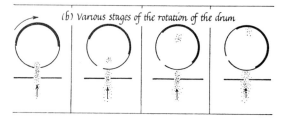

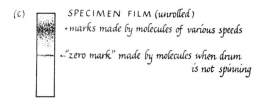

FIG. 25-11. MEASURING MOLECULE VELOCITIES DIRECTLY
(a) Sketch of Zartman's experiment.
(b) These sketches show various stages of the rotation of the drum.
(c) Specimen film (unrolled).

agreed well with the value predicted by simple theory (see sketch of graph in Fig. 25-12).[11]

Molecular Speeds in Other Gases. Diffusion

Weighing a bottle of hydrogen or helium at atmospheric pressure and room temperature shows these gases are much less dense than air; and carbon dioxide is much more dense. Then our predic-

---

[11] Zartman's method is not limited to this measurement. One method of separating uranium 235 used spinning slits, though the uranium atoms were electrically charged and were given high speeds by electric fields. And mechanical "chopper" systems are used to sort out moving neutrons.

Such choppers operate like traffic lights set for some constant speed. The simplest prototype of Zartman's experiment is the scheme shown in Fig. 8-8 for measuring the speed of a rifle bullet.

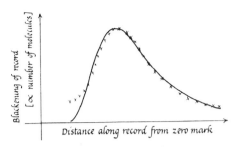

FIG. 25-12. RESULTS OF ZARTMAN'S EXPERIMENT
The curve, drawn by a grayness-measuring-machine, shows the experimental results. The crosses show values predicted by kinetic theory with simple statistics.

tion $pV = (\frac{1}{3}) M \overline{v^2}$ tells us that hydrogen and helium molecules move faster than air molecules (at the same temperature), and carbon dioxide molecules slower. Here are actual values:

Gas	Measurements at Room Temperature and Atmospheric Pressure	
	Volume	Mass
hydrogen	24 cu. meters	2.0 kilograms
helium	24 " "	4.0 kg
carbon dioxide	24 " "	44.0 kg
oxygen	24 " "	32.0 kg
nitrogen	24 " "	28.0 kg
air (⅕ oxygen ⅘ nitrogen)	24 " "	28.8 kg

★ PROBLEM 7. SPEEDS

(i) If oxygen molecules move about ¼ mile/sec at room temperature, how fast do hydrogen molecules move?

(ii) How does the average speed of helium molecules compare with that of hydrogen molecules at the same temperature? (Give the ratio of "average" speeds.)

(iii) How does the speed of carbon dioxide molecules compare with that of air molecules at the same temperature? (Give the ratio of "average" speeds.)

PROBLEM 8

Making a risky guess,* say whether you would expect the speed of sound in helium to be the same as in air, or bigger or smaller. Test your guess by blowing an organ pipe first with air, then with helium (or with carbon dioxide). Or breathe in helium and then talk, using your mouth and nose cavities as miniature echoing organ pipes. A change in the speed of sound changes the time taken by sound waves to

---

* It is obviously risky, since we are not considering the mechanism of sound transmission in detail. In fact there is an unexpected factor, which is different for helium: the ease with which the gas heats up as sound-compressions pass through. This momentary rise of temperature makes sound compressions travel faster. The effect is more pronounced in helium than in air, making the speed of sound 8% bigger than simple comparison with air suggests. Kinetic theory can predict this effect of specific heat, telling us that helium must have a smaller heat capacity, for a good atomic-molecular reason.

bounce up and down the pipe, and thus changes the frequency at which sound pulses emerge from the mouth. And that changes the musical note of the vowel sounds, which rises to higher pitch at higher frequency.

PROBLEM 9

How would you expect the speed of sound in air to change when the pressure is changed without any change of temperature? (Try this question with the following data, for air at room temperature: 28.8 kg of air occupy 24 cubic meters at 1 atmosphere pressure; at 2 atmospheres they occupy 12 cubic meters.)

Diffusion

If molecules of different gases have such different speeds, one gas should outstrip another when they diffuse through long narrow pipes. The pipes must be very long and very narrow so that gas seeps through by the wandering of individual molecules and not in a wholesale rush. The pores of unglazed pottery make suitable "pipes" for this. See Fig. 25-13a, b. The white jar J has fine pores that run right through its walls. If it is filled with compressed gas and closed with a stopper S, the gas will slowly leak out through the pores into the atmosphere, as you would expect. But if the pressure is the same (atmospheric) inside and out you would not expect any leakage even if there are different gases inside and outside. Yet there are changes, showing the effects of different molecular speeds. The demonstrations sketched start with air inside the jar and another gas, also at atmospheric pressure, outside. You see the effects of hydrogen molecules whizzing into the jar faster than air can move out; or of air moving out faster than CO_2 molecules crawl in. These are just qualitative demonstrations of "diffusion," but they suggest a process for separating mixed gases. Put a mixture of hydrogen and CO_2 inside the jar; then, whether there is air or vacuum outside, the hydrogen will diffuse out faster than the CO_2, and by repeating the process in several stages

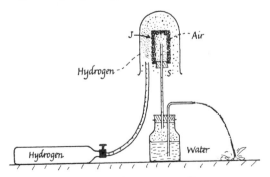

FIG. 25-13a. DIFFUSION OF GASES
Hydrogen diffuses in through the porous wall J faster than air diffuses out.

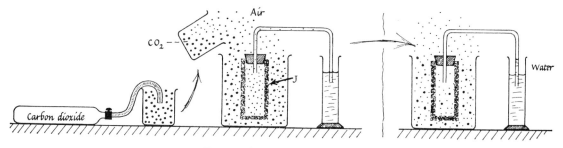

FIG. 25-13b. DIFFUSION OF GASES
Carbon dioxide diffuses in through the porous wall, J, slower than air diffuses out.

you could obtain almost pure hydrogen. This is a *physical* method of separation depending on a difference of molecular speeds that goes with a difference of molecular masses (see Fig. 25-14). It does not require a difference of *chemical* properties; so it can be used to separate "isotopes," those twin-brothers that are chemically identical but differ slightly in atomic masses. When isotopes were first discovered, one neon gas 10% denser than the other, some atoms of lead heavier than the rest, they were interesting curiosities, worth trying to separate just to show. Diffusion of the natural neon mixture from the atmosphere proved the possibility. But now with two uranium isotopes hopelessly mixed as they come from the mines, one easily fissionable, the other not, the separation of the rare fissionable kind is a matter of prime importance. Gas diffusion is now used for this on an enormous scale. See Problem 11, and Figs. 25-15, 16 and 17. Also see Chs. 30 and 43.

Temperature

Heating a gas increases p or V or both. With a rise of temperature there is always an increase of pV, and therefore of $(\frac{1}{3}) N m \overline{v^2}$. Therefore making a gas hotter increases v^2, makes its molecules move faster. This suggests some effects of temperature.

★ PROBLEM 10

(a) Would you expect the speed of sound to be greater, less, or the same in air at higher temperature? Explain.
(b) Would you expect diffusion of gases to proceed faster, slower, or at the same rate, at higher temperature? Explain.

Kinetic Theory To Be Continued

We cannot give more precise answers to such questions until we know more about heat and temperature and energy. Then we can extract more predictions concerning gas friction, heat conduction, specific heats; and we shall find a way of

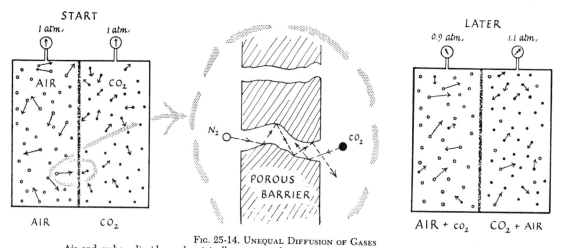

FIG. 25-14. UNEQUAL DIFFUSION OF GASES
Air and carbon dioxide, each originally at atmospheric pressure, are separated by a porous barrier.
At the start, with equal volumes at the same pressure, the two populations have equal numbers of molecules.
On the average, air molecules stagger through the pores faster than CO_2 molecules.
Then the populations are no longer equal so the pressures are unequal.

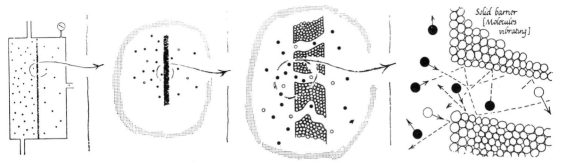

FIG. 25-15. SEPARATION OF URANIUM ISOTOPES BY DIFFUSION OF UF₆ THROUGH A POROUS BARRIER
Gas molecules hit the barrier, and the walls of its pores, many times—net result: a few get through.

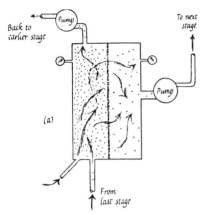

FIG. 25-16a. SEPARATION OF URANIUM ISOTOPES BY DIFFUSION OF UF₆ THROUGH A POROUS BARRIER.

measuring the mass of a single molecule, so that we can count the myriad molecules in a sample of gas. We shall return to kinetic theory after a study of energy. Meanwhile, it is kinetic theory that leads us towards energy by asking a question:

What is mv²?

The expression (⅓) $N m v^2$ is very important in the study of all gases. Apart from the fraction (⅓) it is

THE NUMBER OF MOLECULES · (mv^2 for one molecule)

What is mv^2 for a moving molecule? It *is* just the mass multiplied by the square of the speed; but what kind of thing does it measure? What are its properties? Is it an important member of the series: $m \quad mv \quad mv^2 \quad \ldots\ldots$? We know m, mass, and treat

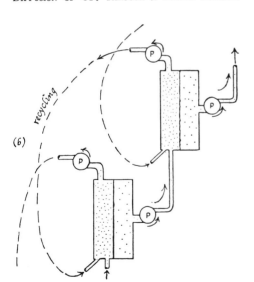

FIG. 25-16b. MULTI-STAGE DIFFUSION SEPARATION
Mixture diffusing through in one stage is pumped to the input of the next stage. Unused mixture from one stage is recycled, pumped back to the input of the preceding stage.

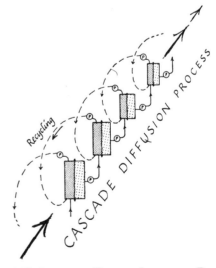

FIG. 25-17. SEPARATING URANIUM ISOTOPES BY DIFFUSION
To effect a fairly complete separation of U²³⁵ F₆, thousands of stages are needed.

it as a constant thing whose total is universally conserved. We know mv, momentum, and trust it as a vector that is universally conserved. Is mv^2 equally useful? Its structure is $mv \cdot v$ or $Ft \cdot v$ or

FORCE · TIME · DISTANCE/TIME.

Then mv^2 is of the form FORCE · DISTANCE. Is that product useful? To push with a force along some distance needs an engine that uses fuel. Fuel . . . money . . . energy. We shall find that mv^2 which appears in our theory of gases needs only a constant factor ($\frac{1}{2}$) to make it an expression of "energy."

PROBLEMS FOR CHAPTER 25

★ 1. DERIVING MOLECULAR PRESSURE

Work through the question sheets of Problem 1 shown earlier in this chapter. These lead up to the use of Newton's mechanics in a molecular picture of gases.

★ 2. KINETIC THEORY WITH ALGEBRA

Work through the question sheets of Problem 2.

Problems 3-10 are in the text of this chapter.

★ 11. URANIUM SEPARATION (For more professional version, see Problem 3 in Ch. 30)

Chemical experiments and arguments show that oxygen molecules contain two atoms so we write them O_2; hydrogen molecules have two atoms, written H_2; and the dense vapor of uranium flouride has structure UF_6.

Chemical experiments tell us that the *relative* masses of single atoms of O, H, F, and U are 16, 1, 19, 238. Chemical evidence and a brilliant guess (Avogadro's) led to the belief that a standard volume of any gas at one atmosphere and room temperature contains *the same number of molecules* whatever the gas (the same for O_2, H_2, or UF_6). Kinetic theory endorses this guess strongly (see Ch. 30).

(a) Looking back to your calculations in Problem 7 you will see that changing from O_2 to H_2 changes the mass of a molecule in the proportion 32 to 2. For the same temperature what change would you expect in the $\overline{v^2}$ and therefore what change in the average velocity? (That is, how fast are hydrogen molecules moving at room temperature compared with oxygen ones? Give a ratio showing the *proportion* of the new speed to the old. Note you do not have to repeat all the arithmetic, just consider the one factor that changes.)

(b) Repeat (a) for the change from oxygen to uranium fluoride vapor. Do *rough* arithmetic to find approximate numerical value.

(c) Actually there are several kinds of uranium atom. The common one has mass 238 (relative to oxygen 16) but a rare one (0.7% of the mixture got from rocks) which is in fact the one that undergoes fission, has mass 235. One of the (very slow) ways of separating this valuable rare uranium from the common one is by converting the mixture to fluoride and letting the fluoride vapor diffuse through a porous wall. Because the fluoride of U^{235} has a different molecular speed the mixture emerging after diffusing through has different proportions.
(i) Does it become richer or poorer in U^{235}?
(ii) Give reasons for your answer to (i).
(iii) Estimate the percentage difference between average speeds of $\left[U_1^{235}F_6\right]$ and $\left[U_1^{238}F_6\right]$ molecules.

(*Note*: As discussed in Ch. 11, a change of x % in some measured quantity Q makes a change of about $\frac{1}{2}$ x % in $\sqrt{Q}$.)

12. Figs. 25-13a and 25-13b show two diffusion demonstrations. Describe what happens and interpret the experiments.

★ 13. MOLECULAR VIEW OF COMPRESSING GAS

(a) When an elastic ball hits a massive wall head-on it rebounds with much the same *speed* as its original speed. The same happens when a ball hits a massive bat which is held firmly. However, *if the bat is moving towards the ball*, the ball rebounds with a different speed. Does it move faster or slower?

(b) (Optional, hard: requires careful thought.) When the bat is moving towards the ball is the time of the elastic impact longer, shorter, or the same as when the bat is stationary? (*Hint*: If elastic . . . . S.H.M. . . .)

(c) When a gas in a cylinder is suddenly compressed by the pushing in of a piston, its temperature rises. Guess at an explanation of this in terms of the kinetic theory of gases, with the help of (a) above.

(d) Suppose a compressed gas, as in (c), is allowed to push a piston out, and expand. What would you expect to observe?

★ 14. MOLECULAR SIZE AND TRAVEL

A closed box contains a large number of gas molecules at fixed temperature. Suppose the molecules magically became more bulky by swelling up to greater volume, without any increase in number or speed, without any change of *mass*, and without any change in the volume of the box.

(a) How would this affect the *average distance apart* of the molecules, center to center (great increase, decrease, or little change)?

(b) Give a reason for your answer to (a).

(c) How would this affect the *average distance travelled by a molecule between one collision and the next* (the "mean free path")?

(d) Give a reason for your answer to (c).

Changes in the visible world are often the result of the rule of probability at work in the submicroscopic world. A survey of principles of probability, reasons why there are no perpetual-motion machines, entropy and time's arrow—and much else.

6   Entropy and the Second Law of Thermodynamics

Kenneth W. Ford

An excerpt from his book *Basic Physics*, 1968.

As profound as any principle in physics is the second law of thermodynamics. Based on uncertainty and probability in the submicroscopic world, it accounts for definite rules of change in the macroscopic world. We shall approach this law, and a new concept, entropy, that goes with it, by considering some aspects of probability. Through the idea of probability comes the deepest understanding of spontaneous change in nature.

14.1   *Probability in nature*

When a spelunker starts down an unexplored cavern, he does not know how far he will get or what he will find. When a gambler throws a pair of dice, he does not know what number will turn up. When a prospector holds his Geiger counter over a vein of uranium ore, he does not know how many radioactive particles he will count in a minute, even if he counted exactly the number in a preceding minute. These are three quite different kinds of uncertainty, and all of them are familiar to the scientist.

The spelunker cannot predict because of total ignorance of what lies ahead. He is in a situation that, so far as he knows, has never occurred before. He is like a scientist exploring an entirely new avenue of research. He can make educated guesses about what might happen, but he can neither say what will happen, nor even assess the probability of any particular outcome of the exploration. His is a situation of uncertain knowledge *and* uncertain probability. The gambler is in a better position. He has uncertain knowledge but certain probability. He knows all the possible outcomes of his throw and knows exactly the chance that any particular outcome will actually occur. His ignorance of any single result is tempered by a definite knowledge of average results.

The probability of atomic multitudes, which is the same as the probability of the gambler, is at the heart of this chapter. It forms the basis for the explanation of some of the most important aspects of the behavior of matter in bulk. This kind of probability we can call a probability of ignorance—not the nearly

Figure 14.1 A tray of coins, a system governed by laws of probability.

total ignorance of the spelunker in a new cave or the researcher on a new frontier, but the ignorance of certain details called initial conditions. If the gambler knew with enough precision every mechanical detail of the throw of the dice and the frictional properties of the surface onto which they are thrown (the initial conditions) he could (in principle) calculate exactly the outcome of the throw. Similarly, the physicist with enough precise information about the whereabouts and velocities of a collection of atoms at one time could (with an even bigger "in principle"*) calculate their exact arrangement at a later time. Because these details are lacking, probability necessarily enters the picture.

The prospector's uncertainty is of still a different kind. He is coming up against what is, so far as we now know, a fundamental probability of nature, a probability not connected with ignorance of specific details, but rather connected with the operation of the laws of nature at the most elementary level. In atomic and nuclear events, such as radioactivity, probability plays a role, even when every possible initial condition is known. This fundamental probability in nature, an essential part of the theory of quantum mechanics, is pursued in Chapter Twenty-Three. In thermodynamics—the study of the average behavior of large numbers of molecules and of the links between the submicroscopic and macroscopic worlds—the fundamental probability in nature is of only secondary importance. It influences the details of individual atomic and molecular collisions, but these details are unknown in any case. Of primary importance is the probability of ignorance stemming from our necessarily scant knowledge of precise details of molecular motion.

The triumphs of thermodynamics are its definite laws of behavior for systems about which we have incomplete knowledge. However, it should be no surprise that laws of probability applied to large enough numbers can become laws of near certainty. The owners of casinos in Nevada are consistent winners.

14.2 *Probability in random events*

We turn our attention now to a system that at first sight has little to do with molecules, temperature, or heat. It is a tray of coins (Figure 14.1). For the purposes of some specific calculations, let us suppose that the tray contains just five coins. For this system we wish to conduct a hypothetical experiment and

---

* Because classical mechanics does not suffice to calculate exactly the outcome of an atomic collision, this hypothetical forecast of future atomic positions and velocities could be extended but a moment forward in time.

make some theoretical predictions. The experiment consists of giving the tray a sharp up-and-down motion so that all the coins flip into the air and land again in the tray, then counting the number of heads and tails displayed, and repeating this procedure many times. The theoretical problem is to predict how often a particular arrangement of heads and tails will appear.

Table 14.1 *Possible Arrangements of Five Coins*

Coin 1	Coin 2	Coin 3	Coin 4	Coin 5	
H	H	H	H	H	1 way to get 5 heads
H	H	H	H	T	
H	H	H	T	H	
H	H	T	H	H	5 ways to get 4 heads and 1 tail
H	T	H	H	H	
T	H	H	H	H	
H	H	H	T	T	
H	H	T	H	T	
H	T	H	H	T	
T	H	H	H	T	
H	H	T	T	H	10 ways to get 3 heads and 2 tails
H	T	H	T	H	
T	H	H	T	H	
H	T	T	H	H	
T	H	T	H	H	
T	T	H	H	H	
H	H	T	T	T	
H	T	H	T	T	
H	T	T	H	T	
H	T	T	T	H	
T	H	H	T	T	10 ways to get 2 heads and 3 tails
T	H	T	H	T	
T	H	T	T	H	
T	T	H	H	T	
T	T	H	T	H	
T	T	T	H	H	
H	T	T	T	T	
T	H	T	T	T	
T	T	H	T	T	5 ways to get 1 head and 4 tails
T	T	T	H	T	
T	T	T	T	H	
T	T	T	T	T	1 way to get 5 tails

The experiment you can easily carry out yourself. Be sure that the tray is shaken vigorously enough each time so that at least some of the coins flip over. Here let us be concerned with the theory. To begin, we enumerate all possible ways in which the coins can land. This is done pictorially in Table 14.1. There are 32 possible results of a tray shaking.* If all we do is count heads and tails without identifying the coins, the number of possible results is 6 instead of 32 (Table 14.1). Ten of the ways the coins can land yield three heads and two tails.

---

* Since each coin can land in two ways, the total number of ways in which five coins can land is $2 \times 2 \times 2 \times 2 \times 2 = 2^5 = 32$. Three coins could land in 8 different ways (2^3), four coins in 16 ways (2^4), and so on. In how many ways could 10 coins land?

There are also ten different ways to get three tails and two heads. Both four heads and one tail and four tails and one head can be achieved in five ways. Only one arrangement of coins yields five heads, and only one yields five tails. These numbers do not yet constitute a prediction of the results of the experiment. We need a postulate about the actual physical process, and a reasonable one is a postulate of randomness: that every coin is equally likely to land heads up or tails up and that every possible arrangement of the five coins is equally likely. This means that after very many trials, every entry in Table 14.1 should have resulted about $\frac{1}{32}$ of the time. Note, however, that equal probability for each arrangement of coins is *not* the same as equal probability for each possible number of heads or tails. After 3,200 trials, for example, we would expect to have seen five heads about 100 times, but three heads and two tails should have showed up ten times more frequently, about 1,000 times. The exact number of appearances of five heads or of three heads and two tails or of any other combination cannot be predicted with certainty. What *can* be stated precisely (provided the postulate of randomness is correct) are probabilities of each such combination.

Table 14.2 *Probabilities for Different Numbers of Heads and Tails When Five Coins Are Flipped*

No. Heads	No. Tails	Probability
5	0	1/32 = 0.031
4	1	5/32 = 0.156
3	2	10/32 = 0.313
2	3	10/32 = 0.313
1	4	5/32 = 0.156
0	5	1/32 = 0.031
		Total probability = 1.000

Shown in Table 14.2 are the basic probabilities for all the possible numbers of heads and tails that can appear in a single trial. It is interesting to present these numbers graphically also, as is done in Figure 14.2. The probability of a certain

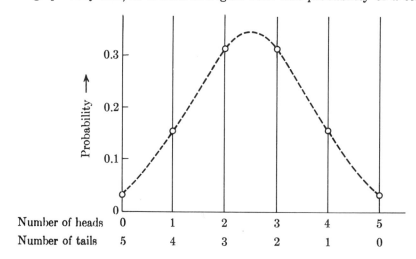

Figure 14.2 Probabilities for various results of tray-shaking experiment with five coins.

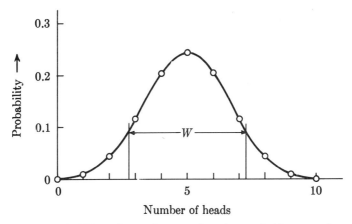

Figure 14.3 Probabilities for various results of tray-shaking experiment with ten coins.

number of heads plotted vs. the numbers of heads gives a bell-shaped curve, high in the middle, low in the wings.

Table 14.3 *Probabilities for Different Numbers of Heads and Tails When Ten Coins Are Flipped*

No. Heads	No. Tails	Probability
10	0	1/1024 = 0.0010
9	1	10/1024 = 0.0098
8	2	45/1024 = 0.0439
7	3	120/1024 = 0.1172
6	4	210/1024 = 0.2051
5	5	252/1024 = 0.2460
4	6	210/1024 = 0.2051
3	7	120/1024 = 0.1172
2	8	45/1024 = 0.0439
1	9	10/1024 = 0.0098
0	10	1/1024 = 0.0010
		Total probability = 1.0000

The same kind of calculation, based on the postulate of randomness can be carried out for any number of coins. For ten coins, the basic probabilities are given in Table 14.3 and in Figure 14.3.* Two changes are evident. First, the probability of all heads or all tails is greatly reduced. Second, the bell-shaped

---

* The reader familiar with binomial coefficients may be interested to know that the number of arrangements of n coins to yield m heads is the binomial coefficient

$$\binom{n}{m} = \frac{n!}{m!(n-m)!}.$$

Thus the probabilities in Table 14.3 are proportional to

$$\binom{10}{0}, \quad \binom{10}{1}, \quad \binom{10}{2},$$

and so on.

probability curve has become relatively narrower. The greater the number of coins, the less likely is it that the result of a single trial will be very different from an equal number of heads and tails. To make this point clear, the probability curve for a tray of 1,000 coins is shown in Figure 14.4. The chance of shaking all heads with this many coins would be entirely negligible even after a lifetime of trying. As Figure 14.4 shows, there is not even much chance of getting a distribution as unequal as 450 heads and 550 tails.

The tendency of the probabilities to cluster near the midpoint of the graph, where the number of heads and the number of tails are nearly equal, can be characterized by a "width" of the curve. The width of the curve is defined to be the distance between a pair of points (see Figures 14.3 and 14.4) outside of which the probabilities are relatively small and inside of which the probabilities are relatively large. Exactly where these points are chosen is arbitrary. One convenient choice is the pair of points where the probability has fallen to about one third of its central value—more exactly to $1/e = 1/2.72$ of its central value. The reason for defining a width is this: It spans a region of highly probable results. After the tray is shaken, the number of heads and the number of tails are most likely to correspond to a point on the central part of the curve within its width. The distribution of heads and tails is unlikely to be so unequal as to correspond to a point on the curve outside of this central region. When the number of coins is reasonably large (more than 100), there is a particularly simple formula for the width of the probability curve. If C is the number of heads (or tails) at the center of the curve, the width W of the curve is given by

$$W = 2\sqrt{C}. \tag{14.1}$$

The half-width, that is, the distance from the midpoint to the $1/e$ point of the curve, is equal to $\sqrt{C}$. This simple square root law is the reason for the particular factor $1/e$ used to define the width. With this choice the probability for the result of a tray-shaking to lie within the width of the curve is 84%.

In Figure 14.4 the value of C, the midpoint number of heads, is 500. The square root of C is roughly 22. Thus the width of the curve is about 44, extending from

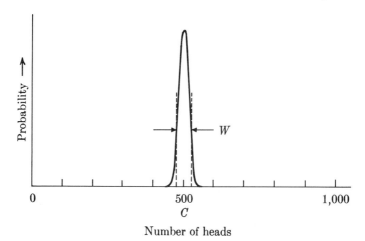

Figure 14.4 Probabilities for various results of tray-shaking experiment with 1,000 coins.

$500 - 22 = 478$ to $500 + 22 = 522$. The total chance for a result to lie within this span is 84%; to lie outside it, 16%.

An important consequence of the square-root law is to sharpen the probability curve as the number of coins increases. The ratio of the width to the total number of coins N $(N = 2C)$ is

$$\frac{W}{N} = \frac{2\sqrt{C}}{2C} = \frac{1}{\sqrt{C}}.$$ (14.2)

This ratio decreases as C (or N) increases. For 100 coins, the width-to-number ratio is about 1/10. For 1,000 coins, it is about 1/32. For 1,000,000 coins, it is 1/1,000. If the number of coins could be increased to be equal to the number of molecules in a drop of water, about 10^{22}, the width-to-number ratio of the probability curve would be $1/10^{11}$. Then the result of vigorous shaking of the coins would produce a number of heads and a number of tails unlikely to differ from equality by more than one part in one hundred billion. The probability curve would have collapsed to a narrow spike (Figure 14.5).

Two more points of interest about these head-and-tail probabilities will bring us closer to the connection between trays of coins and collections of molecules. First is the relation between probability and disorder. Ten coins arranged as all heads can be considered as perfectly orderly, as can an array of all tails. Five heads and five tails, on the other hand, arranged for example as HHTHTTTHTH or as TTHTHTHHHT, form a disorderly array. Evidently a high state of order is associated with low probability, a state of disorder is associated with high probability. This might be called the housewife's rule: Order is improbable, disorder is probable. The reason this is so is exactly the same for the household as for the tray of coins. There are many more different ways to achieve disorder than to achieve order.

The second point of special interest concerns the way probabilities change in time. If a tray of 1,000 coins is carefully arranged to show all heads, and is then shaken repeatedly, its arrangement will almost certainly shift in the direction of nearly equal numbers of heads and tails. The direction of spontaneous change will be from an arrangement of low probability to an arrangement of high

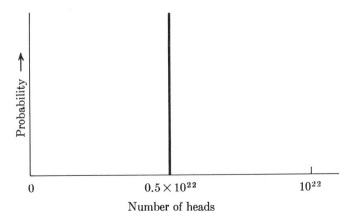

Figure 14.5 For 10^{22} coins, the probability curve is a spike much narrower even than the line on this graph.

probability, from order to disorder. The same will be true whenever the initial arrangement is an improbable one, for instance 700 tails and 300 heads. If instead we start with 498 heads and 502 tails, no amount of shaking will tend to move the distribution to a highly uneven arrangement. This can be considered an equilibrium situation. Repeated trials will then produce results not very different from the starting point. Clearly there is a general rule here—a rule of probability, to be sure, not an absolute rule: Under the action of random influences, a system tends to change from less probable arrangements to more probable arrangements, from order to disorder. The generalization of this rule from trays of coins to collections of molecules, and indeed to complex systems of any kind, is the *second law of thermodynamics*—a law, as we shall see, with remarkably broad and important consequences.

14.3 *Probability of position*

Most of the large-scale properties of substances are, when examined closely enough, probabilistic in nature. Heat and temperature are purely macroscopic concepts that lose their meaning when applied to individual atoms and molecules, for any particular molecule might have more or less energy than the average, or might contribute more or less than the average to a process of energy exchange. Temperature is proportional to an *average* kinetic energy; heat is equal to a *total* energy transferred by molecular collision. Because of our incomplete knowledge about the behavior of any single molecule, and the consequent necessity of describing molecular motion in probabilistic terms, neither of these thermal concepts is useful except when applied to numbers so large that the laws of probability become laws of near certainty. The same can be said of other concepts such as pressure and internal energy.

A single molecule is characterized by position, velocity, momentum, and energy. Of these, position is the simplest concept and therefore the one for which it is easiest to describe the role of probability. Consider, for instance, an enclosure—perhaps the room you are in—divided by a screen into two equal parts. What is the relative number of molecules of air on the two sides of the screen? Not a hard question, you will say. It is obvious that the two halves should contain equal, or very nearly equal, numbers of molecules. But here is a harder question. Why do the molecules divide equally? Why do they not congregate, at least some of the time, in one corner of the room? The answer to this question is exactly the same as the answer to the question: Why does a tray of coins after being shaken display approximately equal numbers of heads and tails? The equal distribution is simply the most probable distribution. Any very unequal distribution is very improbable.

The mathematics of molecules on two sides of a room proves to be identical to the mathematics of coins on a tray. By the assumption of randomness, every single molecule has an equal chance to be on either side of the room, just as every coin has an equal chance to land as heads or as tails. There are many different ways to distribute the molecules in equal numbers on the two sides, but only one way to concentrate them all on one side. If a room contained only five molecules, it would not be surprising to find them sometimes all on a single side. The probability that they be all on the left is 1/32 (see Table 14.1), and there is an equal probability that they be all on the right. The chance of a 3–2 distribution is 20/32, or nearly two thirds. Even for so small a number as five, a nearly equal division is much more likely than a very uneven division. For 10^{28} molecules, the number in a large room, the distribution is unlikely to deviate from equality by more than one part in 10^{14}. The probability for all of the 10^{28} molecules to congregate spontaneously in one half of the room is less than

$$10^{-(10^{+27})}$$

This number is too small even to think about. Suddenly finding ourselves gasping for breath in one part of a room while someone in another part of the room is oversupplied with oxygen is a problem we need not be worried about.

The second law of thermodynamics is primarily a law of change. It states that the direction of spontaneous change within an isolated system is from an arrangement of lower probability to an arrangement of higher probability. Only if the arrangement is already one of maximal probability will no spontaneous change occur. Air molecules distributed uniformly in a room are (with respect to their position) in such a state of maximal probability. This is an equilibrium situation, one that has no tendency for spontaneous change. Nevertheless it is quite easy through external actions to depart from this equilibrium to a less probable arrangement. Air can be pumped from one side of the room to the other. In a hypothetical vacuum-tight room with an impenetrable barrier dividing it in half, almost all of the air can be pumped into one half. When the barrier is punctured, the air rushes to equalize its distribution in space. This behavior can be described as the result of higher pressure pushing air into a region of lower pressure. But it can equally well be described as a simple consequence of the second law of thermodynamics. Once the barrier is punctured or removed, the air is free to change to an arrangement of higher probability, and it does so promptly.

It is worth noting that frequent molecular collisions play the same role for the air as tray-shaking plays for the coins. A stationary tray displaying all heads would stay that way, even though the arrangement is improbable. If molecules were quiescent, they would remain on one side of a room once placed there. Only because of continual molecular agitation do the spontaneous changes predicted by the second law of thermodynamics actually occur.

14.4 *Entropy and the second law of thermodynamics*

There are a variety of ways in which the second law of thermodynamics can be stated, and we have encountered two of them so far: (1) For an isolated system, the direction of spontaneous change is from an arrangement of lesser probability to an arrangement of greater probability; and (2) for an isolated system, the direction of spontaneous change is from order to disorder. Like the conservation laws, the second law of thermodynamics applies only to a system free of external influences. For a system that is not isolated, there is no principle restricting its direction of spontaneous change.

A third statement of the second law of thermodynamics makes use of a new concept called *entropy*. Entropy is a measure of the extent of disorder in a system or of the probability of the arrangement of the parts of a system. For greater probability, which means greater disorder, the entropy is higher. An arrangement of less probability (greater order) has less entropy. This means that the second law can be stated: (3) The entropy of an isolated system increases or remains the same.

Specifically, entropy, for which the usual symbol is S, is defined as Boltzmann's constant multiplied by the logarithm of the probability of any particular state of the system:

$$S = k \log P. \tag{14.3}$$

The appearance of Boltzmann's constant k as a constant of proportionality is a convenience in the mathematical theory of thermodynamics, but is, from a fundamental point of view, entirely arbitrary. The important aspect of the definition is the proportionality of the entropy to the logarithm of the probability P. Note that since the logarithm of a number increases when the number increases, greater probability means greater entropy, as stated in the preceding paragraph.

Exactly how to calculate a probability for the state of a system (a procedure that depends on the energies as well as the positions of its molecules) is a complicated matter that need not concern us here. Even without this knowledge, we can approach an understanding of the reason for the definition expressed by Equation 14.3. At first, entropy might seem to be a superfluous and useless concept, since it provides the same information about a system as is provided by the probability P, and S grows or shrinks as P grows or shrinks. Technically these two concepts *are* redundant, so that either one of them might be considered superfluous. Nevertheless both are very useful. (For comparison, consider the radius and the volume of a sphere; both are useful concepts despite the fact that they provide redundant information about the sphere.) The valuable aspect of the entropy concept is that it is additive. For two or more systems brought together to form a single system, the entropy of the total is equal to the sum of the entropies of the parts. Probabilities, by contrast, are multiplicative. If the probability for one molecule to be in the left half of a container is $\frac{1}{2}$, the probability for two to be there is $\frac{1}{4}$, and the probability for three to congregate on one side is $\frac{1}{8}$. If two containers, each containing three molecules, are encompassed in a single system, the probability that the first three molecules are all on the left side of the first container *and* that the second three are also on the left side of the second container is $\frac{1}{8} \times \frac{1}{8} = \frac{1}{64}$. On the other hand, the entropy of the combination is the sum of the entropies of the two parts. These properties of addition and multiplication are reflected in the definition expressed by Equation 14.3. The logarithm of a product is the sum of the logarithm of the factors:

$$S_{\text{total}} = k \log P_1 P_2 = k \log P_1 + k \log P_2 = S_1 + S_2. \tag{14.4}$$

The additive property of entropy is more than a mathematical convenience. It means that the statement of the second law can be generalized to include a composite system. To restate it: (3) The total entropy of a set of interconnected systems increases or stays the same. If the entropy of one system decreases, the entropy of systems connected to it must increase by at least a compensating amount, so that the sum of the individual entropies does not decrease.

Even though the second law of thermodynamics may be re-expressed in terms of entropy or of order and disorder, probability remains the key underlying idea. The exact nature of this probability must be understood if the second law is to be understood. Implicit in our discussion up to this point but still requiring emphasis is the a priori nature of the probability that governs physical change. The statement that physical systems change from less probable to more probable arrangements might seem anything but profound if the probability is regarded as an after-the-fact probability. If we decided that a uniform distribution of molecules in a box must be more probable than a nonuniform distribution because gas in a box is always observed to spread itself out evenly, the second law would be mere tautology, saying that systems tend to do what they are observed to do. In fact, the probability of the second law of thermodynamics is not based on experience or experiment. It is a before-the-fact (a priori) probability, based on counting the number of different ways in which a particular arrangement could be achieved. To every conceivable arrangement of a system can be assigned an a priori probability, whether or not the system or that arrangement of it has ever been observed. In practice there is no reason why the state of a system with the highest a priori probability need be the most frequently observed. Consider the case of the dedicated housewife. Almost every time an observant friend comes to call, he finds her house to be in perfect condition, nothing out of place, no dust in sight. He must conclude that for this house at least, the most probable state is very orderly state, since that is what he most often observes. This is an after-the-fact probability. As the housewife and the student of physics know, the orderly state has a low a priori probability. Left to itself, the house will tend toward a disorderly state of higher a priori probability. A state of particularly high a priori probability for a house is one not often observed, a pile of rubble. Thus an arrangement of high probability (from here on we shall omit the modifier, a priori) need be neither frequently observed nor quickly achieved, but it is, according to the second law of thermodynamics, the inevitable destination of an isolated system.

In comparison with other fundamental laws of nature, the second law of thermodynamics has two special features. First, it is not given expression by any mathematical equation. It specifies a direction of change, but not a magnitude of change. The nearest we can come to an equation is the mathematical statement,

$$S \geqslant 0. \tag{14.5}$$

In words: The change of entropy (for an isolated system or collection of systems) is either positive or zero. Or, more simply, entropy does not spontaneously decrease.

Every fundamental law of nature is characterized by remarkable generality, yet the second law of thermodynamics is unique among them (its second special feature) in that it finds direct application in a rich variety of settings, physical, biological, and human. In mentioning trays of coins, molecules of gas, and disorder in the house, we have touched only three of a myriad of applications. Entropy and the second law have contributed to discussion of the behavior of organisms, the flow of events in societies and economies, communication and information, and the history of the universe. In much of the physics and chemistry of macroscopic systems, the second law has found a use. Only at the submicroscopic level of single particles and single events is it of little importance. It is a startling and beautiful thought that an idea as simple as the natural trend from order to disorder should have such breadth of impact and power of application.

In most of the remainder of this chapter we shall be concerned with the application of the second law of thermodynamics to relatively simple physical situations. In Section 14.9 we return to some of its more general implications.

14.5 *Probability of velocity: heat flow and equipartition*

Since the velocities as well as the positions of individual molecules are generally unknown, velocity too is subject to considerations of probability. This kind of probability, like the probability of position, follows the rule of spontaneous change from lower to higher probability. It should not be surprising to learn that for a collection of identical molecules the most probable arrangement is one with equal molecular speeds (and randomly oriented velocities). This means that available energy tends to distribute itself uniformly over a set of identical molecules, just as available space tends to be occupied uniformly by the same molecules. In fact, the equipartition theorem and the zeroth law of thermodynamics can both be regarded as *consequences* of the second law of thermodynamics. Energy divides itself equally among the available degrees of freedom, and temperatures tend toward equality, because the resulting homogenized state of the molecules is the state of maximum disorder and maximum probability. The concentration of all of the energy in a system on a few molecules is a highly ordered and improbable situation analogous to the concentration of all of the molecules in a small portion of the available space.

The normal course of heat flow can also be understood in terms of the second law. Heat flow from a hotter to a cooler body is a process of energy transfer tending to equalize temperature and thereby to increase entropy. The proof that equipartition is the most probable distribution of energy is complicated and beyond the scope of this book. Here we seek only to make it plausible through analogy with the probability of spatial distributions.

Heat flow is so central to most applications of thermodynamics that the second law is sometimes stated in this restricted form: (4) Heat never flows spontaneously from a cooler to a hotter body. Notice that this is a statement about macroscopic behavior, whereas the more general and fundamental statements of the second law, which make use of the ideas of probability and order and disorder, refer to the submicroscopic structure of matter. Historically, the first version of the second law, advanced by Sadi Carnot in 1824, came before the submicroscopic basis of heat and temperature was established, in fact before the first law of thermodynamics was formulated. Despite a wrong view of heat and an incomplete view of energy, Carnot was able to advance the important principle that no heat engine (such as a steam engine) could operate with perfect efficiency. In modern terminology, Carnot's version of the second law is this: (5) In a closed system, heat flow out of one part of the system cannot be transformed wholly into mechanical energy (work), but must be accompanied by heat flow into a cooler part of the system. In brief, heat cannot be transformed completely to work.

The consistency of Carnot's form of the second law with the general principle of entropy increase can best be appreciated by thinking in terms of order and disorder. The complete conversion of heat to work would represent a transformation of disordered energy, a replacement of random molecular motion by orderly bulk motion. This violates the second law of thermodynamics. As indicated

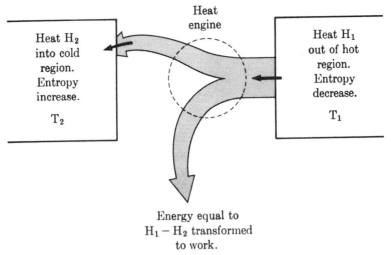

Figure 14.6 Schematic diagram of partial conversion of disordered heat energy to ordered mechanical energy. Heat flow out of a hot region decreases the entropy there. A compensating increase of entropy in a cold region requires less heat. Therefore, some heat can be transformed to work without violating the second law of thermodynamics. Any device that achieves this aim is called a heat engine.

schematically in Figure 14.6, a *partial* conversion of heat to work is possible because a small heat flow into a cool region may increase the entropy there by more than the decrease of entropy produced by a larger heat flow out of a hot region. At absolute zero, the hypothetically motionless molecules have maximum order. Greater temperature produces greater disorder. Therefore heat flow into a region increases its entropy, heat flow out of region decreases its entropy. Fortunately for the feasibility of heat engines, it takes less heat at low temperature than at high temperature to produce a given entropy change. To make an analogy, a pebble is enough to bring disorder to the smooth surface of a calm lake. To produce an equivalent increase in the disorder of an already rough sea requires a boulder. In Section 14.7, the quantitative link between heat flow and entropy is discussed.

The reverse transformation, of total conversion of work to heat, is not only possible but is commonplace. Every time a moving object is brought to rest by friction, all of its ordered energy of bulk motion is converted to disordered energy of molecular motion. This is an entropy-increasing process allowed by the second law of thermodynamics. In general, the second law favors energy dissipation, the transformation of energy from available to unavailable form. Whenever we make a gain against the second law by increasing the order or the available energy in one part of a total system, we can be sure we have lost even more in another part of the system. Thanks to the constant input of energy from the sun, the earth remains a lively place and we have nothing to fear from the homogenizing effect of the second law.

14.6 *Perpetual motion*

We have given so far five different versions of the second law, and will add only one more. Of those given, the first three, expressed in terms of probability, of order-disorder, and of entropy, are the most fundamental. Worth noting in several of the formulations is the recurring emphasis on the negative. Entropy does *not* decrease. Heat does *not* flow spontaneously from a cooler to a hotter region. Heat can *not* be wholly transformed to work. Our sixth version is also expressed in the negative. (6) Perpetual-motion machines cannot be constructed. This statement may sound more like a staff memorandum in the Patent Office than a fundamental law of nature. It may be both. In any event, it is certainly the latter, for from it can be derived the spontaneous increase of probability, of disorder, or of entropy. It is specialized only in that it assumes some friction, however small, to be present to provide some energy dissipation. If we overlook the nearly frictionless motion of the planets in the solar system and the frictionless motion of single molecules in a gas, everything in between is encompassed.

A perpetual-motion machine can be defined as a closed system in which bulk motion persists indefinitely, or as a continuously operating device whose output work provides its own input energy. Some proposed perpetual-motion machines violate the law of energy conservation (the first law of thermodynamics). These are called perpetual-motion machines of the first kind. Although they can be elaborate and subtle, they are less interesting than perpetual-motion machines of the second kind, hypothetical devices that conserve energy but violate the principle of entropy increase (the second law of thermodynamics).

As operating devices, perpetual-motion machines are the province of crackpot science and science fiction. As *inoperable* devices they have been of some signif-

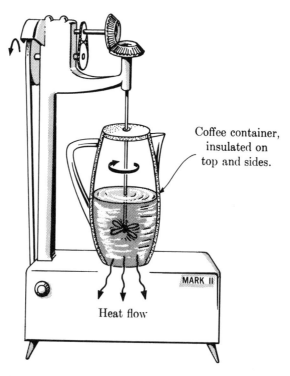

Figure 14.7 A perpetual-motion machine of the second kind. The device labeled MARK II receives heat energy from the coffee and converts this to mechanical energy which turns a paddle wheel, agitating the coffee, returning to the coffee the energy it lost by heat flow. It is not patentable.

icance in the development of science. Carnot was probably led to the second law of thermodynamics by his conviction that perpetual motion should be impossible. Arguments based on the impossibility of perpetual motion can be used to support Newton's third law of mechanics and Lenz's law of electromagnetic reaction, which will be discussed in Chapter Sixteen. Any contemporary scientist with a speculative idea can subject it to at least one quick test: Is it consistent with the impossibility of perpetual motion?

Suppose that an inventor has just invented a handy portable coffee warmer (Figure 14.7). It takes the heat which flows from the coffee container and, by a method known only to him, converts this heat to work expended in stirring the coffee. If the energy going back into the coffee is equal to that which leaks off as heat, the original temperature of the coffee will be maintained. Is it patentable? No, for it is a perpetual-motion machine of the second kind. Although it conserves energy, it performs the impossible task of maintaining a constant entropy in the face of dissipative forces that tend to increase entropy. Specifically it violates Carnot's version of the second law (No. 5, page 441), for in one part of its cycle it converts heat wholly to work. Of course it also violates directly our sixth version of the second law.

One of the chief strengths of the second law is its power to constrain the behavior of complex systems without reference to any details. Like a corporate director, the second law rules the overall behavior of systems or interlocked sets of system in terms of their total input and output and general function. Given a proposed scheme for the operation of the automatic coffee warmer, it might be quite a complicated matter to explain in terms of its detailed design why it cannot work. Yet the second law reveals at once that no amount of ingenuity can make it work.

14.7 *Entropy on two levels*

The mathematical roots of thermodynamics go back to the work of Pierre Laplace and other French scientists concerned with the caloric theory of heat in the years around 1800, and even further to the brilliant but forgotten invention of the kinetic theory of gases by Daniel Bernoulli in 1738. Not until after 1850 did these and other strands come together to create the theory of thermodynamics in something like its modern form. No other great theory of physics has traveled such a rocky road to success over so many decades of discovery, argumentation, buried insights, false turns, and rediscovery, its paths diverging and finally rejoining in the grand synthesis of statistical mechanics which welded together the macroscopic and submicroscopic domains in the latter part of the nineteenth century.

In the long and complex history of thermodynamics, the generalization of the principle of energy conservation to include heat stands as probably the most significant single landmark. Joule's careful experiments on the mechanical equivalent of heat in the 1840's not only established the first law of thermodynamics, but cleared the way for a full understanding of the second law, provided a basis for an absolute temperature scale, and laid the groundwork for the submicroscopic mechanics of the kinetic theory. Progress in the half century before Joule's work had been impeded by a pair of closely related difficulties: an incorrect view of the nature of heat, and an incomplete understanding of the way in which heat engines provide work. To be sure, there had been important insights in this period, such as Carnot's statement of the second law of thermodynamics in 1824. But such progress as there was did not fit together into a single structure, nor did it provide a base on which to build. Not until 1850, when the great significance of the general principle of energy conservation was appreciated by at least a few scientists, was Carnot's work incorporated into a developing theoretical structure. The way was cleared for a decade of rapid progress. In the 1850's, the first and second laws of thermodynamics were first stated as general unifying principles, the kinetic theory was rediscovered and refined, the concepts of heat and temperature were given submicroscopic as well as macroscopic definitions, and the full significance of the ideal-gas law was understood. The great names of the period were James Joule, William Thomson (Lord Kelvin), and James Clerk Maxwell in England, Rudolph Clausius and August Krönig in Germany.

One way to give structure to the historical development of a major theory is to follow the evolution of its key concepts. This is particularly instructive for the study of thermodynamics, because its basic concepts—heat, temperature, and entropy—exist on two levels, the macroscopic and the submicroscopic. The refinement of these concepts led both to a theoretical structure for understanding a great part of nature and to a bridge between two worlds, the large and the small. Of special interest here is the entropy concept.

Like heat and temperature, entropy was given first a macroscopic definition, later a molecular definition. Being a much subtler concept than either heat or temperature (in that it does not directly impinge on our senses), entropy was defined only after its need in the developing theory of thermodynamics became obvious. Heat and temperature were familiar ideas refined and revised for the needs of quantitative understanding. Entropy was a wholly new idea, formally introduced and arbitrarily named when it proved to be useful in expressing the second law of thermodynamics in quantitative form. As a useful but unnamed quantity, entropy entered the writings of both Kelvin and Clausius in the early 1850's. Finally in 1865, it was formally recognized and christened "entropy" by Clausius, after a Greek word for transformation. Entropy, as he saw it, measured the potentiality of a system for transformation.

The proportionality of entropy to the logarithm of an intrinsic probability for the arrangement of a system, as expressed by Equation 14.3, was stated first by Ludwig Boltzmann in 1877. This pinnacle of achievement in what had come to be called statistical mechanics fashioned the last great thermodynamics link between the large-scale and small-scale worlds. Although we now regard Boltzmann's definition based on the molecular viewpoint as the more fundamental, we must not overlook the earlier macroscopic definition of entropy given by Clausius (which in most applications is easier to use). Interestingly, Clausius expressed entropy simply and directly in terms of the two already familiar basic concepts, heat and temperature. He stated that a change of entropy of any part of a system is equal to the increment of heat added to that part of the system divided by its temperature at the moment the heat is added, provided the change is from one equilibrium state to another:

$$\Delta S = \frac{\Delta H}{T}.$$

(14.6)

Here S denotes entropy, H denotes heat, and T denotes the absolute temperature. For heat gain, ΔH is positive and entropy increases. For heat loss, ΔH is negative and entropy decreases. How much entropy change is produced by adding or subtracting heat depends on the temperature. Since the temperature T appears in the denominator in Equation 14.6, a lower temperature enables a given increment of heat to produce a greater entropy change.

There are several reasons why Clausius defined not the entropy itself, but the change of entropy. For one reason, the absolute value of entropy is irrelevant, much as the absolute value of potential energy is irrelevant. Only the change of either of these quantities from one state to another matters. Another more important reason is that there is no such thing as "total heat." Since heat is energy transfer (by molecular collisions), it is a dynamic quantity measured only in processes of change. An increment of heat ΔH can be gained or lost by part of a system, but it is meaningless to refer to the total heat H stored in that part. (This was the great insight about heat afforded by the discovery of the general principle of energy conservation in the 1840's). What is stored is internal energy, a quantity that can be increased by mechanical work as well as by heat flow. Finally, it should be remarked that Clausius' definition refers not merely to change, but to *small* change. When an otherwise inactive system gains heat, its temperature rises. Since the symbol T in Equation 14.6 refers to the temperature at which heat is added, the equation applies strictly only to increments so small that the temperature does not change appreciably as the heat is added. If a large amount of heat is added, Equation 14.6 must be applied over and over to the successive small increments, each at slightly higher temperature.

To explain how the macroscopic definition of entropy given by Clausius (Equation 14.6) and the submicroscopic definition of entropy given by Boltzmann (Equation 14.3) fit together is a task beyond the scope of this book. Nevertheless we can, through an idealized example, make it reasonable that these two definitions, so different in appearance, are closely related. To give the Clausius definition a probability interpretation we need to discuss two facts: (1) Addition of heat to a system increases its disorder and therefore its entropy; (2) The disordering influence of heat is greater at low temperature than at high temperature. The first of these facts is related to the apparance of the factor ΔH on the right of Equation 14.6; the second is related to the inverse proportionality of entropy change to temperature.

Not to prove these facts but to make them seem reasonable, we shall consider an idealized simple system consisting of just three identical molecules, each one capable of existing in any one of a number of equally spaced energy states. The overall state of this system can be represented by the triple-ladder diagram of Figure 14.8, in which each rung corresponds to a molecular energy state. Dots on the three lowest rungs would indicate that the system possesses no internal energy. The pictured dots on the second, third, and bottom rungs indicate that the system has a total of five units of internal energy, two units possessed by the first molecule, three by the second, and none by the third. The intrinsic probability associated with any given total energy is proportional to the number of different ways in which that energy can be divided. This is now a probability of *energy* distribution, not a probability of spatial distribution. However, the reasoning is much the same as in Section 14.3. There the intrinsic (a priori)

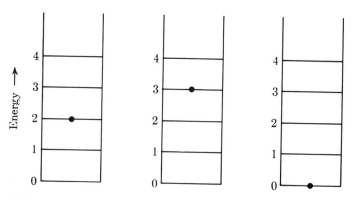

Figure 14.8 Idealized energy diagram for a system of three molecules, each with equally spaced energy states. Each ladder depicts the possible energies of a particular molecule, and the heavy dot specifies the actual energy of that molecule.

probability for a distribution of molecules in space was taken to be proportional to the number of different ways in which that distribution could be obtained. Or, to give another example, the probability of throwing 7 with a pair of dice is greater than the probability of throwing 2, because there are more different ways to get a total of 7 than to get a total of 2.

Table 14.4 enumerates all the ways in which up to five units of energy can be divided among our three idealized molecules. The triplets of numbers in the second column indicate the occupied rungs of the three energy ladders. It is an interesting and instructive problem to deduce a formula for the numbers in the

Table 14.4 *Internal Energy Distribution for Idealized System of Three Molecules*

Total Energy	Distribution of Energy			Number of Ways to Distribute Energy
0	000			1
1	100	010	001	3
2	200	020	002	
	110	101	011	6
3	300	030	003	
	210	201	012	
	120	102	021	
	111			10
4	400	040	004	
	310	301	031	
	130	103	013	
	220	202	022	
	211	121	112	15
5	500	050	005	
	410	401	041	
	140	104	014	
	320	302	032	
	230	203	023	
	311	131	113	
	122	212	221	21

last column. (HINT: The number of ways to distribute 6 units of energy is **28**.) However, since this is a highly idealized picture of very few molecules, precise numerical details are less important than are the qualitative features of the overall pattern. The first evident feature is that the greater the energy, the more different ways there are to divide the energy. Thus a higher probability is associated with greater internal energy. This does not mean that the system, if isolated and left alone, will spontaneously tend toward a higher probability state, for that would violate the law of energy conservation. Nevertheless, we associate with the higher energy state a greater probability and a greater disorder. When energy is added from outside via heat flow, the entropy increase is made possible. This makes reasonable the appearance of the heat increment factor, ΔH, in Equation 14.6.

Looking further at Table 14.4, we ask whether the addition of heat produces a greater disordering effect at low temperature than at high temperature. For simplicity we can assume that temperature is proportional to total internal energy, as it is for a simple gas, so that the question can be rephrased: Does adding a unit of heat at low energy increase the entropy of the system more than adding the same unit of heat at higher energy? Answering this question requires a little care, because of the logarithm that connects probability to entropy. The relative probability accelerates upward in Table 14.4. In going from 1 to 2 units of energy, the number of ways to distribute the energy increases by three, from 2 to 3 units it increases by four, from 3 to 4 units it increases by five, and so on. However, the entropy, proportional to the logarithm of the probability, increases more slowly at higher energy. The relevant measure for the increase of a logarithm is the *factor* of growth.* From 0 to 1 unit of energy, the probability trebles, from 1 to 2 units it doubles, from 2 to 3 units it grows by 67%, and so on, by ever decreasing factors of increase. Therefore the entropy grows most rapidly at low internal energy (low temperature). This makes reasonable the appearance of the temperature factor "downstairs" on the right of Equation 14.6.

This example focuses attention on a question that may have occurred to you already. Why is it that energy addition by heat flow increases entropy, but energy addition by work does not? The definition, Equation 14.6, makes reference to only one kind of energy, heat energy. The difference lies basically in the recoverability of the energy. When work is done on a system without any accompanying heat flow, as when gas is compressed in a cylinder (Figure **14.9**), the energy can be fully recovered, with the system and its surroundings returning precisely to the state they were in before the work was done. No entropy change is involved. On the other hand, when energy in the form of heat flows from a hotter to a cooler place, there is no mechanism that can cause the heat to flow spontaneously back from the cooler to the hotter place. It is not recoverable. Entropy has increased. In a realistic as opposed to an ideal cycle of compression and expansion, there will in fact be some entropy increase because there will be some flow of heat from the compressed gas to the walls of the container.

---

*Logarithms are defined in such a way that the logarithms of 10, 100, 1,000, and 10,000 or of 5, 10, 20, 40, and 80 differ by equal steps. It is this feature which makes the multiplication of a pair of numbers equivalent to the addition of their logarithms.

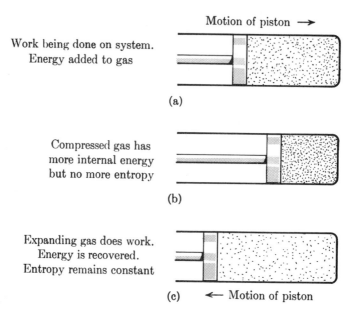

Motion of piston →

Work being done on system.
Energy added to gas

(a)

Compressed gas has
more internal energy
but no more entropy

(b)

Expanding gas does work.
Energy is recovered.
Entropy remains constant

(c)   ← Motion of piston

Figure 14.9 Idealized cycle of compression and expansion of gas, accompanied by no change of entropy. If any heat flow occurs in the cycle, entropy does increase.

Another useful way to look at the difference between heat and work is in molecular terms, merging the ideas of position probability and velocity or energy probability. If a confined gas [Figure 14.9(b)] is allowed to expand until its volume doubles [Figure 14.9(c)] what we learned about position probability tells us that, so far as its spatial arrangement is concerned, it has experienced an entropy increase, having spread out into an intrinsically more probable arrangement. In doing so, however, it has done work on its surroundings and has lost internal energy. This means that, with respect to its velocity and energy, it has approached a state of greater order and lesser entropy. Its increase of spatial disorder has in fact been precisely canceled by its decrease of energy disorder, and it experiences no net change of entropy. Had we instead wanted to keep its temperature constant during the expansion, it would have been necessary to add heat (equal in magnitude to the work done). Then after the expansion, the unchanged internal energy would provide no contribution to entropy change, so that a net entropy increase would be associated with the expansion—arising from the probability of position. This would match exactly the entropy increase $\Delta H/T$ predicted by the Clausius formula, for this change required a positive addition of heat.

Although the macroscopic entropy definition of Clausius and the submicroscopic entropy definition of Boltzmann are, in many physical situations, equivalent, Boltzmann's definition remains the more profound and the more general. It makes possible a single grand principle, the spontaneous trend of systems from arrangements of lower to higher probability, that describes not only gases and solids and chemical reactions and heat engines, but also dust and disarray, erosion and decay, the deterioration of fact in the spread of rumor, the fate of mismanaged corporations, and perhaps the fate of the universe.

14.8 *Application of the second law*

That heat flows spontaneously only from a warmer to a cooler place is a fact which can itself be regarded as a special form of the second law of thermodynamics. Alternatively the direction of heat flow can be related to the general principle of entropy increase with the help of the macroscopic definition of entropy. If body 1 at temperature T_1 loses an increment of heat ΔH, its entropy change—a decrease—is

$$\Delta S_1 = -\frac{\Delta H}{T_1}. \qquad (14.7)$$

If this heat is wholly transferred to body 2 at temperature T_2, its entropy gain is

$$\Delta S_2 = \frac{\Delta H}{T_2}. \qquad (14.8)$$

The total entropy change of the system (bodies 1 and 2) is the sum,

$$\Delta S = \Delta S_1 + \Delta S_2 = \Delta H\left(\frac{1}{T_2} - \frac{1}{T_1}\right). \qquad (14.9)$$

This entropy change must, according to the second law, be positive if the heat transfer occurs spontaneously. It is obvious algebraically from Equation 14.9 that this requirement implies that the temperature T_1 is greater than the temperature T_2. In short, heat flows from the warmer to the cooler body. In the process, the cooler body gains energy equal to that lost by the warmer body but gains entropy greater than that lost by the warmer body. When equality of temperature is reached, heat flow in *either* direction would decrease the total entropy. Therefore it does not occur.

A heat engine is, in simplest terms, a device that transforms heat to mechanical work. Such a transformation is, *by itself*, impossible. It is an entropy-decreasing process that violates the second law of thermodynamics. We need hardly conclude that heat engines are impossible, for we see them all around us. Gasoline engines, diesel engines, steam engines, jet engines, and rocket engines are all devices that transform heat to work. They do so by incorporating in the same system a mechanism of entropy increase that more than offsets the entropy decrease associated with the production of work. The simple example of heat flow with which this section began shows that one part of a system can easily lose entropy if another part gains more. In almost all transformations of any complexity, and in particular in those manipulated by man for some practical purpose, entropy gain and entropy loss occur side by side, with the total gain inevitably exceeding the total loss.

The normal mechanism of entropy gain in a heat engine is heat flow. Carnot's great insight that provided the earliest version of the second law was the realization that a heat engine must be transferring heat from a hotter to a cooler place at the same time that it is transforming heat to work. How this is accomplished varies from one heat engine to another, and the process can be quite complicated and indirect. Nevertheless, without reference to details, it is possible to discover in a very simple way what fraction of the total energy supplied by fuel can be transformed into usable work. This fraction is called the efficiency of the engine. Refer to Figure 14.6, which shows schematically a process of partial transformation of heat to work. From the hotter region, at temperature T_1, flows an increment of heat H_1. Into the cooler region, at temperature T_2, flows heat H_2. The output work is W. The first and second laws of thermodynamics applied to this idealized heat engine can be given simple mathematical expression.

1. Energy conservation: $H_1 = H_2 + W.$ (14.10)

2. Entropy increase: $S = \dfrac{H_2}{T_2} - \dfrac{H_1}{T_1} > 0.$ (14.11)

If this heat engine were "perfect"—free of friction and other dissipative effects—the entropy would remain constant instead of increasing. Then the right side of Equation 14.11 could be set equal to zero, and the ratio of output to input heat would be

$$\frac{H_2}{H_1} = \frac{T_2}{T_1}.$$ (14.12)

From Equation 14.10 follows another equation containing the ratio H_2/H_1,

$$\frac{W}{H_1} = 1 - \frac{H_2}{H_1}.$$ (14.13)

Substitution of Equation 14.12 into Equation 14.13 gives for the ratio of output work to initial heat supply,

$$\frac{W_{\max}}{H_1} = 1 - \frac{T_2}{T_1}.$$ (14.14)

Here we have written $W_{\max}$ instead of W, since this equation gives the maximum possible efficiency of the idealized heat engine. If the temperatures T_1 and T_2 are nearly the same, the efficiency is very low. If T_2 is near absolute zero, the theoretical efficiency can be close to 1—that is, almost perfect.

The modern marvels of technology that populate our present world—automobiles, television, airplanes, radar, pocket radios—all rest ultimately on basic principles of physics. Nevertheless they are usually not instructive as illustrations of fundamental laws, for the chain of connection from their practical function to the underlying principles is complex and sophisticated. The refrigerator is such a device. Despite its complexity of detail, however, it is worth considering in general terms. Because it transfers heat from a cooler to a warmer place, the refrigerator appears at first to violate the second law of thermodynamics. The fact that it must not do so allows us to draw an important conclusion about the minimum expenditure of energy required to run it. The analysis is quite similar to that for a heat engine. Suppose that the mechanism of the refrigerator is required to transfer an amount of heat H_1 out of the refrigerator each second. If the interior of the refrigerator is at temperature T_1, this heat loss contributes an entropy decrease equal to $-H_1/T_1$. This heat is transferred to the surrounding room at temperature T_2 (higher than T_1), where it contributes an entropy increase equal to H_1/T_2. The sum of these two entropy changes is negative. Some other contribution to entropy change must be occurring in order that the total change may be positive, in consonance with the second law. This extra contribution comes from the degradation of the input energy that powers the refrigerator.

The energy supplied by electricity or by the combustion of gas eventually reaches the surrounding room as heat. If the external energy (usually electrical) supplied in one second is called W, and the total heat added to the room in the same time is called H_2, energy conservation requires that H_2 be the sum of H_1 and W:

$$H_2 = H_1 + W. \tag{14.15}$$

The energy flow is shown schematically in Figure 14.10. At the same time the total entropy change is given by

$$\Delta S = \frac{H_2}{T_2} - \frac{H_1}{T_1}. \tag{14.16}$$

Since ΔS must be zero or greater, the ratio H_2/H_1 [= (heat added to room)/(heat extracted from refrigerator)] must be at least equal to T_2/T_1. If the energy conservation equation is written in the form

$$W = H_1\left[\frac{H_2}{H_1} - 1\right],$$

we can conclude that

$$W \geqslant H_1\left[\frac{T_2}{T_1} - 1\right]. \tag{14.17}$$

The right side of this inequality gives the minimum amount of external energy input required in order to transfer an amount of heat H_1 "uphill" from temperature T_1 to temperature T_2. As might be expected, the input energy requirement increases as the temperature difference increases. If the temperature T_1 is near absolute zero, as it is in a helium liquefier, the external energy expended is much greater than the heat transferred.

The real beauty of the result expressed by Equation 14.17 is its generality for all refrigerators regardless of their construction and mode of operation. The input energy W could be supplied by an electric motor, a gas flame, or a hand crank. It is characteristic of the second law of thermodynamics, just as it is characteristic of the fundamental conservation laws, that it has something important to say about the overall behavior of a system without reference to details, perhaps

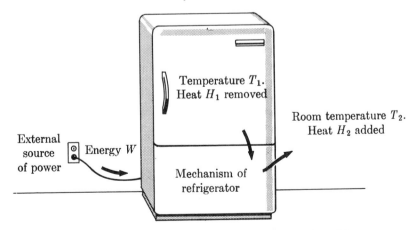

Figure 14.10   Energy and heat flow in the operation of a refrigerator.

without knowledge of details. In the small-scale world, our inability to observe precise features of individual events is one reason for the special importance of conservation laws. In the large-scale world, the elaborate complexity of many systems is one reason for the special importance of the second law of thermodynamics. Like the conservation laws, it provides an overall constraint on the system as a whole.

In many applications of the second law, the concept of available energy is the easiest key to understanding. In general, the trend of nature toward greater disorder is a trend toward less available energy. A jet plane before takeoff has a certain store of available energy in its fuel. While it is accelerating down the runway, a part of the energy expended is going into bulk kinetic energy (ordered energy), a part is going into heat that is eventually dissipated into unavailable energy. At constant cruising speed, all of the energy of the burning fuel goes to heat the air. Thermodynamically speaking, the net result of a flight is the total loss of the available energy originally present in the fuel. A rocket in free space operates with greater efficiency. Being free of air friction, it continues to accelerate as long as the fuel is burning. When its engine stops, a certain fraction (normally a small fraction) of the original available energy in the fuel remains available in the kinetic energy of the vehicle. This energy may be "stored" indefinitely in the orbital motion of the space vehicle. If it re-enters the atmosphere, however, this energy too is transformed into the disordered and unavailable form of internal energy of the air. To get ready for the next launching, more rocket fuel must be manufactured. The energy expended in the chemical factory that does this job is inevitably more than the energy stored in the fuel that is produced.

In general the effect of civilization is to encourage the action of the second law of thermodynamics. Technology greatly accelerates the rate of increase of entropy in man's immediate environment. Fortunately the available energy arriving each day from the sun exceeds by a very large factor the energy degraded by man's activity in a day. Fortunately too, nature, with no help from man, stores in usable form some of the sun's energy—for periods of months or years in the cycle of evaporation, precipitation, and drainage; for decades or centuries in lumber; for millennia in coal and oil. In time, as we deplete the long-term stored supply of available energy, we shall have to rely more heavily on the short-term stores and probably also devise new storage methods to supplement those of nature.

14.9 *The arrow of time*

Familiarity breeds acceptance. So natural and normal seem the usual events of our everyday life that it is difficult to step apart and look at them with a scientific eye.

Men with the skill and courage to do so led the scientific revolution of the seventeenth century. Since then, the frontiers of physics have moved far from the world of direct sense perception, and even the study of our immediate environment more often than not makes use of sophisticated tools and controlled experiment. Nevertheless, the ability to take a fresh look at the familiar and to contrast it with what would be the familiar in a different universe with different laws of nature remains a skill worth cultivating. For the student, and often for the scientist as well, useful insights come from looking at the familiar as if it were unfamiliar.

Consider the second law of thermodynamics. We need not go to the laboratory or to a machine or even to the kitchen to witness its impact on events. It is unlikely that you get through any five minutes of your waking life without seeing the second law at work. The way to appreciate this fact is by thinking backward. Imagine a motion picture of any scene of ordinary life run backward. You might watch a student untyping a paper, each keystroke erasing another letter as the keys become cleaner and the ribbon fresher. Or bits of hair clippings on a barber-shop floor rising to join the hair on a customer's head as the barber unclips. Or a pair of mangled automobiles undergoing instantaneous repair as they back apart. Or a dead rabbit rising to scamper backward into the woods as a crushed bullet reforms and flies backward into a rifle while some gunpowder is miraculously manufactured out of hot gas. Or something as simple as a cup of coffee on a table gradually becoming warmer as it draws heat from its cooler surroundings. All of these backward-in-time views and a myriad more that you can quickly think of are ludicrous and impossible for one reason only—they violate the second law of thermodynamics. In the actual sequence of events, entropy is increasing. In the time reversed view, entropy is decreasing. We recognize at once the obvious impossibility of the process in which entropy decreases, even though we may never have thought about entropy increase in the everyday world. In a certain sense everyone "knows" the second law of thermodynamics. It distinguishes the possible from the impossible in ordinary affairs.

In some of the examples cited above, the action of the second law is obvious, as in the increasing disorder produced by an automobile collision, or the increasing entropy associated with heat flow from a cup of coffee. In others, it is less obvious. But whether we can clearly identify the increasing entropy or not, we can be very confident that whenever a sequence of events occurs in our world in one order and not in the other, it is because entropy increase is associated with the possible order, entropy decrease with the impossible order. The reason for this confidence is quite simple. We know of no law other than the second law of thermodynamics that assigns to processes of change in the large-scale world a preferred direction in time. In the submicroscopic world too, time-reversal invariance is a principle governing all or nearly all fundamental processes.* Here we have an apparent paradox. In order to understand the paradox and its resolution, we must first understand exactly what is meant by time-reversal invariance.

The principle of time-reversal invariance can be simply stated in terms of hypothetical moving pictures. If the filmed version of any physical process, or sequence of events, is shown backward, the viewer sees a picture of something that could have happened. In slightly more technical language, any sequence of events, if executed in the opposite order, is a physically possible sequence of events. This leads to the rather startling conclusion that it is, in fact, impossible

---

* For the first time in 1964, some doubt was cast on the universal validity of time-reversal invariance, which had previously been supposed to be an absolute law of nature. In 1968 the doubt remains unresolved. Even if found to be imperfect, the principle will remain valid to a high degree of approximation, since it has already been tested in many situations. In particular, since all interactions that have any effect on the large-scale world do obey the principle of time-reversal invariance, the discussion in this section will be unaffected.

to tell by watching a moving picture of events in nature whether the film is running backward or forward. How can this principle be reconciled with the gross violations of common sense contained in the backward view of a barber cutting hair, a hunter firing a gun, a child breaking a plate, or the President signing his name? Does it mean that time-reversal invariance is not a valid law in the macroscopic world? No. As far as we know, time-reversal invariance governs every interaction that underlies processes of change in the large-scale world. The key to resolving the paradox is to recognize that possibility does not mean probability. Although the spontaneous reassembly of the fragments of an exploded bomb into a whole, unexploded bomb is wildly, ridiculously improbable, it is not, from the most fundamental point of view, impossible.

At every important point where the macroscopic and submicroscopic descriptions of matter touch, the concept of probability is crucial. The second law of thermodynamics is basically a probabilistic law whose approach to absolute validity increases as the complexity of the system it describes increases. For a system of half a dozen molecules, entropy decrease is not only possible, it is quite likely, at least some of the time. All six molecules might cluster in one corner of their container, or the three less energetic molecules might lose energy via collisions to the three more energetic molecules ("uphill" heat flow). For a system of 10^{20} molecules, on the other hand, entropy decrease becomes so improbable that it deserves to be called impossible. We could wait a billion times the known lifetime of the universe and still never expect to see the time-reversal view of something as simple as a piece of paper being torn in half. Nevertheless, it is important to realize that the time-reversed process is possible in principle.

Even in the world of particles, a sequence of events may occur with much higher probability in one direction than in the opposite direction. In the world of human experience, the imbalance of probabilities is so enormous that it no longer makes sense to speak of the more probable direction and the less probable direction. Instead we speak of the possible and the impossible. The action of molecular probabilities gives to the flow of events in the large-scale world a unique direction. The (almost complete) violation of time-reversal invariance by the second law of thermodynamics attaches an arrow to time, a one-way sign for the unfolding of events. Through this idea, thermodynamics impinges on philosophy.

In the latter part of the nineteenth century, long before time-reversal invariance was appreciated as a fundamental law of submicroscopic nature, physicists realized that the second law had something quite general to say about our passage through time. There are two aspects of the idea of the arrow of time: first, that the universe, like a wound-up clock, is running down, its supply of available energy ever dwindling; second, that the spontaneous tendency of nature toward greater entropy is what gives man a conception of the unique one-way direction of time.

The second law of thermodynamics had not long been formulated in a general way before men reflected on its implications for the universe at large. In 1865, Clausius wrote, without fanfare, as grand a pair of statements about the world as any produced by science: "We can express the fundamental laws of the universe which correspond to the two fundamental laws of the mechanical theory of heat in the following simple form.

"**1.** The energy of the universe is constant.
"**2.** The entropy of the universe tends toward a maximum."

These are the first and second laws of thermodynamics extended to encompass all of nature. Are the extensions justifiable? If so, what are their implications? We know in fact no more than Clausius about the constancy of energy and the steady increase of entropy in the universe at large. We do know that energy conservation has withstood every test since he wrote, and that entropy increase is founded on the very solid principle of change from arrangements of lesser to those of greater probability. Nevertheless, all that we have learned of nature in the century since Clausius leaped boldly to the edge of existence should make us cautious about so great a step. In 1865, the single theory of Newtonian mechanics seemed to be valid in every extremity of nature, from the molecular to the planetary. A century later we know instead that it fails in every extremity—in the domain of small sizes, where quantum mechanics rules; in the domain of high speed, where special relativity changes the rules; and in the domain of the very large, where general relativity warps space and time.

The logical terminus of the universe, assuming it to be a system obeying the same laws as the macroscopic systems accessible to experiment, is known as the "heat death," a universal soup of uniform density and uniform temperature, devoid of available energy, incapable of further change, a perfect and featureless final disorder. If this is where the universe is headed, we have had no hints of it as yet. Over a time span of ten billion years or more, the universe has been a vigorously active place, with new stars still being born as old ones are dying. It is quite possible that the long-range fate of the universe will be settled within science and need not remain forever a topic of pure speculation. At present, however, we have no evidence at all to confirm or contradict the applicability of thermodynamics to the universe as a whole. Even if we choose to postulate its applicability, we need not be led inevitably to the idea of the ultimate heat death. The existence of a law of time-reversal invariance in the world of the small and the essential probabilistic nature of the second law leave open the possibility that one grand improbable reversal of probability could occur in which disorder is restored to order. Finally, we can link this line of thought to the second aspect of the arrow of time, the uniqueness of the direction of man's course through time, with this challenging thought. If it is the second law that gives to man his sense of time's direction, the very construction of the human machine forces us to see the universe running down. In a world that we might look in upon from the outside to see building order out of disorder, the less probable from the more probable, we would see creatures who remembered their future and not their past. For them the trend of events would seem to be toward disorder and greater probability and it is we who would seem to be turned around.

In the three centuries since Newton, time has evolved from the obvious to the mysterious. In the *Principia*, Newton wrote, "Absolute, true, and mathematical time, of itself, and from its own nature flows equably without regard to anything external, and by another name is called duration." This view of time as something flowing constantly and inexorably forward, carrying man with it, persisted largely intact until the revolution of relativity at the beginning of this century. The nineteenth century brought only hints of a deeper insight, when it was appreciated that the second law of thermodynamics differentiated between forward and backward in time, as the laws of mechanics had failed to do. If time were run backward, the reversed planetary orbits would be reasonable and possible, obeying the same laws as the actual forward-in-time orbits. But the reversal of any entropy-changing transformation would be neither reasonable nor possible. The second law of thermodynamics points the way for Newton's equable flow.

Relativity had the most profound effect on our conception of time. The merger of space and time made unreasonable a temporal arrow when there was no spatial arrow. More recently, time-reversal invariance has confirmed the equal status of both directions in time. Relativity also brought time to a stop. It is more consistent with the viewpoint of modern physics to think of man and matter moving through time (as they move through space) than to think of time itself as flowing.

All of the new insights about time make clear that we must think about it in very human terms—its definition, its measurement, its apparently unique direction stem not from "absolute, true and mathematical time" but from psychological time. These insights also reinforce the idea that the second law of thermodynamics must ultimately account for our sense of time.

It is a stimulating idea that the only reason man is aware of the past and not the future is that he is a complicated and highly organized structure. Unfortunately, simpler creatures are no better off. They equalize future and past by remembering neither. An electron, being precisely identical with every other electron, is totally unmarked by its past or by its future. Man is intelligent enough to be scarred by his past. But the same complexity that gives him a memory at all is what keeps his future a mystery.

EXERCISES

14.1. Section 14.1 describes three kinds of uncertainty, associated respectively with a spelunker, a gambler, and a uranium prospector. Which of these kinds of uncertainty characterizes each of the following situations? (1) A pion of known energy enters a bubble chamber. The number of bubbles formed along its first centimeter of track is measured. The number of bubbles along its second centimeter of track can then be predicted approximately, but not exactly. (2) Another pion is created in the chamber. How long it will live before decaying is uncertain. (3) Still another pion, of energy higher than any previously studied, strikes a nucleus. The result of the collision is uncertain. Which, if any, of these examples of uncertainty is governed by thermodynamic probability (the probability of atomic multitudes)?

14.2. Suppose that a small cylinder (see figure) could be so nearly perfectly evacuated that only 100 molecules remained within it. (1) Using Figures 14.3 and 14.4 and Equation 14.1 as guides, sketch a curve of relative probability for any number of these molecules to be found in region A, which is half of the container. (2) If you placed a bet at even money that a measurement would reveal exactly 50 molecules in region A, would this be, from your point of view, a good bet or a poor bet? (3) If you bet, also at even money, that a series of measurements would show less than 60 molecules in region A more often than not, would you be making a good bet or a poor bet?

Completely random motion, such as the thermal motion
of molecules, might seem to be out of the realm of law-
fulness. But on the contrary, just because the motion
is completely disorderly, it is subject to statistical laws.

7 The Law of Disorder

George Gamow

A chapter from his book *One, Two, Three . . . Infinity*, 1947.

IF YOU pour a glass of water and look at it, you will see a clear
uniform fluid with no trace of any internal structure or motion
in it whatsoever (provided, of course, you do not shake the glass).
We know, however, that the uniformity of water is only apparent
and that if the water is magnified a few million times, there will
be revealed a strongly expressed granular structure formed by a
large number of separate molecules closely packed together.

Under the same magnification it is also apparent that the water
is far from still, and that its molecules are in a state of violent
agitation moving around and pushing one another as though they
were people in a highly excited crowd. This irregular motion of
water molecules, or the molecules of any other material substance,
is known as *heat (or thermal) motion,* for the simple reason that
it is responsible for the phenomenon of heat. For, although
molecular motion as well as molecules themselves are not directly
discernible to the human eye, it is molecular motion that produces
a certain irritation in the nervous fibers of the human organism
and produces the sensation that we call heat. For those organisms
that are much smaller than human beings, such as, for example,
small bacteria suspended in a water drop, the effect of thermal
motion is much more pronounced, and these poor creatures are
incessantly kicked, pushed, and tossed around by the restless
molecules that attack them from all sides and give them no rest
(Figure 77). This amusing phenomenon, known as *Brownian
motion,* named after the English botanist Robert Brown, who first
noticed it more than a century ago in a study of tiny plant spores,
is of quite general nature and can be observed in the study of any
kind of sufficiently small particles suspended in any kind of
liquid, or of microscopic particles of smoke and dust floating
in the air.

If we heat the liquid the wild dance of tiny particles suspended in it becomes more violent; with cooling the intensity of the motion noticeably subsides. This leaves no doubt that we are actually watching here the effect of the hidden thermal motion of matter, and that what we usually call temperature is nothing else but a measurement of the degree of molecular agitation. By studying the dependence of Brownian motion on temperature, it was found that at the temperature of $-273°$ C or $-459°$ F,

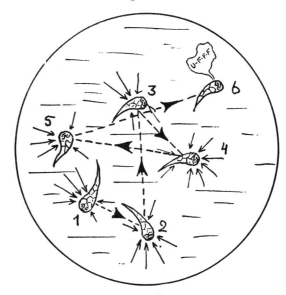

FIGURE 77

Six consecutive positions of a bacterium which is being tossed around by molecular impacts (physically correct; bacteriologically not quite so).

thermal agitation of matter completely ceases, and all its molecules come to rest. This apparently is the lowest temperature and it has received the name of *absolute zero*. It would be an absurdity to speak about still lower temperatures since apparently there is no motion slower than absolute rest!

Near the absolute zero temperature the molecules of any substance have so little energy that the cohesive forces acting upon them cement them together into one solid block, and all they can do is only quiver slightly in their frozen state. When the temperature rises the quivering becomes more and more intense, and at a certain stage our molecules obtain some freedom of motion and are able to slide by one another. The rigidity of the frozen substance disappears, and it becomes a fluid. The temperature at which the melting process takes place depends on the strength of the cohesive forces acting upon the molecules. In some materials such as hydrogen, or a mixture of nitrogen and oxygen which form atmospheric air, the cohesion of molecules is very weak, and the thermal agitation breaks up the frozen state at comparatively low temperatures. Thus hydrogen exists in the frozen state only at temperatures below 14° abs (i.e., below −259° C), whereas solid oxygen and nitrogen melt at 55° abs and 64° abs, respectively (i.e. −218° C and −209° C). In other substances the cohesion between molecules is stronger and they remain solid up to higher temperatures: thus pure alcohol remains frozen up to −130° C, whereas frozen water (ice) melts only at 0° C. Other substances remain solid up to much higher temperatures; a piece of lead will melt only at +327° C, iron at +1535° C, and the rare metal known as osmium remains solid up to the temperature of +2700° C. Although in the solid state of matter the molecules are strongly bound to their places, it does not mean at all that they are not affected by thermal agitation. Indeed, according to the fundamental law of heat motion, the amount of energy in every molecule is the same for all substances, solid, liquid, or gaseous at a given temperature, and the difference lies only in the fact that whereas in some cases this energy suffices to tear off the molecules from their fixed positions and let them travel around, in other cases they can only quiver on the same spot as angry dogs restricted by short chains.

This thermal quivering or vibration of molecules forming a solid body can be easily observed in the X-ray photographs described in the previous chapter. We have seen indeed that, since taking a picture of molecules in a crystal lattice requires a considerable time, it is essential that they should not move away from their fixed positions during the exposure. But a constant quivering around the fixed position is not conducive to good photography, and results in a somewhat blurred picture. This

FIGURE 78

effect is shown in the molecular photograph which is reproduced in Plate I. To obtain sharper pictures one must cool the crystals as much as possible. This is sometimes accomplished by dipping them in liquid air. If, on the other hand, one warms up the crystal to be photographed, the picture becomes more and more blurred, and, at the melting point the pattern completely vanishes, owing to the fact that the molecules leave their places and begin to move in an irregular way through the melted substance.

After solid material melts, the molecules still remain together, since the thermal agitation, though strong enough to dislocate them from the fixed position in the crystalline lattice, is not yet sufficient to take them completely apart. At still higher temperatures, however, the cohesive forces are not able to hold the molecules together any more and they fly apart in all directions unless prevented from doing so by the surrounding walls. When this happens, of course, the result is matter in a gaseous state. As in the melting of a solid, the evaporation of liquids takes place at different temperatures for different materials, and the substances with a weaker internal cohesion will turn into vapor at lower temperatures than those in which cohesive forces are stronger. In this case the process also depends rather essentially on the pressure under which the liquid is kept, since the outside pressure evidently helps the cohesive forces to keep the molecules together. Thus, as everybody knows, water in a tightly closed kettle boils at a lower temperature than will water in an open one. On the other hand, on the top of high mountains, where atmospheric pressure is considerably less, water will boil well below 100° C. It may be mentioned here that by measuring the temperature at which water will boil, one can calculate atmospheric pressure and consequently the distance above sea level of a given location.

But do not follow the example of Mark Twain who, according to his story, once decided to put an aneroid barometer into a boiling kettle of pea soup. This will not give you any idea of the elevation, and the copper oxide will make the soup taste bad.

The higher the melting point of a substance, the higher is its boiling point. Thus liquid hydrogen boils at −253° C, liquid oxygen and nitrogen at $-183°$ C and $-196°$ C, alcohol at $+78°$ C, lead at $+1620°$ C, iron at $+3000°$ C and osmium only above $+5300°$ C.[1]

The breaking up of the beautiful crystalline structure of solid bodies forces the molecules first to crawl around one another like a pack of worms, and then to fly apart as though they were a flock of frightened birds. But this latter phenomenon still does not represent the limit of the destructive power of increasing thermal motion. If the temperature rises still farther the very existence of the molecules is threatened, since the ever increasing violence of intermolecular collisions is capable of breaking them up into separate atoms. This *thermal dissociation*, as it is called, depends on the relative strength of the molecules subjected to it. The molecules of some organic substances will break up into separate atoms or atomic groups at temperatures as low as a few hundred degrees. Other more sturdily built molecules, such as those of water, will require a temperature of over a thousand degrees to be destroyed. But when the temperature rises to several thousand degrees no molecules will be left and the matter will be a gaseous mixture of pure chemical elements.

This is the situation on the surface of our sun where the temperature ranges up to 6000° C. On the other hand, in the comparatively cooler atmospheres of the red stars,[2] some of the molecules are still present, a fact that has been demonstrated by the methods of spectral analysis.

The violence of thermal collisions at high temperatures not only breaks up the molecules into their constituent atoms, but also damages the atoms themselves by chipping off their outer electrons. This *thermal ionization* becomes more and more pronounced when the temperature rises into tens and hundreds of thousands of degrees, and reaches completion at a few million degrees above zero. At these tremendously hot temperatures, which are high above everything that we can produce in our laboratories but which are common in the interiors of stars and in particular inside our sun, the atoms as such cease to exist. All electronic shells are completely stripped off, and the matter

[1] All values given for atmospheric pressure.
[2] See Chapter XI.

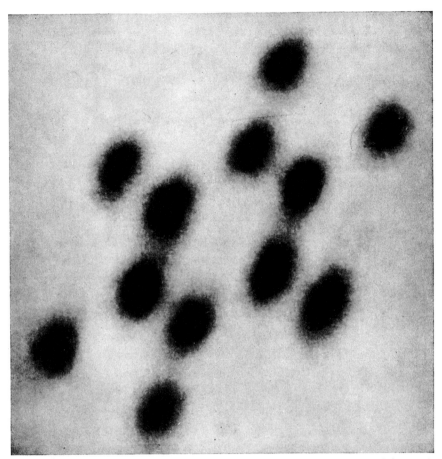

(Courtesy of Dr. M. L. Huggins. Eastman Kodak Laboratory.)

PLATE I

Photograph of Hexamethylbenzene molecule magnified 175,000,000 times.

becomes a mixture of bare nuclei and free electrons rushing wildly through space and colliding with one another with tremendous force. However, in spite of the complete wreckage of atomic bodies, the matter still retains its fundamental chemical

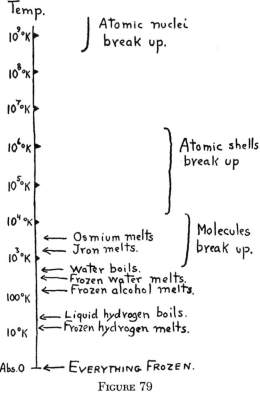

FIGURE 79

The destructive effect of temperature.

characteristics, inasmuch as atomic nuclei remain intact. If the temperature drops, the nuclei will recapture their electrons and the integrity of atoms will be reestablished.

In order to attain complete thermal dissociation of matter, that is to break up the nuclei themselves into the separate nucleons (protons and neutrons) the temperature must go up to at least several billion degrees. Even inside the hottest stars we do not find such high temperatures, though it seems very likely that temperatures of that magnitude did exist several billion years ago when our universe was still young. We shall return to this exciting question in the last chapter of this book.

Thus we see that the effect of thermal agitation is to destroy step by step the elaborate architecture of matter based on the law of quantum, and to turn this magnificent building into a mess of widely moving particles rushing around and colliding with one another without any apparent law or regularity.

2. HOW CAN ONE DESCRIBE DISORDERLY MOTION?

It would be, however, a grave mistake to think that because of the irregularity of thermal motion it must remain outside the scope of any possible physical description. Indeed the fact itself that thermal motion is *completely irregular* makes it subject to a new kind of law, the *Law of Disorder* better known as the *Law of Statistical Behavior*. In order to understand the above statement let us turn our attention to the famous problem of a "Drunkard's Walk." Suppose we watch a drunkard who has been leaning against a lamp post in the middle of a large paved city square (nobody knows how or when he got there) and then has suddenly decided to go nowhere in particular. Thus off he goes, making a few steps in one direction, then some more steps in another, and so on and so on, changing his course every few steps in an entirely unpredictable way (Figure 80). How far will be our drunkard from the lamp post after he has executed, say, a hundred phases of his irregular zigzag journey? One would at first think that, because of the unpredictability of each turn, there is no way of answering this question. If, however, we consider the problem a little more attentively we will find that, although we really cannot tell where the drunkard will be at the end of his walk, we can answer the question about his *most probable* distance from the lamp post after a given large number of turns. In order to approach this problem in a vigorous mathematical way let us draw on the pavement two co-ordinate axes with the origin in the lamp post; the X-axis coming toward us and the Y-axis to the right. Let R be the distance of the drunkard from the lamp post after the total of N zigzags (14 in Figure 80). If now X_N and Y_N are the projections of the Nth leg of the track on the corresponding axis, the Pythagorean theorem gives us apparently:

$$R^2 = (X_1 + X_2 + X_3 \cdots + X_N)^2 + (Y_1 + Y_2 + Y_3 + \cdots Y_N)^2$$

where X's and Y's are positive or negative depending on whether our drunkard was moving to or from the post in this particular

FIGURE 80
Drunkard's walk.

phase of his walk. Notice that since his motion is *completely disorderly*, there will be about as many positive values of X's and Y's as there are negative. In calculating the value of the square of the terms in parentheses according to the elementary rules of algebra, we have to multiply each term in the bracket by itself and by each of all other terms.

Thus:

$$(X_1+X_2+X_3+\cdots X_N)^2$$
$$=(X_1+X_2+X_3+\cdots X_N) \ (X_1+X_2+X_3+\cdots X_N)$$
$$=X_1{}^2+X_1X_2+X_1X_3+\cdots X_2{}^2+X_1X_2+\cdots X_N{}^2$$

This long sum will contain the square of all X's ($X_1{}^2$, $X_2{}^2 \cdots X_N{}^2$), and the so-called "mixed products" like X_1X_2, X_2X_3, etc.

So far it is simple arithmetic, but now comes the statistical point based on the disorderliness of the drunkard's walk. Since he was moving entirely at random and would just as likely make a step toward the post as away from it, the values of X's have a fifty-fifty chance of being either positive or negative. Consequently in looking through the "mixed products" you are likely to find always the pairs that have the same numerical value but opposite signs thus canceling each other, and the larger the total number of turns, the more likely it is that such a compensation takes place. What will be left are only the squares of X's, since the square is always positive. Thus the whole thing can be written as $X_1{}^2+X_2{}^2+\cdots X_N{}^3=N\ X^2$ where X is the average length of the projection of a zigzag link on the X-axis.

In the same way we find that the second bracket containing Y's can be reduced to: NY^2, Y being the average projection of the link on the Y-axis. It must be again repeated here that what we have just done is not strictly an algebraic operation, but is based on the statistical argument concerning the mutual cancellation of "mixed products" because of the random nature of the pass. For the most probable distance of our drunkard from the lamp post we get now simply:

$$R^2=N\ (X^2+Y^2)$$

or

$$R=\sqrt{N}\cdot\sqrt{X^2+Y^2}$$

But the average projections of the link on both axes is simply a 45° projection, so that $\sqrt{X^2+Y^2}$ right is (again because of the Pythagorean theorem) simply equal to the average length of the link. Denoting it by 1 we get:

$$R=1\cdot\sqrt{N}$$

In plain words our result means: *the most probable distance of our drunkard from the lamp post after a certain large number of irregular turns is equal to the average length of each straight track that he walks, times the square root of their number.*

Thus if our drunkard goes one yard each time before he turns (at an unpredictable angle!), he will most probably be only ten yards from the lamp post after walking a grand total of a hundred yards. If he had not turned, but had gone straight, he would be a hundred yards away—which shows that it is definitely advantageous to be sober when taking a walk.

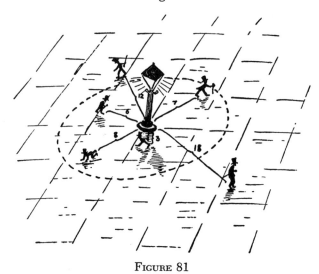

FIGURE 81

Statistical distribution of six walking drunkards around the lamp post.

The statistical nature of the above example is revealed by the fact that we refer here only to the *most probable* distance and not to the exact distance in each individual case. In the case of an individual drunkard it may happen, though this is not very probable, that he does not make any turns at all and thus goes far away from the lamp post along the straight line. It may also happen, that he turns each time by, say, 180 degrees thus returning to the lamp post after every second turn. But if a large number of drunkards all start from the same lamp post walking in different zigzag paths and not interfering with one another you will find after a sufficiently long time that they are spread over a certain area around the lamp post in such a way that their *average distance* from the post may be calculated by the above rule. An example of such spreading due to irregular motion is given in Figure 81, where we consider six walking drunkards. It goes without saying that the larger the number of drunkards, and the larger the number of turns they make in their disorderly walk, the more accurate is the rule.

Now substitute for the drunkards some microscopic bodies such as plant spores or bacteria suspended in liquid, and you will have exactly the picture that the botanist Brown saw in his microscope. True the spores and bacteria are not drunk, but, as we have said above, they are being incessantly kicked in all possible directions by the surrounding molecules involved in thermal motion, and are therefore forced to follow exactly the same irregular zigzag trajectories as a person who has completely lost his sense of direction under the influence of alcohol.

If you look through a microscope at the Brownian motion of a large number of small particles suspended in a drop of water, you will concentrate your attention on a certain group of them that are at the moment concentrated in a given small region (near the "lamp post"). You will notice that in the course of time they become gradually dispersed all over the field of vision, and that their average distance from the origin increases in proportion to the square root of the time interval as required by the mathematical law by which we calculated the distance of the drunkard's walk.

The same law of motion pertains, of course, to each separate molecule in our drop of water; but you cannot see separate molecules, and even if you could, you wouldn't be able to distinguish between them. To make such motion visible one must use two different kinds of molecules distinguishable for example by their different colors. Thus we can fill one half of a chemical test tube with a water solution of potassium permanganate, which will give to the water a beautiful purple tint. If we now pour on the top of it some clear fresh water, being careful not to mix up the two layers, we shall notice that the color gradually penetrates the clear water. If you wait sufficiently long you will find that all the water from the bottom to the surface becomes uniformly colored. This phenomenon, familiar to everybody, is known as *diffusion* and is due to the irregular thermal motion of the molecules of dye among the water molecules. We must imagine each molecule of potassium permanganate as a little drunkard who is driven to and fro by the incessant impacts received from other molecules. Since in water the molecules are packed rather tightly (in contrast to the arrangement of those in a gas) the average free path of each molecule between two successive collisions is very short, being only about one hundred millionths of an inch. Since on the other hand the molecules at room temperature move with the speed of about one tenth of a mile per second, it takes only one million-millionth part of a second for a molecule to go from one collision to another. Thus in the course of a single second

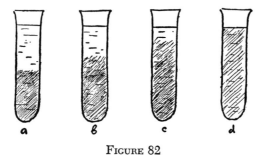

FIGURE 82

each dye molecule will be engaged in about a million million consecutive collisions and will change its direction of motion as many times. The average distance covered during the first second will be one hundred millionth of an inch (the length of free path) times the square root of a million millions. This gives the average diffusion speed of only one hundredth of an inch per second; a rather slow progress considering that if it were not deflected by collisions, the same molecule would be a tenth of a mile away! If you wait 100 sec, the molecule will have struggled through 10 times ($\sqrt{100} = 10$) as great distance, and in 10,000 sec, that is, in about 3 hr, the diffusion will have carried the coloring 100 times farther ($\sqrt{10000} = 100$), that is, about 1 in. away. Yes, diffusion is a rather slow process; when you put a lump of sugar into your cup of tea you had better stir it rather than wait until the sugar molecules have been spread throughout by their own motion.

Just to give another example of the process of diffusion, which is one of the most important processes in molecular physics, let us consider the way in which heat is propagated through an iron poker, one end of which you put into the fireplace. From your own experience you know that it takes quite a long time until the other end of the poker becomes uncomfortably hot, but you probably do not know that the heat is carried along the metal stick by the process of diffusion of electrons. Yes, an ordinary iron poker is actually stuffed with electrons, and so is any metallic object. The difference between a metal, and other materials, as for example glass, is that the atoms of the former lose some of their outer electrons, which roam all through the metallic lattice, being involved in irregular thermal motion, in very much the same way as the particles of ordinary gas.

The surface forces on the outer boundaries of a piece of metal prevent these electrons from getting out,[3] but in their motion inside the material they are almost perfectly free. If an electric force is applied to a metal wire, the free unattached electrons will rush headlong in the direction of the force producing the phenomenon of electric current. The nonmetals on the other hand are usually good insulators because all their electrons are bound to be atoms and thus cannot move freely.

When one end of a metal bar is placed in the fire, the thermal motion of free electrons in this part of the metal is considerably increased, and the fast-moving electrons begin to diffuse into the other regions carrying with them the extra energy of heat. The process is quite similar to the diffusion of dye molecules through water, except that instead of having two different kinds of particles (water molecules and dye molecules) we have here the *diffusion of hot electron gas into the region occupied by cold electron gas.* The drunkard's walk law applies here, however, just

[3] When we bring a metal wire to a high temperature, the thermal motion of electrons in its inside becomes more violent and some of them come out through the surface. This is the phenomenon used in electron tubes and familiar to all radio amateurs.

as well and the distances through which the heat propagates along a metal bar increase as the square roots of corresponding times.

As our last example of diffusion we shall take an entirely different case of cosmic importance. As we shall learn in the following chapters the energy of our sun is produced deep in its interior by the alchemic transformation of chemical elements. This energy is liberated in the form of intensive radiation, and the "particles of light," or the light quanta begin their long journey through the body of the sun towards its surface. Since light moves at a speed of 300,000 km per second, and the radius of the sun is only 700,000 km it would take a light quantum only slightly over two seconds to come out provided it moved without any deviations from a straight line. However, this is far from being the case; on their way out the light quanta undergo innumerable collisions with the atoms and electrons in the material of the sun. The free pass of a light quantum in solar matter is about a centimeter (much longer than a free pass of a molecule!) and since the radius of the sun is 70,000,000,000 cm, our light quantum must make $(7 \cdot 10^{10})^2$ or $5 \cdot 10^{21}$ drunkard's steps to reach the surface. Since each step requires $\dfrac{1}{3 \cdot 10^{10}}$ or $3 \cdot 10^{-9}$ sec, the entire time of travel is $3 \cdot 10^{-9} \times 5 \cdot 10^{21} = 1.5 \cdot 10^{13}$ sec or about 200,000 yr! Here again we see how slow the process of diffusion is. It takes light 2000 centuries to travel from the center of the sun to its surface, whereas after coming into empty intraplanetary space and traveling along a straight line it covers the entire distance from the sun to the earth in only eight minutes!

3. COUNTING PROBABILITIES

This case of diffusion represents only one simple example of the application of the statistical law of probability to the problem of molecular motion. Before we go farther with that discussion, and make the attempt to understand the all-important *Law of Entropy*, which rules the thermal behavior of every material body, be it a tiny droplet of some liquid or the giant universe of stars, we have first to learn more about the ways in which the probability of different simple or complicated events can be calculated.

By far the simplest problem of probability calculus arises when you toss a coin. Everybody knows that in this case (without cheating) there are equal chances to get heads or tails. One usually says that there is a *fifty-fifty chance* for heads or tails, but it is more customary in mathematics to say that the chances are *half and half*. If you add the chances of getting heads and getting tails you get $\frac{1}{2}+\frac{1}{2}=1$. Unity in the theory of probability means a certainty; you are in fact quite certain that in tossing a

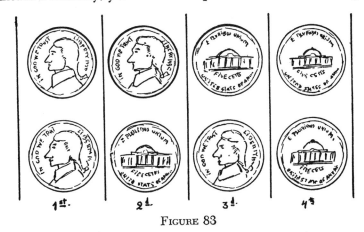

FIGURE 83

Four possible combinations in tossing two coins.

coin you get either heads or tails, unless it rolls under the sofa and vanishes tracelessly.

Suppose now you drop the coin twice in succession or, what is the same, you drop 2 coins simultaneously. It is easy to see that you have here 4 different possibilities shown in Figure 83.

In the first case you get heads twice, in the last case tails twice, whereas the two intermediate cases lead to the same result since it does not matter to you in which order (or in which coin) heads or tails appear. Thus you say that the chances of getting heads twice are 1 out of 4 or $\frac{1}{4}$ the chances of getting tails twice are also $\frac{1}{4}$, whereas the chances of heads once and tails once are 2 out of 4 or $\frac{1}{2}$. Here again $\frac{1}{4}+\frac{1}{4}+\frac{1}{2}=1$ meaning that you are certain to get one of the 3 possible combinations. Let us see now what happens if we toss the coin 3 times. There are altogether 8 possibilities summarized in the following table:

First tossing	h	h	h	h	t	t	t	t
Second	h	h	t	t	h	h	t	t
Third	h	t	h	t	h	t	h	t
	I	II	II	III	II	III	III	IV

If you inspect this table you find that there is 1 chance out of 8 of getting heads three times, and the same of getting tails three times. The remaining possibilities are equally divided between heads twice and tails once, or heads once and tails twice, with the probability three eighths for each event.

Our table of different possibilities is growing rather rapidly, but let us take one more step by tossing 4 times. Now we have the following 16 possibilities:

First tossing	h	h	h	h	h	h	h	h	t	t	t	t	t	t	t	t
Second	h	h	h	h	t	t	t	t	h	h	h	h	t	t	t	t
Third	h	h	t	t	h	h	t	t	h	h	t	t	h	h	t	t
Fourth	h	t	h	t	h	t	h	t	h	t	h	t	h	t	h	t
	I	II	II	III	II	III	III	IV	II	III	III	IV	III	IV	IV	V

Here we have $\frac{1}{16}$ for the probability of heads four times, and exactly the same for tails four times. The mixed cases of heads three times and tails once or tails three times and heads once have the probabilities of $\frac{4}{16}$ or $\frac{1}{4}$ each, whereas the chances of heads and tails the same number of times are $\frac{6}{16}$ or $\frac{3}{8}$.

If you try to continue in a similar way for larger numbers of tosses the table becomes so long that you will soon run out of paper; thus for example for ten tosses you have 1024 different possibilities (i.e., $2\times2\times2\times2\times2\times2\times2\times2\times2\times2$). But it is not at all necessary to construct such long tables since the simple laws of probability can be observed in those simple examples that we already have cited and then used directly in more complicated cases.

First of all you see that the probability of getting heads twice is equal to the product of the probabilities of getting it separately in the first and in the second tossing; in fact $\frac{1}{4}=\frac{1}{2}\times\frac{1}{2}$. Similarly the probability of getting heads three or four times in succession is the product of probabilities of getting it separately in each tossing ($\frac{1}{8} = \frac{1}{2} \times \frac{1}{2} \times \frac{1}{2}$; $\frac{1}{16} = \frac{1}{2} \times \frac{1}{2} \times \frac{1}{2} \times \frac{1}{2}$). Thus if somebody asks you what the chances are of getting heads each time in ten tossings you can easily give the answer by multiplying $\frac{1}{2}$ by $\frac{1}{2}$ ten times. The result will be .00098, indicating that the chances are very low indeed: about one chance out of a thousand! Here we have the rule of "multiplication of probabilities," which states that *if you want several different things, you may determine the mathematical probability of getting them by multiplying the mathematical probabilities of getting the several individual ones.* If there are many things you want, and each of them is not particularly probable, the chances that you get them *all* are discouragingly low!

There is also another rule, that of the "addition of probabilities," which states that *if you want only one of several things (no matter which one), the mathematical probability of getting it is the sum of mathematical probabilities of getting individual items on your list.*

This can be easily illustrated in the example of getting an equal division between heads and tails in tossing a coin twice. What you actually want here is *either* "heads once, tails twice" or "tails twice, heads once." The probability of each of the above combinations is $\frac{1}{4}$, and the probability of getting either one of them is $\frac{1}{4}$ plus $\frac{1}{4}$ or $\frac{1}{2}$. Thus: If you want "that, *and* that, *and* that . . ." you *multiply* the individual mathematical probabilities of different items. If, however, you want "that, *or* that, *or* that" you *add* the probabilities.

In the first case your chances of getting everything you ask for will decrease as the number of desired items increases. In the second case, when you want only one out of several items your chances of being satisfied increase as the list of items from which to choose becomes longer.

The experiments with tossing coins furnish a fine example of what is meant by saying that the laws of probability become more exact when you deal with a large number of trials. This is illustrated in Figure 84, which represents the probabilities of getting a different relative number of heads and tails for two, three, four, ten, and a hundred tossings. You see that with the increasing number of tossings the probability curve becomes sharper and sharper and the maximum at fifty-fifty ratio of heads and tails becomes more and more pronounced.

Thus whereas for 2 or 3, or even 4 tosses, the chances to have heads each time or tails each time are still quite appreciable, in 10 tosses even 90 per cent of heads or tails is very improbable.

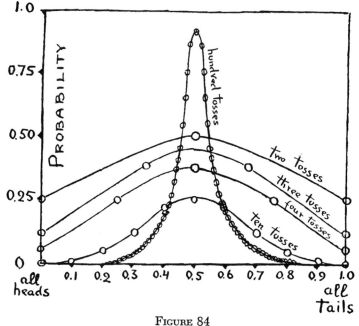

FIGURE 84

Relative number of tails and heads.

For a still larger number of tosses, say 100 or 1000, the probability curve becomes as sharp as a needle, and the chances of getting even a small deviation from fifty-fifty distribution becomes practically nil.

Let us now use the simple rules of probability calculus that we have just learned in order to judge the relative probabilities of various combinations of five playing cards which one encounters in the well-known game of poker.

In case you do not know, each player in this game is dealt 5 cards and the one who gets the highest combination takes the bank. We shall omit here the additional complications arising from the possibility of exchanging some of your cards with the hope of getting better ones, and the psychological strategy of bluffing your opponents into submission by making them believe that you have much better cards than you actually have. Although this bluffing actually is the heart of the game, and once led the famous Danish physicist Niels Bohr to propose an entirely new type of game in which no cards are used, and the players simply bluff one another by talking about the imaginary combinations they have, it lies entirely outside the domain of probability calculus, being a purely psychological matter.

FIGURE 85

A flush (of spades).

In order to get some exercise in probability calculus, let us calculate the probabilities of some of the combinations in the game of poker. One of these combinations is called a "flush" and represents 5 cards all of the same suit (Figure 85).

If you want to get a flush it is immaterial what the first card you get is, and one has only to calculate the chances that the other four will be of the same suit. There are altogether 52 cards in the pack, 13 cards of each suit,[4] so that after you get your first card, there remain in the pack 12 cards of the same suit. Thus the chances that your second card will be of the proper suit are 12/51. Similarly the chances that the third, fourth, and fifth cards

[4] We omit here the complications arising from the presence of the "joker," an extra card which can be substituted for any other card according to the desire of the player.

will be of the same suit are given by the fractions: 11/50, 10/49 and 9/48. Since you want *all* 5 cards to be of the same suit you have to apply the rule of probability-multiplications. Doing this you find that the probability of getting a flush is:

$$\frac{12}{51}\times\frac{11}{50}\times\frac{10}{49}\times\frac{9}{48}=\frac{13068}{5997600} \text{ or about 1 in 500.}$$

But please do not think that in 500 hands you are sure to get a flush. You may get none, or you may get two. This is only probability calculus, and it may happen that you will be dealt many more than 500 hands without getting the desired combination, or on the contrary that you may be dealt a flush the very first time you have the cards in your hands. All that the theory of prob-

FIGURE 86
Full house.

ability can tell you is that you will *probably* be dealt 1 flush in 500 hands. You may also learn, by following the same methods of calculation, that in playing 30,000,000 games you will probably get 5 aces (including the joker) about ten times.

Another combination in poker, which is even rarer and therefore more valuable, is the so-called "full hand," more popularly called "full house." A full house consists of a "pair" and "three of a kind" (that is, 2 cards of the same value in 2 suits, and 3 cards of the same value in 3 suits—as, for example, the 2 fives and 3 queens shown in Figure 86).

If you want to get a full house, it is immaterial which 2 cards you get first, but when you get them you must have 2 of the remaining 3 cards match one of them, and the other match the other one. Since there are 6 cards that will match the ones you have (if you have a queen and a five, there are 3 other queens and 3 other fives) the chances that the third card is a right one are 6 out of 50 or 6/50. The chances that the fourth card will be the right one are 5/49 since there are now only 5 right cards out of 49 cards left, and the chance that the fifth card will be right is 4/48. Thus the total probability of a full house is:

$$\frac{6}{50}\times\frac{5}{49}\times\frac{4}{48}=\frac{120}{117600}$$

or about one half of the probability of the flush.

In a similar way one can calculate the probabilities of other combinations as, for example, a "straight" (a sequence of cards), and also take into account the changes in probability introduced by the presence of the joker and the possibility of exchanging the originally dealt cards.

By such calculations one finds that the sequence of seniority used in poker does really correspond to the order of mathematical probabilities. It is not known by the author whether such an arrangement was proposed by some mathematician of the old times, or was established purely empirically by millions of players risking their money in fashionable gambling salons and little dark haunts all over the world. If the latter was the case, we must admit that we have here a pretty good statistical study of the relative probabilities of complicated events!

Another interesting example of probability calculation, an example that leads to a quite unexpected answer, is the problem of "Coinciding Birthdays." Try to remember whether you have ever been invited to two different birthday parties on the same day. You will probably say that the chances of such double invitations are very small since you have only about 24 friends who are likely to invite you, and there are 365 days in the year on which their birthdays may fall. Thus, with so many possible dates to choose from, there must be very little chance that any 2 of your 24 friends will have to cut their birthday cakes on the same day.

However, unbelievable as it may sound, your judgment here is quite wrong. The truth is that there is a rather high probability that in a company of 24 people there are a pair, or even several pairs, with coinciding birthdays. As a matter of fact, there are more chances that there is such a coincidence than that there is not.

You can verify that fact by making a birthday list including about 24 persons, or more simply, by comparing the birth dates of 24 persons whose names appear consecutively on any pages of some such reference book as "Who's Who in America," opened at random. Or the probabilities can be ascertained by using the simple rules of probability calculus with which we have become acquainted in the problems of coin tossing and poker.

Suppose we try first to calculate the chances that in a company of twenty-four persons everyone has a different birth date. Let us ask the first person in the group what is his birth date; of course this can be any of the 365 days of the year. Now, what is the chance that the birth date of the second person we approach is *different* from that of the first? Since this (second) person could have been born on any day of the year, there is one chance out of 365 that his birth date coincides with that of the first one, and 364 chances out of 365 (i.e., the probability of 364/365) that it does not. Similarly, the probability that the third person has a birth date different from that of either the first or second is 363/365, since two days of the year have been excluded. The probabilities that the next persons we ask have different birth dates from the ones we have approached before are then: 362/365, 361/365, 360/365 and so on up to the last person for whom the probability is $\dfrac{(365-23)}{365}$ or $\dfrac{342}{365}$.

Since we are trying to learn what the probability is that one of these coincidences of birth dates exists, we have to multiply all the above fractions, thus obtaining for the probability of all the persons having different birth dates the value:

$$\frac{364}{365} \times \frac{363}{365} \times \frac{362}{365} \times \cdots \frac{342}{365}$$

One can arrive at the product in a few minutes by using certain methods of higher mathematics, but if you don't know them you can do it the hard way by direct multiplication,[5] which would not take so very much time. The result is 0.46, indicating that the probability that there will be no coinciding birthdays is slightly less than one half. In other words there are only 46 chances in 100 that no two of your two dozen friends will have

[5] Use a logarithmic table or slide rule if you can!

birthdays on the same day, and 54 chances in 100 that two or more will. Thus if you have 25 or more friends, and have never been invited to two birthday parties on the same date you may conclude with a high degree of probability that either most of your friends do not organize their birthday parties, or that they do not invite you to them!

The problem of coincident birthdays represents a very fine example of how a common-sense judgment concerning the probabilities of complex events can be entirely wrong. The author has put this question to a great many people, including many prominent scientists, and in all cases except one[6] was offered bets ranging from 2 to 1 to 15 to 1 that no such coincidence will occur. If he had accepted all these bets he would be a rich man by now!

It cannot be repeated too often that if we calculate the probabilities of different events according to the given rules and pick out the most probable of them, we are not at all sure that this is exactly what is going to happen. Unless the number of tests we are making runs into thousands, millions or still better into billions, the predicted results are only "likely" and not at all "certain." This slackening of the laws of probability when dealing with a comparatively small number of tests limits, for example, the usefulness of statistical analysis for deciphering various codes and cryptograms which are limited only to comparatively short notes. Let us examine, for example, the famous case described by Edgar Allan Poe in his well-known story "The Gold Bug." He tells us about a certain Mr. Legrand who, strolling along a deserted beach in South Carolina, picked up a piece of parchment half buried in the wet sand. When subjected to the warmth of the fire burning gaily in Mr. Legrand's beach hut, the parchment revealed some mysterious signs written in ink which was invisible when cold, but which turned red and was quite legible when heated. There was a picture of a skull, suggesting that the document was written by a pirate, the head of a goat, proving beyond any doubt that the pirate was none other than the famous Captain Kidd, and several lines of typographical signs apparently indicating the whereabouts of a hidden treasure (see Figure 87).

We take it on the authority of Edgar Allan Poe that the pirates of the seventeenth century were acquainted with such typo-

[6] This exception was, of course, a Hungarian mathematician (see the beginning of the first chapter of this book).

graphical signs as semicolons and quotation marks, and such others as: ‡, +, and ¶.

Being in need of money, Mr. Legrand used all his mental powers in an attempt to decipher the mysterious cryptogram and

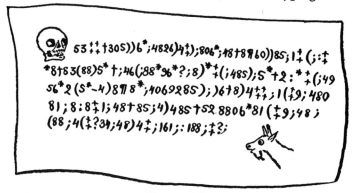

FIGURE 87

Captain Kidd's Message.

finally did so on the basis of the relative frequency of occurrence of different letters in the English language. His method was based on the fact that if you count the number of different letters of any English text, whether in a Shakespearian sonnet or an Edgar Wallace mystery story, you will find that the letter "e" occurs by far most frequently. After "e" the succession of most frequent letters is as follows:

a, o, i, d, h, n, r, s, t, u, y, c, f, g, l, m, w, b, k, p, q, x, z

By counting the different symbols appearing in Captain Kidd's cryptogram, Mr. Legrand found that the symbol that occurred most frequently in the message was the figure 8. "Aha," he said, "that means that 8 most probably stands for the letter e."

Well, he was right in this case, but of course it was only *very probable* and not at all certain. In fact if the secret message had been "You will find a lot of gold and coins in an iron box in woods two thousand yards south from an old hut on Bird Island's north tip" it would not have contained a single "e"! But the laws of chance were favorable to Mr. Legrand, and his guess was really correct.

Having met with success in the first step, Mr. Legrand became overconfident and proceeded in the same way by picking up the letters in the order of the probability of their occurrence. In the following table we give the symbols appearing in Captain Kidd's message in the order of their relative frequency of use:

Of the character 8 there are 33		e ← ⟶ e
;	26	a t
4	19	o h
‡	16	i o
(	16	d r
*	13	h n
5	12	n a
6	11	r i
†	8	s d
1	8	t
0	6	u
g	5	y
2	5	c
i	4	
3	4	g ← ⟶ g
?	3	l u
¶	2	m
-	1	w
.	1	b

The first column on the right contains the letters of the alphabet arranged in the order of their relative frequency in the English language. Therefore it was logical to assume that the signs listed in the broad column to the left stood for the letters listed opposite them in the first narrow column to the right. But using this arrangement we find that the beginning of Captain Kidd's message reads: *ngiisgunddrhaoecr* . . .

No sense at all!

What happened? Was the old pirate so tricky as to use special words that do not contain letters that follow the same rules of frequency as those in the words normally used in the English language? Not at all; it is simply that the text of the message is not long enough for good statistical sampling and the most probable distribution of letters does not occur. Had Captain Kidd hidden his treasure in such an elaborate way that the instructions for its recovery occupied a couple of pages, or, still better an entire volume, Mr. Legrand would have had a much better chance to solve the riddle by applying the rules of frequency.

If you drop a coin 100 times you may be pretty sure that it will fall with the head up about 50 times, but in only 4 drops you may have heads three times and tails once or vice versa. To make a rule of it, the larger the number of trials, the more accurately the laws of probability operate.

Since the simple method of statistical analysis failed because of an insufficient number of letters in the cryptogram, Mr. Legrand had to use an analysis based on the detailed structure of different words in the English language. First of all he strengthened his hypothesis that the most frequent sign *8* stood for *e* by noticing that the combination *88* occurred very often (5 times) in this comparatively short message, for, as everyone knows, the letter e is very often doubled in English words (as in: *meet, fleet, speed, seen, been, agree, etc.*). Furthermore if *8* really stood for *e* one would expect it to occur very often as a part of the word "the." Inspecting the text of the cryptogram we find that the combination *;48* occurs seven times in a few short lines. But if this is true, we must conclude that *;* stands for *t* and *4* for *h*.

We refer the reader to the original Poe story for the details concerning the further steps in the deciphering of Captain Kidd's message, the complete text of which was finally found to be: "A good glass in the bishop's hostel in the devil's seat. Forty-one degrees and thirteen minutes northeast by north. Main branch seventh limb east side. Shoot from the left eye of the death's head. A bee-line from the tree through the shot fifty feet out."

The correct meaning of the different characters as finally deciphered by Mr. Legrand is shown in the second column of the table on page 217, and you see that they do not correspond exactly to the distribution that might reasonably be expected on the basis of the laws of probability. It is, of course, because the text is too short and therefore does not furnish an ample opportunity for the laws of probability to operate. But even in this small "statistical sample" we can notice the tendency for the letters to arrange themselves in the order required by the theory of probability, a tendency that would become almost an unbreak-

FIGURE 88

able rule if the number of letters in the message were much larger.

There seems to be only one example (excepting the fact that insurance companies do not break up) in which the predictions of the theory of probability have actually been checked by a very large number of trials. This is a famous problem of the American flag and a box of kitchen matches.

To tackle this particular problem of probability you will need an American flag, that is, the part of it consisting of red and white stripes; if no flag is available just take a large piece of paper and draw on it a number of parallel and equidistant lines. Then you need a box of matches—any kind of matches, provided they are shorter than the width of the stripes. Next you will need a Greek pi, which is not something to eat, but just a letter of the Greek alphabet equivalent to our "p." It looks like this: π. In addition to being a letter of the Greek alphabet, it is used to signify the ratio of the circumference of a circle to its diameter. You may know that numerically it equals 3.1415926535 . . . (many more digits are known, but we shall not need them all.)

Now spread the flag on a table, toss a match in the air and watch it fall on the flag (Figure 88). It may fall in such a way that it all remains within one stripe, or it may fall across the boundary between two stripes. What are the chances that one or another will take place?

Following our procedure in ascertaining other probabilities, we must first count the number of cases that correspond to one or another possibility.

But how can you count all the possibilities when it is clear that a match can fall on a flag in an infinite number of different ways?

Let us examine the question a little more closely. The position of the fallen match in respect to the stripe on which it falls can be characterized by the distance of the middle of the match

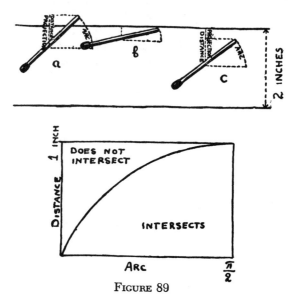

FIGURE 89

from the nearest boundary line, and by the angle that the match forms with the direction of the stripes in Figure 89. We give three typical examples of fallen matches, assuming, for the sake of simplicity, that the length of the match equals the width of the stripe, each being, say, two inches. If the center of the match is rather close to the boundary line, and the angle is rather large (as in case *a*) the match will intersect the line. If, on the contrary, the angle is small (as in case *b*) or the distance is large (as in case *c*) the match will remain within the boundaries of one stripe. More exactly we may say that the match will intersect the line if the projection of the half-of-the-match on the vertical direction is larger than the half width of the stripe (as in case *a*), and that no intersection will take place if the opposite is true (as in case b). The above statement is represented graphically on the diagram in the lower part of the picture. We plot on the horizontal axis (abscissa) the angle of the fallen match as given by the length of the corresponding arc of radius 1. On the vertical axis (ordinate) we plot the length of the projection of the half-match length on the vertical direction; in trigonometry this length is known as the *sinus* corresponding to the given arc. It is clear that the sinus is zero when the arc is zero since in that case the match occupies a horizontal position. When the arc is $\frac{1}{2}\pi$, which corresponds to a straight angle,[7] the sinus is equal to unity, since the match occupies a vertical position and thus coincides with its projection. For intermediate values of the arc the sinus is given by the familiar mathematical wavy curve known as sinusoid. (In Figure 89 we have only one quarter of a complete wave in the interval between 0 and $\pi/2$.)

Having constructed this diagram we can use it with convenience for estimating the chances that the fallen match will or will not cross the line. In fact, as we have seen above (look again at the three examples in the upper part of Figure 89) the match will cross the boundary line of a stripe if the distance of the center of the match from the boundary line is less than the corresponding projection, that is, less than the sinus of the arc. That means that in plotting that distance and that arc in our diagram we get a point *below* the sinus line. On the contrary the match that falls entirely within the boundaries of a stripe will give a point *above* the sinus line.

Thus, according to our rules for calculating probabilities, the chances of intersection will stand in the same ratio to the chances of nonintersection as the area below the curve does to the area above it; or the probabilities of the two events may be calculated by dividing the two areas by the entire area of the rectangle. It can be proved mathematically (*cf.* Chapter II) that the area of the sinusoid presented in our diagram equals exactly 1. Since the total area of the rectangle is $\frac{\pi}{2}\times 1=\frac{\pi}{2}$ we find the probability that the match will fall across the boundary (for matches equal in length to the stripe width) is: $\dfrac{1}{\pi/2}=\dfrac{2}{\pi}$.

[7] The circumference of a circle with the radius 1 is π times its diameter or 2π. Thus the length of one quadrant of a circle is $2\pi/4$ or $\pi/2$.

The interesting fact that π pops up here where it might be least expected was first observed by the eighteenth century scientist Count Buffon, and so the match-and-stripes problem now bears his name.

An actual experiment was carried out by a diligent Italian mathematician, Lazzerini, who made 3408 match tosses and observed that 2169 of them intersected the boundary line. The exact record of this experiment, checked with the Buffon formula, substitutes for π a value of $\dfrac{2+3408}{2169}$ or 3.1415929, differing from the exact mathematical value only in the seventh decimal place!

This represents, of course, a most amusing proof of the validity of the probability laws, but not more amusing than the determination of a number "2" by tossing a coin several thousand times and dividing the total number of tosses by the number of times heads come up. Sure enough you get in this case: 2.000000 . . . with just as small an error as in Lazzerini's determination of π.

4. THE "MYSTERIOUS" ENTROPY

From the above examples of probability calculus, all of them pertaining to ordinary life, we have learned that predictions of that sort, being often disappointing when small numbers are involved, become better and better when we go to really large numbers. This makes these laws particularly applicable to the description of the almost innumerable quantities of atoms or molecules that form even the smallest piece of matter we can conveniently handle. Thus, whereas the statistical law of Drunkard's Walk can give us only approximate results when applied to a half-dozen drunkards who make perhaps two dozen turns each, its application to billions of dye molecules undergoing billions of collisions every second leads to the most rigorous physical law of diffusion. We can also say that the dye that was originally dissolved in only one half of the water in the test tube tends through the process of diffusion to spread uniformly through the entire liquid, because, such uniform distribution is *more probable* than the original one.

For exactly the same reason the room in which you sit reading this book is filled uniformly by air from wall to wall and from floor to ceiling, and it never even occurs to you that the air in the room can unexpectedly collect itself in a far corner, leaving you to suffocate in your chair. However, *this horrifying event is not at all physically impossible, but only highly improbable.*

To clarify the situation, let us consider a room divided into two equal halves by an imaginary vertical plane, and ask ourselves about the most probable distribution of air molecules between the two parts. The problem is of course identical with the coin-tossing problem discussed in the previous chapter. If we pick up one single molecule it has equal chances of being in the right or in the left half of the room, in exactly the same way as the tossed coin can fall on the table with heads or tails up.

The second, the third, and all the other molecules also have equal chances of being in the right or in the left part of the room regardless of where the others are.[8] Thus the problem of distributing molecules between the two halves of the room is equivalent to the problem of heads-and-tails distribution in a large number of tosses, and as you have seen from Figure 84, the fifty-fifty distribution is in this case by far the most probable one. We also see from that figure that with the increasing number of tosses (the number of air molecules in our case) the probability at 50 per cent becomes greater and greater, turning practically into a certainty when this number becomes very large. Since in the average-size room there are about 10^{27} molecules,[9] the probability that all of them collect simultaneously in, let us say, the right part of the room is:

$$(\tfrac{1}{2})^{10^{27}} \cong 10^{-3 \cdot 10^{26}}$$

i.e., 1 out of $10^{.3 \cdot 10^{26}}$

On the other hand, since the molecules of air moving at the speed of about 0.5 km per second require only 0.01 sec to move from one end of the room to the other, their distribution in the room will be reshuffled 100 times each second. Consequently the waiting time for the right combination is

[8] In fact, owing to large distances between separate molecules of the gas, the space is not at all crowded and the presence of a large number of molecules in a given volume does not at all prevent the entrance of new molecules.

[9] A room 10 ft by 15 ft, with a 9 ft ceiling has a volume of 1350 cu ft, or $5 \cdot 10^{7}$ cu cm, thus containing $5 \cdot 10^{4}$ g of air. Since the average mass of air molecules is $3 \cdot 1 \cdot 66 \times 10^{-24} = 5 \times 10^{-23}$ g, the total number of molecules is $5 \cdot 10^{4}/5 \cdot 10^{-23} = 10^{+27}$. ($\cong$ means: approximately equal to.)

$10^{299,999,999,999,999,999,999,999,998}$ sec as compared with only 10^{17} sec representing the total age of the universe! Thus you may go on quietly reading your book without being afraid of being suffocated by chance.

To take another example, let us consider a glass of water standing on the table. We know that the molecules of water, being involved in the irregular thermal motion, are moving at high speed in all possible directions, being, however, prevented from flying apart by the cohesive forces between them.

Since the direction of motion of each separate molecule is governed entirely by the law of chance, we may consider the possibility that at a certain moment the velocities of one half of the molecules, namely those in the upper part of the glass, will all be directed upward, whereas the other half, in the lower part of the glass, will move downwards.[10] In such a case, the cohesive forces acting along the horizontal plane dividing two groups of molecules will not be able to oppose their "unified desire for parting," and we shall observe the unusual physical phenomenon of half the water from the glass being spontaneously shot up with the speed of a bullet toward the ceiling!

Another possibility is that the total energy of thermal motion of water molecules will be concentrated by chance in those located in the upper part of the glass, in which case the water near the bottom suddenly freezes, whereas its upper layers begin to boil violently. Why have you never seen such things happen? Not because they are absolutely impossible, but only because they are extremely improbable. In fact, if you try to calculate the probability that molecular velocities, originally distributed at random in all directions, will by pure chance assume the distribution described above, you arrive at a figure that is just about as small as the probability that the molecules of air will collect in one corner. In a similar way, the chance that, because of mutual collisions, some of the molecules will lose most of their kinetic energy, while the other part gets a considerable excess of it, is also negligibly small. Here again the distribution of velocities that corresponds to the usually observed case is the one that possesses the largest probability.

If now we start with a case that does not correspond to the

[10] We must consider this half-and-half distribution, since the possibility that *all* molecules move in the same direction is ruled out by the mechanical law of the conservation of momentum.

most probable arrangement of molecular positions or velocities, by letting out some gas in one corner of the room, or by pouring some hot water on top of the cold, a sequence of physical changes will take place that will bring our system from this less probable to a most probable state. The gas will diffuse through the room until it fills it up uniformly, and the heat from the top of the glass will flow toward the bottom until all the water assumes an equal temperature. Thus we may say that *all physical processes depending on the irregular motion of molecules go in the direction of increasing probability, and the state of equilibrium, when nothing more happens, corresponds to the maximum of probability.* Since, as we have seen from the example of the air in the room, the probabilities of various molecular distributions are often expressed by inconveniently small numbers (as $10^{-3 \cdot 10^{26}}$ for the air collecting in one half of the room), it is customary to refer to their logarithms instead. This quantity is known by the name of *entropy*, and plays a prominent role in all questions connected with the irregular thermal motion of matter. The foregoing statement concerning the probability changes in physical processes can be now rewritten in the form: *Any spontaneous changes in a physical system occur in the direction of increasing entropy, and the final state of equilibrium corresponds to the maximum possible value of the entropy.*

This is the famous *Law of Entropy*, also known as the Second Law of Thermodynamics (the First Law being the Law of Conservation of Energy), and as you see there is nothing in it to frighten you.

The Law of Entropy can also be called the *Law of Increasing Disorder* since, as we have seen in all the examples given above, the entropy reaches its maximum when the position and velocities of molecules are distributed completely at random so that any attempt to introduce some order in their motion would lead to the decrease of the entropy. Still another, more practical, formulation of the Law of Entropy can be obtained by reference to the problem of turning the heat into mechanical motion. Remembering that the heat is actually the disorderly mechanical motion of molecules, it is easy to understand that the complete transformation of the heat content of a given material body into mechanical energy of large-scale motion is equivalent to the task of forcing all molecules of that body to move in the same direction. However, in the example of the glass of water that might spontaneously shoot one half of its contents toward the ceiling, we have seen that such a phenomenon is sufficiently improbable to be considered as being practically impossible. Thus, *although the energy of mechanical motion can go completely over into heat (for example, through friction), the heat energy can never go completely into mechanical motion.* This rules out the possibility of the so-called "perpetual motion motor of the second kind,"[11] which would extract the heat from the material bodies at normal temperature, thus cooling them down and utilizing for doing mechanical work the energy so obtained. For example, it is impossible to build a steamship in the boiler of which steam is generated not by burning coal but by extracting the heat from the ocean water, which is first pumped into the engine room, and then thrown back overboard in the form of ice cubes after the heat is extracted from it.

But how then do the ordinary steam-engines turn the heat into motion without violating the Law of Entropy? The trick is made possible by the fact that in the steam engine *only a part of the heat liberated by burning fuel is actually turned into energy,* another larger part being thrown out into the air in the form of exhaust steam, or absorbed by the specially arranged steam coolers. In this case we have two opposite changes of entropy in our system: (1) the increase of entropy corresponding to the transformation of a part of the heat into mechanical energy of the pistons, and (2) the decrease of entropy resulting from the flow of another part of the heat from the hot-water boilers into the coolers. The Law of Entropy requires only that *the total amount* of entropy of the system increase, and this can be easily arranged by making the second factor larger than the first. The situation can probably be understood somewhat better by considering an example of a 5 lb weight placed on a shelf 6 ft above the floor. According to the Law of Conservation of Energy, it is quite impossible that this weight will spontaneously and without any external help rise toward the ceiling. On the other hand it is possible to drop one part of this weight to the floor and use the energy thus released to raise another part upward.

In a similar way we can decrease the entropy in one part of our system if there is a compensating increase of entropy in its other part. In other words *considering a disorderly motion of*

[11] Called so in contrast to the "perpetual motion motor of the first kind" which violates the law of conservation of energy working without any energy supply.

*molecules we can bring some order in one region, if we do not
mind the fact that this will make the motion in other parts still
more disorderly.* And in many practical cases, as in all kinds of
heat engines, we do not mind it.

5. STATISTICAL FLUCTUATION

The discussion of the previous section must have made it clear
to you that the Law of Entropy and all its consequences is based
entirely on the fact that in large-scale physics we are always
dealing with an immensely large number of separate molecules,
so that any prediction based on probability considerations becomes almost an absolute certainty. However, this kind of prediction becomes considerably less certain when we consider very
small amounts of matter.

Thus, for example, if instead of considering the air filling a
large room, as in the previous example, we take a much smaller
volume of gas, say a cube measuring one hundredth of a
micron[12] each way, the situation will look entirely different. In
fact, since the volume of our cube is 10^{-18} cu cm it will contain
only $\dfrac{10^{-18} \cdot 10^{-3}}{3 \cdot 10^{-23}}$ 30 molecules, and the chance that all of them
will collect in one half of the original volume is $(\frac{1}{2})^{30} = 10^{-10}$.

On the other hand, because of the much smaller size of the
cube, the molecules will be reshuffled at the rate of $5 \cdot 10^9$ times
per second (velocity of 0.5 km per second and the distance of
only 10^{-6} cm) so that about once every second we shall find that
one half of the cube is empty. It goes without saying that the
cases when only a certain fraction of molecules become concentrated at one end of our small cube occur considerably more
often. Thus for example the distribution in which 20 molecules
are at one end and 10 molecules at the other (i.e only 10 extra
molecules collected at one end) will occur with the frequency
of $(\frac{1}{2})^{10} \times 5 \cdot 10^{10} = 10^{-3} \times 5 \times 10^{10} = 5 \times 10^7$, that is, 50,000,000 times
per second.

Thus, on a small scale, the distribution of molecules in the air is
far from being uniform. If we could use sufficient magnification,
we should notice the small concentration of molecules being
instantaneously formed at various points of the gas, only to be
dissolved again, and be replaced by other similar concentrations

[12] One micron, usually denoted by Greek letter *Mu* (μ), is 0.0001 cm.

appearing at other points. This effect is known as *fluctuation of density* and plays an important role in many physical phenomena. Thus, for example, when the rays of the sun pass through the atmosphere these inhomogeneities cause the scattering of blue rays of the spectrum, giving to the sky its familiar color and making the sun look redder than it actually is. This effect of reddening is especially pronounced during the sunset, when the sun rays must pass through the thicker layer of air. Were these fluctuations of density not present the sky would always look completely black and the stars could be seen during the day.

Similar, though less pronounced, fluctuations of density and pressure also take place in ordinary liquids, and another way of describing the cause of Brownian motion is by saying that the tiny particles suspended in the water are pushed to and fro because of rapidly varying changes of pressure acting on their opposite sides. When the liquid is heated until it is close to its boiling point, the fluctuations of density become more pronounced and cause a slight opalescence.

We can ask ourselves now whether the Law of Entropy applies to such small objects as those to which the statistical fluctuations become of primary importance. Certainly a bacterium, which through all its life is tossed around by molecular impacts, will sneer at the statement that heat cannot go over into mechanical motion! But it would be more correct to say in this case that the Law of Entropy loses its sense, rather than to say that it is violated. In fact all that this law says is that molecular motion cannot be transformed completely into the motion of large objects containing immense numbers of separate molecules. For a bacterium, which is not *much* larger than the molecules themselves, the difference between the thermal and mechanical motion has practically disappeared, and it would consider the molecular collisions tossing it around in the same way as we would consider the kicks we get from our fellow citizens in an excited crowd. If we were bacteria, we should be able to build a perpetual motion motor of the second kind by simply tying ourselves to a flying wheel, but then we should not have the brains to use it to our advantage. Thus there is actually no reason for being sorry that we are not bacteria!

The "law of averages" applies to all randomly moving objects whether in kinetic theory or in city traffic. This story from The New Yorker magazine raises in fictional form the question of the meaning of a statistical law.

8 The Law

Robert M. Coates

An article from *The New Yorker Magazine,* 1947.

THE first intimation that things were getting out of hand came one early-fall evening in the late nineteen-forties. What happened, simply, was that between seven and nine o'clock on that evening the Triborough Bridge had the heaviest concentration of outbound traffic in its entire history.

This was odd, for it was a weekday evening (to be precise, a Wednesday), and though the weather was agreeably mild and clear, with a moon that was close enough to being full to lure a certain number of motorists out of the city, these facts alone were not enough to explain the phenomenon. No other bridge or main highway was affected, and though the two preceding nights had been equally balmy and moonlit, on both of these the bridge traffic had run close to normal.

The bridge personnel, at any rate, was caught entirely unprepared. A main artery of traffic, like the Triborough, operates under fairly predictable conditions. Motor travel, like most other large-scale human activities, obeys the Law of Averages—that great, ancient rule that states that the actions of people in the mass will always follow consistent patterns—and on the basis of past experience it had always been possible to foretell, almost to the last digit, the number of cars that would cross the bridge at any given hour of the day or night. In this case, though, all rules were broken.

The hours from seven till nearly midnight are normally quiet ones on the bridge. But on that night it was as if all the motorists in the city, or at any rate a staggering proportion of them, had conspired together to upset tradition. Beginning almost exactly at seven o'clock, cars poured onto the bridge in such numbers and with such rapidity that the staff at the toll booths was overwhelmed almost from the start. It was soon apparent that this was no momentary congestion, and as it became more and more obvious that the traffic jam promised to be one of truly monumental proportions, added details of police were rushed to the scene to help handle it.

Cars streamed in from all directions—from the Bronx approach and the Manhattan one, from 125th Street and the East River Drive. (At the peak of the crush, about eight-fifteen, observers on the bridge reported that the drive was a solid line of car headlights as far south as the bend at Eighty-ninth Street, while the congestion crosstown in Manhattan disrupted traffic as far west as Amsterdam Avenue.) And perhaps the most confusing thing about the whole manifestation was that there seemed to be no reason for it.

Now and then, as the harried toll-booth attendants made change for the seemingly endless stream of cars, they would question the occupants, and it soon became clear that the very participants in the monstrous tieup were as ignorant of its cause as anyone else was. A report made by Sergeant Alfonse O'Toole, who commanded the detail in charge of the Bronx approach, is typical. "I kept askin' them," he said, " ' Is there night football somewhere that we don't know about? Is it the races you're goin' to?' But the funny thing was half the time they'd be askin' *me*. 'What's the crowd for, Mac?' they would say. And

I'd just look at them. There was one guy I mind, in a Ford convertible with a girl in the seat beside him, and when he asked me, I said to him, 'Hell, you're *in* the crowd, ain't you?' I said. 'What brings *you* here?' And the dummy just looked at me. 'Me?' he says. 'I just come out for a drive in the moonlight. But if I'd known there'd be a crowd like this . . .' he says. And then he asks me, 'Is there any place I can turn around and get out of this?' " As the *Herald Tribune* summed things up in its story next morning, it "just looked as if everybody in Manhattan who owned a motorcar had decided to drive out on Long Island that evening."

THE incident was unusual enough to make all the front pages next morning, and because of this, many similar events, which might otherwise have gone unnoticed, received attention. The proprietor of the Aramis Theatre, on Eighth Avenue, reported that on several nights in the recent past his auditorium had been practically empty, while on others it had been jammed to suffocation. Lunchroom owners noted that increasingly their patrons were developing a habit of making runs on specific items; one day it would be the roast shoulder of veal with pan gravy that was ordered almost exclusively, while the next everyone would be taking the Vienna loaf, and the roast veal went begging. A man who ran a small notions store in Bayside revealed that over a period of four days two hundred and seventy-four successive customers had entered his shop and asked for a spool of pink thread.

These were news items that would ordinarily have gone into the papers as fillers or in the sections reserved for oddities. Now, however, they seemed to have a more serious significance. It was apparent at last that something decidedly strange was happening to people's habits, and it was as unsettling as those occasional moments on excursion boats when the passengers are moved, all at once, to rush to one side or the other of the vessel. It was not till one day in December when, almost incredibly, the Twentieth Century Limited left New York for Chicago with just three passengers aboard that business leaders discovered how disastrous the new trend could be, too.

Until then, the New York Central, for instance, could operate confidently on the assumption that although there might be several thousand men in New York who had business relations in Chicago, on any single day no more—and no less—than some hundreds of them would have occasion to go there. The play producer could be sure that his patronage would sort itself out and that roughly as many persons would want to see the performance on Thursday as there had been on Tuesday or Wednesday. Now they couldn't be sure of anything. The Law of Averages had gone by the board, and if the effect on business promised to be catastrophic, it was also singularly unnerving for the general customer.

The lady starting downtown for a day of shopping, for example, could never be sure whether she would find Macy's department store a seething mob of other shoppers or a wilderness of empty, echoing aisles and unoccupied salesgirls. And the uncertainty produced a strange sort of jitteriness in the individual when faced with any impulse to action. "Shall we do it or shan't we?" people kept asking themselves, knowing that if they did do it, it might turn out that thousands of other individuals had decided similarly; knowing, too, that if they *didn't*, they might miss the one glorious chance of all chances to have Jones Beach, say, practically to themselves. Business languished, and a sort of desperate uncertainty rode everyone.

AT this juncture, it was inevitable that Congress should be called on for action. In fact, Congress called on itself, and it must be said that it rose nobly to the occasion. A committee was appointed, drawn from both Houses and headed by Senator J. Wing Sloop-

er (R.), of Indiana, and though after considerable investigation the committee was forced reluctantly to conclude that there was no evidence of Communist instigation, the unconscious subversiveness of the people's present conduct was obvious at a glance. The problem was what to do about it. You can't indict a whole nation, particularly on such vague grounds as these were. But, as Senator Slooper boldly pointed out, "You can control it," and in the end a system of reëducation and reform was decided upon, designed to lead people back to—again we quote Senator Slooper—"the basic regularities, the homely averageness of the American way of life."

In the course of the committee's investigations, it had been discovered, to everyone's dismay, that the Law of Averages had never been incorporated into the body of federal jurisprudence, and though the upholders of States' Rights rebelled violently, the oversight was at once corrected, both by Constitutional amendment and by a law—the Hills-Slooper Act—implementing it. According to the Act, people were *required* to be average, and, as the simplest way of assuring it, they were divided alphabetically and their permissible activities catalogued accordingly. Thus, by the plan, a person whose name began with "G," "N," or "U," for example, could attend the theatre only on Tuesdays, and he could go to baseball games only on Thursdays, whereas his visits to a haberdashery were confined to the hours between ten o'clock and noon on Mondays.

The law, of course, had its disadvantages. It had a crippling effect on theatre parties, among other social functions, and the cost of enforcing it was unbelievably heavy. In the end, too, so many amendments had to be added to it—such as the one permitting gentlemen to take their fiancées (if accredited) along with them to various events and functions no matter what letter the said fiancées' names began with—that the courts were frequently at a loss to interpret it when confronted with violations.

In its way, though, the law did serve its purpose, for it did induce—rather mechanically, it is true, but still adequately—a return to that average existence that Senator Slooper desired. All, indeed, would have been well if a year or so later disquieting reports had not begun to seep in from the backwoods. It seemed that there, in what had hitherto been considered to be marginal areas, a strange wave of prosperity was

making itself felt. Tennessee mountaineers were buying Packard convertibles, and Sears, Roebuck reported that in the Ozarks their sales of luxury items had gone up nine hundred per cent. In the scrub sections of Vermont, men who formerly had barely been able to scratch a living from their rock-strewn acres were now sending their daughters to Europe and ordering expensive cigars from New York. It appeared that the Law of Diminishing Returns was going haywire, too. —ROBERT M. COATES

How can a viewer distinguish whether a film is being run forward or backward? The direction of increasing disorder helps to fix the direction of the arrow of time.

9   The Arrow of Time

Jacob Bronowski

A chapter from his book *Insight,* 1964.

This chapter and those that follow deal with time. In particular, this chapter looks at the direction of time. Why does time go one way only? Why cannot we turn time backwards? Why are we not able to travel in time, back and forth?

The idea of time travel has fascinated men. Even folklore contains legends about travel in time. And science fiction, from *The Time Machine* onwards, has been pre-occupied with this theme. Plainly, men feel themselves to be imprisoned in the single direction of time. They would like to move about in time as freely as they can move in space.

And time is in some way like space. Like space, time is not a thing but a relation between things. The essence of space is that it describes an order among things—higher or lower, in front or behind, to left or to right. The essence of time also is that it describes an order—earlier or later. Yet we cannot move things in time as we can in space. Time must therefore describe some fundamental process in nature which we do not control.

It is not easy to discuss time without bringing in some way of measuring it—a clock of one sort or another. Yet if all the clocks in the world stopped, and if we all lost all inner sense of time, we could still tell earlier from later. The essential nature of time does not depend on clocks. That is the point of this chapter, and we will begin by illustrating it from very simple and common experiences.

The three pairs of pictures point the way. They help to show what it is that enables us to tell earlier from later without a clock. In each pair, the pictures are arranged at random, and not necessarily in the sequence of time. Yet in all except the first pair, it is easy to arrange the pictures; the sequence in time is obvious. Only the first pair does not betray its time sequence. What is the difference between the first pair of pictures and the other two pairs?

We get a clue to the difference when we study the arrangement of the things in each picture. In the first pair, we cannot really distinguish one arrangement from another; they are equally tidy and orderly. The two pictures of the first pair show a shot at billiards. The billiard balls are as well arranged after the shot as before; there is no obvious difference between the arrangements.

The situation is different in the other two pairs. A broken egg is an entirely different arrangement

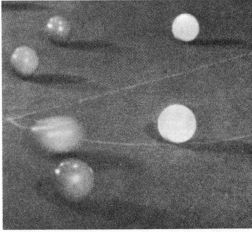

from a whole egg. A snooker pyramid is quite different from a jumble of balls.

And not only are the arrangements here different. Once they are different, it is quite clear which arrangement comes before the other. Whole eggs come before broken ones. The snooker pyramid comes before the spread of the balls.

In each case, the earlier arrangement is more ordered than the later. Time produces disorder; that is the lesson of these pictures. And it is also the lesson of this chapter. The arrow of time is loss of order.

In a game of snooker, we know quite well that the highly ordered arrangement of the balls at the beginning of the game comes before the disordered arrangement at the end of the first shot. Indeed, the first shot is called 'breaking the pyramid'; and breaking is a destructive action—it destroys order. It is just not conceivable that fifteen balls would gather themselves up into a pyramid, however skilful the player. The universe does not suddenly create order out of disorder.

These pictures show the same thing again. When a spot of powdered dye is put on the surface of

water, it spreads out and gradually dissolves. Dye would never come out of solution and stream together by itself to gather in a spot on the surface. Again time is breaking down order and making disorder. It disperses the dye randomly through the water.

We know at once that the stones in the picture below were shaped and erected a very long time ago. Their rough, weathered surfaces bear the mark of time. It is still possible to reconstruct the once orderly arrangement of the stones of Stonehenge. But the once orderly surface of each stone cannot be recovered. Atom by atom, the smooth surface has been carried away, and is lost to chaos.

And here finally is the most interesting of all the pictures in which time betrays itself. In these shots from an old film the heroine has been tied to the rails—a splendid tradition of silent films. A train is approaching, but of course it stops just in time. The role of the heroine would seem to call for strong nerves as well as dramatic ability, if she has to trust the engine driver to stop the locomotive exactly where he is told. However, the last few yards of the approach are in fact done by a trick. The locomotive

is *started* close to the heroine and is backed away: and the film is then run backwards.

There is only one thing that gives this trick away. When the film is run backwards, the smoke visibly goes into the funnel instead of coming out of it. We know that in reality, smoke behaves like the spreading dye: it becomes more disorderly, the further it gets from the funnel. So when we see disorder coming before order, we realise that something is wrong. Smoke does not of itself collect together and stream down a funnel.

One thing remains to clear up in these examples. We began with an example in which earlier and later were equally well ordered. The example was a shot at billiards. The planets in their orbits would be another example, in which there would be nothing to say which arrangement comes first.

Then does time stand still in billiards and planetary motion? No, time is still doing its work of disorder. We may not see the effects at once, but they are there. For billiard balls and planets gradually lose material from their surface, just like the stones of Stonehenge. Time destroys their orderly shape too. A billiard ball is not quite the same after a shot as before it. A planet is not quite the same in each successive orbit. And the changes are in the direction

of disorder. Atoms are lost from ordered structures and return to chaos. The direction of time is from order to disorder.

That is one reason why perpetual motion machines are impossible. Time cannot be brought to a standstill. We cannot freeze the arrangement of the atoms, even in a tiny corner of the universe. And that is what we should have to do to make a perpetual motion machine. The machine would have to remain the same, atom for atom, for all time. Time would have to stand still for it.

For example, take the first of these three machines from a famous book of Perpetual Motion Machines. It is meant to be kept going by balls in each sector, which roll from the centre to the rim and back again as the wheel turns. Of course it does not work. There is friction in the bearing of the wheel, and more friction between the balls and the tracks they run on. Every movement rubs off a few atoms. The bearings wear, the balls lose their smooth roundness. Time does not stand still.

The second machine is more complicated and sillier. It is designed to work like a waterwheel with little balls instead of water. At the bottom the balls roll out of their compartments down the chute, and on to a moving belt which is to lift them to the top

again. That is how the machine is meant to keep going. In fact, when we built it, it came to a stop every few minutes.

The pendulum arrangement in the third picture also comes from the book of Perpetual Motion Machines. A ball runs backwards and forwards in the trough on top to keep it going. There are also elastic strings at each end for good measure. This machine at least works for short bursts. But as a perpetual motion machine, it has the same defects as the others. Nothing can be done to get rid of friction; and where there is friction, there must be wear.

This last point is usually put a little differently. Every machine has friction. It has to be supplied with energy to overcome the friction. And this energy cannot be recovered. In fact, this energy is lost in heat, and in wear—that is, in moving atoms out of their order, and in losing them. That is another way of putting the same reasoning, and shows equally (in different language) why a perpetual motion machine cannot work.

Before we put these fanciful monsters out of mind, it is worth seeing how beautifully a fine machine can be made. It cannot conquer the disorder of time, it cannot get rid of friction, but it can keep them to a minimum. So on page 132 are two splendid clocks which make no pretence to do the impossible, yet which go as far as it is possible to go by means of exact and intelligent craftsmanship.

These clocks are not intended to be perpetual motion machines. Each has an outside source of energy to keep it going. In the clock at the top, it is ordinary clockwork which tips the platform whenever the ball has completed a run. The clock below is more tricky: it has no clockwork spring, and instead is driven by temperature differences in the air. But even if there was someone to wind one clock, and suitable air conditions for the other, they could not run for ever. They would wear out. That is, their ordered structure would slowly become more disordered until they stopped. The clock with no spring would run for several hundred years, but it could not run for ever.

To summarise: the direction of time in the universe is marked by increasing disorder. Even without clocks and without an inner sense of time, we could tell later and earlier. Later' is characterised by the greater disorder, by the growing randomness of the universe.

We ought to be clear what these descriptive phrases mean. Order is a very special arrangement; and disorder means the loss of what makes it special. When we say that the universe is becoming more disordered, more random, we mean that the special arrangements in this place or that are being evened out. The peaks are made lower, the holes are filled

in. The extremes disappear, and all parts sink more and more towards a level average. Disorder and randomness are not wild states; they are simply states which have no special arrangement, and in which everything is therefore near the average.

Even in disorder, of course, things move and deviate round their average. But they deviate by chance, and chance then takes them back to the average. It is only in exceptional cases that a deviation becomes fixed, and perpetuates itself. These exceptions are fascinating and important, and we now turn to them.

The movement towards randomness, we repeat, is not uniform. It is statistical, a general trend. And (as we saw in Chapter 8) the units that make up a general trend do not all flow in the same direction. Here and there, in the midst of the flow towards an average of chaos, there are places where the flow is reversed for a time. The most remarkable of these reversals is life. Life as it were is running against time. Life is the very opposite of randomness.

How this can come about can be shown by an analogy. The flow of time is like an endless shuffling of a pack of cards. A typical hand dealt after long shuffling will be random—say four diamonds, a couple of spades, four clubs, and three hearts. This is the sort of hand a bridge player expects to pick up several times in an evening. Yet every now and then a bridge player picks up a freak hand. For example, from time to time a player picks up all thirteen spades. And this does not mean that the pack was not properly shuffled. A hand of thirteen spades can arise by chance, and does; the odds against it are high, but they are not astronomic. Life started with a chance accident of this kind. The odds against it were high, but they were not astronomic.

The special thing about life is that it is self-perpetuating. The freak hand, instead of disappearing in the next shuffle, reproduces itself. Once the thirteen spades of life are dealt, they keep their order, and they impose it on the pack from then on. This is what distinguishes life from other freaks, other deviations from the average.

There are other happenings in the universe that run against the flow of time for a while. The formation of a star from the interstellar dust is such a happening. When a star is formed, the dust that forms it becomes less random; its order is increased, not decreased. But stars do not reproduce themselves. Once the star is formed, the accident is over. The flow towards disorder starts again. The deviation begins to ebb back towards the average.

Life is a deviation of a special kind; it is a self-reproducing accident. Once its highly ordered arrangement occurs, once the thirteen spades happen to be dealt in one hand, it repeats itself. The order was reached by chance, but it then survives because it is able to perpetuate itself, and to impose itself on other matter.

It is rare to find in *dead* matter behaviour of this kind which illustrates the way in which *life* imposes its order. An analogy of a kind, however, is found in the growth of crystals. When a supercooled solution is ready to form crystals, it needs something to start it off. Now we introduce the outside accident, the freak hand at bridge. That is, we introduce a tiny crystal that we have made, and we drop it in. At once the crystal starts to grow and to impose its own shape round it.

In this analogy, the first crystal is a seed, like the seed of life. Without it, the supercooled solution would remain dead, unchanged for hours or even days. And like the seed of life, the first crystal imposes its order all round it. It reproduces itself many times over.

Nearly five hundred years ago, Leonardo da Vinci described time as the destroyer of all things. So we have seen it in this chapter. It is the nature of time to destroy things, to turn order into disorder. This indeed gives time its single direction—its arrow.

But the arrow of time is only statistical. The general trend is towards an average chaos; yet there are deviations which move in the opposite direction. Life is the most important deviation of this kind. It is able to reproduce itself, and so to *perpetuate the order which began by accident*. Life runs against the disorder of time.

The biography of this great Scottish physicist, renowned both for kinetic theory and for his mathematical formulation of the laws of electricity and magnetism, is presented in two parts. The second half of this selection is in Reader 4.

---

10   **James Clerk Maxwell**

James R. Newman

An article from the *Scientific American*, 1955.

J AMES CLERK MAXWELL was the greatest theoretical physicist of the nineteenth century. His discoveries opened a new epoch of science, and much of what distinguishes our world from his is due to his work. Because his ideas found perfect expression in mathematical symbolism, and also because his most spectacular triumph — the prophecy of the existence of electromagnetic waves — was the fruit of theoretical rather than experimental researches, he is often cited as the supreme example of a scientist who builds his systems entirely with pencil and paper. This notion is false. He was not, it is true, primarily an experimentalist. He had not the magical touch of Faraday, of whom Helmholtz once observed after a visit to his laboratory that "a few wires and some old bits of wood and iron seem to serve him for the greatest discoveries." Nonetheless he combined a profound physical intuition with a formidable mathematical capacity to produce results "partaking of both natures." On the one hand, Maxwell never lost sight of the phenomena to be explained, nor permitted himself, as he said, to be drawn aside from the subject in pursuit of "analytical subtleties"; on the other hand, the use of mathematical methods conferred freedom on his inquiries and enabled him to gain physical insights without committing himself to a physical theory. This blending of the concrete and the abstract was the characteristic of almost all his researches.

Maxwell was born at Edinburgh on November 13, 1831, the same year Faraday announced his famous discovery of electromagnetic induction. He was descended of the Clerks of Penicuick in Midlothian, an old Scots family distinguished no less for their individuality, "verging on eccentricity," than for their talents. His forbears included eminent lawyers, judges, politicians, mining speculators, merchants, poets, musicians, and also the author (John Clerk) of a thick book on naval tactics, whose naval experience appears to have been confined entirely to sailing mimic men of war on the fishponds at Penicuick. The name Maxwell was assumed by James's father, John Clerk, on inheriting the small estate of Middlebie from his grandfather Sir George Clerk Maxwell.

At Glenlair, a two-day carriage ride from Edinburgh and "very much in the wilds," in a house built by his father shortly after he married, Maxwell passed his infancy and early boyhood. It was a happy time. He was an only son (a sister, born earlier, died in infancy) in a close-knit, comfortably-off family. John Clerk Maxwell had been called to the Scottish bar but took little interest in the grubby pursuits of an advocate. Instead the laird managed his small estates, took part in county affairs and gave loving attention to the education of his son. He was a warm and rather simple man with a nice sense of humor and a penchant for doing things with what he called "judiciosity"; his main characteristic, according to Maxwell's

James Clerk Maxwell.
(The Bettmann Archive)

biographer Lewis Campbell,* was a "persistent practical interest in all useful purposes." Maxwell's mother, Frances Cay, who came of a well-known Northumbrian family, is described as having a "sanguine, active temperament."

Jamesie, as he was called, was a nearsighted, lively, affectionate little boy, as persistently inquisitive as his father and as fascinated by mechanical contrivances. To discover of anything "how it doos" was his constant aim. "What's the go of that?" he would ask, and if the answer did not satisfy him he would add, "But what's the *particular* go of that?" His first creation was a set of figures for a "wheel of life," a scientific toy that produced the illusion of continuous movement; he was fond of making things with his hands, and in later life knew how to design models embodying the most complex motions and other physical processes.

When Maxwell was nine, his mother died of cancer, the same disease that was to kill him forty years later. Her death drew father and son even more closely together, and many intimate glimpses of Maxwell in his younger years emerge from the candid and affectionate letters he wrote to his father from the time he entered school until he graduated from Cambridge.

Maxwell was admitted to Edinburgh Academy as a day student when he was ten years old. His early school experiences were painful. The master, a dryish Scotsman whose reputation derived from a book titled *Account of the Irregular Greek Verbs* and from the fact that he was a good disciplinarian, expected his students to be orderly, well-grounded in the usual subjects and unoriginal. Maxwell was deficient in all these departments. He created something of a sensation because of his clothes, which had been designed by his strong-

---

* The standard biography (London, 1882) is by Lewis Campbell and William Garnett. Campbell wrote the first part, which portrays Maxwell's life; Garnett the second part, dealing with Maxwell's contributions to science. A shorter biography, especially valuable for the scientific exposition, is by the mathematician R. T. Glazebrook (*James Clerk Maxwell and Modern Physics*, London, 1901). In this essay, material in quotation marks, otherwise unattributed, is from Campbell and Garnett.

Illuminated letter was written by Maxwell to his father in 1843, when the younger Maxwell was 11. The letter refers to a lecture by the American frontier artist, George Catlin. (Scientific American)

minded father and included such items as "hygienic" square-toed shoes and a lace-frilled tunic. The boys nicknamed him "Dafty" and mussed him up, but he was a stubborn child and in time won the respect of his classmates even if he continued to puzzle them. There was a gradual awakening of mathematical interests. He wrote his father that he had made a "tetra hedron, a dodeca hedron, and two more hedrons that I don't know the wright names for," that he enjoyed playing with the "boies," that he attended a performance of some "Virginian minstrels," that he was composing Latin verse and making a list of the Kings of Israel and Judah. Also, he sent him the riddle of the simpleton who "wishing to swim was nearly drowned. As soon as he got out he swore that he would never touch water till he had learned to swim." In his fourteenth year he won the Academy's mathematical medal and wrote a paper on a mechanical method, using pins and thread, of constructing perfect oval curves. Another prodigious little boy, René Descartes, had anticipated Maxwell in this field, but Maxwell's contributions were completely independent and original. It was a wonderful day for father and son when they heard "Jas's" paper on ovals read before the Royal Society of Edinburgh by Professor James Forbes: "Met," Mr. Maxwell wrote of the event in his diary, "with very great attention and approbation generally."

After six years at the Academy, Maxwell entered the University of Edinburgh. He was sixteen, a restless, enigmatic, brilliantly talented adolescent who wrote not very good but strangely prophetic verse about the destiny of matter and energy:

> When earth and sun are frozen clods,
> When all its energy degraded
> Matter to aether shall have faded

His friend and biographer Campbell records that James was completely neat in his person "though with a rooted objection to the vanities of starch and gloves," and that he had a "pious horror of destroying anything — even a scrap of writing paper." He had a quaint humor, read voraciously and passed much time in mathematical speculations and in chemical, magnetic and optical experiments. "When at table he often seemed abstracted from what was going on, being absorbed in observing the effects of refracted light in the finger glasses, or in trying some experiment with his eyes — seeing around a corner, making invisible stereoscopes, and the like. Miss Cay [his aunt] used to call his attention by crying, 'Jamesie, you're in a prop!' [an abbreviation for mathematical proposition]." He was by now a regular visitor at the meetings of the Edinburgh Royal Society, and two of his papers, on "Rolling Curves" and on the "Equilibrium of Elastic Solids," were published in the *Transactions*. The papers were read before the Society by others "for it was not thought proper for a boy in a round jacket to mount the rostrum there." During vacations at Glenlair he was tremendously active and enjoyed reporting his multifarious doings in long letters to friends. A typical communication, when Maxwell was seventeen, tells Campbell of building an "electro-magnetic machine," taking off an hour to read Poisson's papers on electricity and magnetism ("as I am pleased with him today"), swimming and engaging in "aquatic experiments," making a centrifugal pump, reading Herodotus, designing regular geometric figures, working on an electric telegraph, recording thermometer and barometer readings, embedding a beetle in wax to see if it was a good conductor of electricity ("not at all cruel, because I slew him in boiling water in which he never kicked"), taking the dogs out, picking fruit, doing "violent exercise" and solving props. Many of his letters exhibit his metaphysical leanings, especially an intense interest in moral philosophy. This bent of his thought, while showing no particular originality, reflects his social sympathy, his Christian earnestness, the not uncommon nineteenth-century mixture of rationalism and simple faith. It was a period when men still shared the eighteenth-century belief that questions of wisdom, happiness and virtue could be studied as one studies optics and mechanics.

In 1850 Maxwell quit the University of Edinburgh for Cambridge. After a term at Peterhouse College he migrated to Trinity where the opportunity seemed better of obtaining ultimately a mathematical fellowship. In his second year he became a private pupil of William Hopkins, considered the ablest mathematics coach of his time. It was Hopkins's job to prepare his pupils for the stiff competitive examinations, the mathematical tripos, in which the attainment of high place insured academic preferment. Hopkins was not easily impressed; the brightest students begged to join his group, and the famous physicists George Stokes and William Thomson (later Lord Kelvin) had been among his pupils. But from the beginning he recognized the talents of the black-haired young Scotsman, describing him as "the most extraordinary man I have ever met," and adding that "it appears impossible for [him] to think incorrectly on physical subjects." Maxwell worked hard as an undergraduate, attending the lectures of Stokes and others and faithfully doing what he called "old Hop's props." He joined fully in social and intellectual activities and was made one of the Apostles, a club limited to twelve members, which for many years included the outstanding young men at Cambridge. A contemporary describes him as "the most genial and amusing of companions, the propounder of many a strange theory, the composer of many a poetic *jeu d'esprit*." Not the least strange of his theories related to finding an effective economy of work and sleep. He would sleep from 5 in the afternoon to 9:30, read very hard from 10 to 2, exercise by running along the corridors and up and down stairs from 2 to 2:30 A.M. and sleep again from 2:30 to 7. The occupants of the rooms along his track were not pleased, but Maxwell persisted in his bizarre experiments. Less disturbing were his investigations of the process by which a cat lands always on her feet. He demonstrated that a cat could right herself even when dropped upside down on a table or bed from about two inches. A complete record of these valuable researches is unfortunately not available.

A severe illness, referred to as a "sort of brain fever,"

seized Maxwell in the summer of 1853. For weeks he was totally disabled and he felt effects of his illness long afterward. Despite the abundance of details about his life, it is hard to get to the man underneath. From his letters one gleans evidence of deep inner struggles and anxieties, and the attack of "brain fever" was undoubtedly an emotional crisis; but its causes remain obscure. All that is known is that his illness strengthened Maxwell's religious conviction — a deep, earnest piety, leaning to Scottish Calvinism yet never completely identified with any particular system or sect. "I have no nose for heresy," he used to say.

In January, 1854, with a rug wrapped round his feet and legs (as his father had advised) to mitigate the perishing cold in the Cambridge Senate House where the elders met and examinations were given, he took the tripos. His head was warm enough. He finished second wrangler, behind the noted mathematician, Edward Routh. (In another competitive ordeal, for the "Smith's Prize," where the subjects were more advanced, Maxwell and Routh tied for first.)

After getting his degree, Maxwell stayed on for a while at Trinity, taking private pupils, reading Berkeley's *Theory of Vision*, which he greatly admired, and Mill's *Logic*, which he admired less: ("I take him slowly . . . I do not think him the last of his kind"), and doing experiments on the effects produced by mixing colors. His apparatus consisted of a top, which he had designed himself, and colored paper discs that could be slipped one over the other and arranged round the top's axis so that any given portion of each color could be exposed. When the top was spun rapidly, the sectors of the different colors became indistinguishable and the whole appeared of one uniform tint. He was able to show that suitable combinations of three primary colors — red, green and blue — produced "to a very near degree of approximation" almost every color of the spectrum. In each case the required combination could be quantitatively determined by measuring the sizes of the exposed sectors of the primary-color discs. Thus, for example, 66.6 parts of red and 33.4 parts of green gave the same chromatic effect as 29.1 parts of yellow and 24.1 parts of blue. In general, color composition could be expressed by an equation of the form

$$xX = aA + bB + cC$$

— shorthand for the statement that x parts of X can be matched by a parts of A, b parts of B and c parts of C. This symbolism worked out very prettily, for "if the sign of one of the quantities, a, b, or c was negative, it simply meant that that color had to be combined with X to match the other two."[*] The problem of color perception drew Maxwell's attention on and off for several years, and enlarged his scientific reputation. The work was one phase of his passionate interest in optics, a subject to which he made many contributions ranging from papers on geometrical optics to the invention of an ophthalmoscope and studies in the "Art of Squinting." Hermann von Helmholtz was of course the great leader in the field of color sensation, but Maxwell's work was independent and of high merit and in 1860 won him the Rumford Medal of the Royal Society.

These investigations, however, for all their importance, cannot be counted the most significant activity of the two post-graduate years at Trinity. For during this same period he was reading with intense absorption Faraday's *Experimental Researches*, and the effect of this great record on his mind is scarcely to be overestimated. He had, as he wrote his father, been "working away at Electricity again, and [I] have been working my way into the views of heavy German writers. It takes a long time to reduce to order all the notions one gets from these men, but I hope to see my way through the subject, and arrive at something intelligible in the way of a theory." Faraday's wonderful mechanical analogies suited Maxwell perfectly; they were what he needed to stimulate his own conjectures. Like Faraday, he thought more easily in images than

[*] Glazebrook, *op. cit.*, pp. 101-102. See also Maxwell's paper, "Experiments on Colour, as perceived by the Eye, with remarks on Colour-Blindness," *Transactions of the Royal Society of Edinburgh*, vol. XXI, part II; collected in *The Scientific Papers of James Clerk Maxwell*, edited by W. D. Niven, Cambridge, 1890.

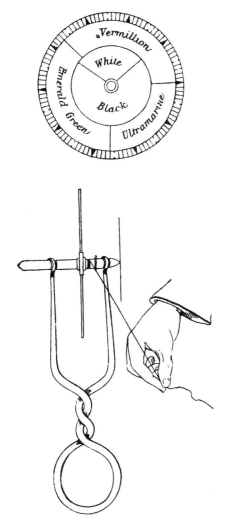

Color wheel is depicted in Maxwell's essay "Experiments in Colour, as perceived by the Eye, with remarks on Colour-Blindness." The wheel is shown at the top. The apparatus for rotating it is at the bottom.
(Scientific American)

abstractions: the models came first, the mathematics later. A Cambridge contemporary said that in their student days, whenever the subject admitted of it, Maxwell "had recourse to diagrams, though the rest [of the class] might solve the question more easily by a train of analysis." It was his aim, he wrote, to take Faraday's ideas and to show how "the connexion of the very different orders of phenomena which he had discovered may be clearly placed before the mathematical mind."* Before the year 1855 was out, Maxwell had published his first major contribution to electrical science, the beautiful paper "On Faraday's Lines of Force," to which I shall return when considering his over-all achievements in the field.

Trinity elected Maxwell to a fellowship in 1855, and he began to lecture in hydrostatics and optics. But his father's health, unsettled for some time, now deteriorated further, and it was partly to avoid their being separated that he became a candidate for the chair of natural philosophy at Marischal College, Aberdeen. In 1856 his appointment was announced; his father, however, had died a few days before, an irreparable personal loss to Maxwell. They had been as close as father and son could be. They confided in each other, understood each other and were in certain admirable traits much alike.

The four years at Aberdeen were years of preparation as well as achievement. Management of his estate, the design of a new "compendious" color machine, and the reading of metaphysics drew on his time. The teaching load was rather light, a circumstance not unduly distressing to Maxwell. He took his duties seriously, prepared lectures and demonstration experiments very carefully, but it cannot be said he was a great teacher. At Cambridge, where he had picked students, his lectures were well attended, but with classes that were, in his own words, "not bright," he found it difficult to hit a suitable pace. He was unable himself to heed the advice he once gave a friend whose duty it was to preach to a country congregation:

* The following quotation from the preface to Maxwell's *Treatise on Electricity and Magnetism* (Cambridge, 1873) gives Maxwell's views of Faraday in his own words: "Before I began the study of electricity I resolved to read no mathematics on the subject till I had first read through Faraday's *Experimental Researches in Electricity*. I was aware that there was supposed to be a difference between Faraday's way of conceiving phenomena and that of the mathematicians so that neither he nor they were satisfied with each other's language. I had also the conviction that this discrepancy did not arise from either party being wrong. ... As I proceeded with the study of Faraday, I perceived that his method of conceiving the phenomena was also a mathematical one, though not exhibited in the conventional form of mathematical symbols. I also found that these methods were capable of being expressed in the ordinary mathematical forms, and these compared with those of the professed mathematicians."

"Why don't you give it to them thinner?"* Electrical studies occupied him both during term and in vacation at Glenlair. "I have proved," he wrote in a semijocular vein to his friend C. J. Monro, "that if there be nine coefficients of magnetic induction, perpetual motion will set in, and a small crystalline sphere will inevitably destroy the universe by increasing all velocities till the friction brings all nature into a state of incandescence. . . ."

Then suddenly the work on electricity was interrupted by a task that engrossed him for almost two years. In competition for the Adams prize of the University of Cambridge (named in honor of the discoverer of Neptune), Maxwell prepared a brilliant essay on the subject set by the electors: "The Structure of Saturn's Rings."

Beginning with Galileo, the leading astronomers had observed and attempted to explain the nature of the several concentric dark and bright rings encircling the planet Saturn. The great Huygens had studied the problem, as had the Frenchman, Jean Dominique Cassini, Sir William Herschel and his son John, Laplace, and the Harvard mathematician and astronomer Benjamin Peirce. The main question at the time Maxwell entered the competition concerned the stability of the ring system: Were the rings solid? Were they fluid? Did they consist of masses of matter "not mutually coherent"? The problem was to demonstrate which type of structure adequately explained the motion and permanence of the rings.

Maxwell's sixty-eight-page essay was a mixture of common sense, subtle mathematical reasoning and profound insight into the principles of mechanics.* There was no point, he said at the outset, in imagining that the motion of the rings was the result of forces unfamiliar to us. We must assume that gravitation is the regulating principle and reason accordingly. The hypothesis that the rings are solid and uniform he quickly demonstrated to be untenable; indeed Laplace had already

* Occasionally he enjoyed mystifying his students, but at Aberdeen, where, he wrote Campbell, "No jokes of any kind are understood," he did not permit himself such innocent enjoyments.

* A summary of the work was published in the *Proceedings of the Royal Society of Edinburgh*, vol. IV; this summary and the essay "On the Stability of the Motion of Saturn's Rings" appear in the *Scientific Papers* (op. cit.).

shown that an arrangement of this kind would be so precarious that even a slight displacement of the center of the ring from the center of the planet "would originate a motion which would never be checked, and would inevitably precipitate the ring upon the planet. . . ."

Suppose the rings were not uniform, but loaded or thickened on the circumference — a hypothesis for which there appeared to be observational evidence. A mechanically stable system along these lines was theoretically possible; yet here too, as Maxwell proved mathematically, the delicate adjustment and distribution of mass required could not survive the most minor perturbations. What of the fluid hypothesis? To be sure, in this circumstance the rings would not collide with the planet. On the other hand, by the principles of fluid motion it can be proved that waves would be set up in the moving rings. Using methods devised by the French mathematician Joseph Fourier for studying heat conduction, by means of which complex wave motions can be resolved into their simple harmonic, sine-cosine elements, Maxwell succeeded in demonstrating that the waves of one ring will force waves in another and that, in due time, since the wave amplitudes will increase indefinitely, the rings will break up into drops. Thus the continuous-fluid ring is no better a solution of the problem than the solid one.

The third possibility remained, that the rings consist of disconnected particles, either solid or liquid, but necessarily independent. Drawing on the mathematical theory of rings, Maxwell proved that such an arrangement is fairly stable and its disintegration very slow; that the particles may be disposed in a series of narrow rings or may move through each other irregularly. He called this solution his "dusky ring, which is something like the state of the air supposing the siege of Sebastopol conducted from a forest of guns 100 miles one way, and 30,000 miles from the other, and the shot never to stop, but go spinning away around a circle, radius 170,000 miles. . . ."

Besides the mathematical demonstration, Maxwell devised an elegantly ingenious model to exhibit the motions of the satellites in a disturbed ring, "for the edification of sensible

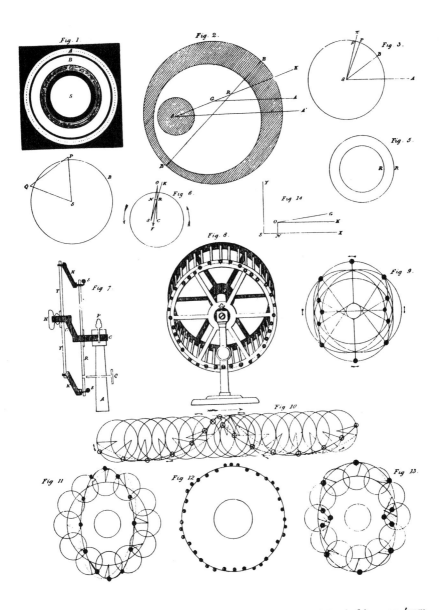

Mechanical model is depicted here in Figures 7 and 8 of this page from Maxwell's essay "On the Stability of the Motion of Saturn's Rings." In this essay, Maxwell demonstrated that the rings were neither liquid nor solid, but composed of particles. (Scientific American)

image-worshippers." His essay — which Sir George Airy, the Astronomer Royal, described as one of the most remarkable applications of mathematics he had ever seen — won the prize and established him as a leader among mathematical physicists.

In 1859 Maxwell read before the British Association his paper "Illustrations of the Dynamical Theory of Gases."* This marked his entry into a branch of physics that he enriched almost as much as he did the science of electricity. Two circumstances excited his interest in the kinetic theory of gases. The first was the research on Saturn, when he encountered the mathematical problem of handling the irregular motions of the particles in the rings — irregular but resulting nonetheless in apparent regularity and uniformity — a problem analogous to that of the behavior of the particles of gas. The second was the publication by the German physicist Rudolf Clausius of two famous memoirs: on the heat produced by molecular motion and on the average length of the path a gas molecule travels before colliding with a neighbor.

Maxwell's predecessors in this field — Daniel Bernoulli, James Joule, Clausius, among others — had been successful in explaining many of the properties of gases, such as pressure, temperature, and density, on the hypothesis that a gas is composed of swiftly moving particles. However, in order to simplify the mathematical analysis of the behavior of enormous aggregates of particles, it was thought necessary to make an altogether implausible auxiliary assumption, namely, that all the particles of a gas moved at the same speed. The gifted British physicist J. J. Waterson alone rejected this assumption, in a manuscript communicated to the Royal Society in 1845: he argued cogently that various collisions among the molecules must produce different velocities and that the gas temperature is proportional to the square of the velocities of all the molecules. But his manuscript lay forgotten for half a century in the archives of the Society.

Maxwell, without knowledge of Waterson's work, arrived at the same conclusions. He realized that further progress in the science of gases was not to be cheaply won. If the subject was

* *Philosophical Magazine*, January and July, 1860; also Maxwell's *Scientific Papers, op. cit.*

to be developed on "strict mechanical principles" — and for him this rigorous procedure was essential — it was necessary, he said, not only to concede what was in any case obvious, that the particles as a result of collisions have different speeds, but to incorporate this fact into the mathematical formulation of the laws of motion of the particles.

Now, to describe how two spheres behave on colliding is hard enough; Maxwell analyzed this event, but only as a prelude to the examination of an enormously more complex phenomenon — the behavior of an "indefinite number of small, hard and perfectly elastic spheres acting on one another only during impact."* The reason for this mathematical investigation was clear. For as he pointed out, if the properties of this assemblage are found to correspond to those of molecular assemblages of gases, "an important physical analogy will be established, which may lead to more accurate knowledge of the properties of matter."

The mathematical methods were to hand but had hitherto not been applied to the problem. Since the many molecules cannot be treated individually, Maxwell introduced the statistical method for dealing with the assemblage. This marked a great forward step in the study of gases. A fundamental Maxwellian innovation was to regard the molecules as falling into groups, each group moving within a certain range of velocity. The groups lose members and gain them, but group population is apt to remain pretty steady. Of course the groups differ in size; the largest, as Maxwell concluded, possesses the most probable velocity, the smaller groups the less probable. In other words, the velocities of the molecules in a gas can be conceived as distributed in a pattern — the famous bell-shaped frequency curve discovered by Gauss, which applies to so many phenomena from observational errors and distribution of shots on a target to groupings of men based on height and weight, and the longevity of electric light bulbs. Thus while the velocity of an individual molecule might elude description, the velocity of a crowd of molecules would not. Because this

* "Illustrations of the Dynamical Theory of Gases," *op. cit.*

method afforded knowledge not only of the velocity of a body of gas as a whole, but also of the groups of differing velocities composing it, Maxwell was now able to derive a precise formula for gas pressure. Curiously enough this expression did not differ from that based on the assumption that the velocity of all the molecules is the same, but at last the right conclusions had been won by correct reasoning. Moreover the generality and elegance of Maxwell's mathematical methods led to the extension of their use into almost every branch of physics.

Maxwell went on, in this same paper, to consider another factor that needed to be determined, namely, the average number of collisions of each molecule per unit of time, and its mean free path (i.e., how far it travels, on the average, between collisions). These data were essential to accurate formulations of the laws of gases. He reasoned that the most direct method of computing the path depended upon the viscosity of the gas. This is the internal friction that occurs when (in Maxwell's words) "different strata of gas slide upon one another with different velocities and thus act upon one another with a tangential force tending to prevent this sliding, and similar in its results to the friction between two solid surfaces sliding over each other in the same way." According to Maxwell's hypothesis, the viscosity can be explained as a statistical consequence of innumerable collisions between the molecules and the resulting exchange of momentum. A very pretty illustration by the Scotch physicist Balfour Stewart helps to an understanding of what is involved. Imagine two trains running with uniform speed in opposite directions on parallel tracks close together. Suppose the passengers start to jump across from one train to the other. Each passenger carries with him a momentum opposite to that of the train onto which he jumps; the result is that the velocity of both trains is slowed just as if there were friction between them. A similar process, said Maxwell, accounts for the apparent viscosity of gases.

Having explained this phenomenon, Maxwell was now able to show its relationship to the mean free path of the molecules. Imagine two layers of molecules sliding past each other. If a molecule passing from one layer to the other travels only a short distance before colliding with another molecule, the two particles do not exchange much momentum, because near the boundary or interface the friction and difference of velocity between the two layers is small. But if the molecule penetrates deep into the other layer before a collision, the friction and velocity differential will be greater; hence the exchange of momentum between the colliding particles will be greater. This amounts to saying that in any gas with high viscosity the molecules must have a long mean free path.

Maxwell deduced further the paradoxical and fundamental fact that the viscosity of gas is independent of its density. The reason is that a particle entering a dense — i.e., highly crowded — gas will not travel far before colliding with another particle; but penetration on the average will be deeper when the gas entered is only thinly populated, because the chance of a collision is smaller. On the other hand, there will be more collisions in a dense than in a less dense gas. On balance, then, the momentum conveyed across each unit area per second remains the same regardless of density, and so the coefficient of viscosity is not altered by varying the density.

These results, coupled with others arrived at in the same paper, made it possible for Maxwell to picture a mechanical model of phenomena and relationships hitherto imperfectly understood. The various properties of a gas — diffusion, viscosity, heat conduction — could now be explained in precise quantitative terms. All are shown to be connected with the motion of crowds of particles "carrying with them their momenta and their energy," traveling certain distances, colliding, changing their motion, resuming their travels, and so on. Altogether it was a scientific achievement of the first rank. The reasoning has since been criticized on the ground, for example, that molecules do not possess the tiny-billiard-ball properties Maxwell ascribed to them; that they are neither hard, nor perfectly elastic; that their interaction is not confined to the actual moment of impact. Yet despite the inadequacies of the model and the errors of reasoning, the results that, as Sir James Jeans has said, "ought to have been hopelessly wrong," turned out to be exactly right, and the formula tying the relationships together is in use to this day, known as Maxwell's law.*

This is perhaps a suitable place to add a few lines about Maxwell's later work in the theory of gases. Clausius, Max Planck tells us, was not profoundly impressed by the law of distribution of velocities, but the German physicist Ludwig Boltzmann at once recognized its significance. He set to work refining and generalizing Maxwell's proof and succeeded, among other results, in showing that "not only does the Maxwell distribution [of velocities] remain stationary, once it is attained, but that it is the only possible equilibrium state, since any system will eventually attain it, whatever its initial state."* This final equilibrium state, as both men realized, is the thermodynamic condition of maximum entropy — the most disordered state, in which the least amount of energy is available for useful work. But since this condition is in the long run also the most probable, purely from the mathematical standpoint, one of the great links had been forged in modern science between the statistical law of averages and the kinetic theory of matter.

The concept of entropy led Maxwell to one of the celebrated images of modern science, namely, that of the sorting demon. Statistical laws, such as the kinetic theory of gases, are good enough in their way, and, at any rate, are the best man can arrive at, considering his limited powers of observations and understanding. Increasing entropy, in other words, is the explanation we are driven to — and indeed our fate in physical reality — because we are not very bright. But a demon more favorably endowed could sort out the slow- and fast-moving particles of a gas, thereby changing disorder into order and

* "Maxwell, by a train of argument which seems to bear no relation at all to molecules, or to the dynamics of their movements, or to logic, or even to ordinary common sense, reached a formula which, according to all precedents and all the rules of scientific philosophy ought to have been hopelessly wrong. In actual fact it was subsequently shown to be exactly right. . . ." (James Jeans, "Clerk Maxwell's Method," in *James Clerk Maxwell, A Commemoration Volume, 1831-1931*, New York, 1931.)

* Max Planck, "Maxwell's Influence on Theoretical Physics in Germany," in James Jeans, *ibid.*

converting unavailable into available energy. Maxwell imagined one of these small, sharp fellows "in charge of a frictionless, sliding door in a wall separating two compartments of a vessel filled with gas. When a fast-moving molecule moves from left to right the demon opens the door, when a slow moving molecule approaches, he (or she) closes the door. The fast-moving molecules accumulate in the right-hand compartment, and slow ones in the left. The gas in the first compartment grows hot and that in the second cold." Thus the demon would thwart the second law of thermodynamics. Living organisms, it has been suggested, achieve an analogous success; as Erwin Schrödinger has phrased it, they suck negative entropy from the environment in the food they eat and the air they breathe.

Maxwell and Boltzmann, working independently and in a friendly rivalry, at first made notable progress in explaining the behavior of gases by statistical mechanics. After a time, however, formidable difficulties arose, which neither investigator was able to overcome. For example, they were unable to write accurate theoretical formulas for the specific heats of certain gases (the quantity of heat required to impart a unit increase in temperature to a unit mass of the gas at constant pressure and volume).* The existing mathematical techniques

* In order to resolve discrepancies between theory and experiment, as to the viscosity of gases and its relationship to absolute temperature, Maxwell suggested a new model of gas behavior, in which the molecules are no longer considered as elastic spheres of definite radius but as more or less undefined bodies repelling one another inversely as the fifth power of the distance between the centers of gravity. By this trick he hoped to explain observed properties of gases and to bypass mathematical obstacles connected with computing the velocity of a gas not in a steady state. For, whereas in the case of hard elastic bodies molecular collisions are a discontinuous process (each molecule retaining its velocity until the moment of impact) and the computation of the distribution of velocities is essential in solving questions of viscosity, if the molecular interaction is by repulsive force, acting very weakly when the molecules are far away from each other and strongly when they approach closely, each collision may be conceived as a rapid but *continuous* transition from the initial to the final velocity, and the computation both of relative velocities of the colliding molecules and of the velocity distribution of the gas as a whole can be dispensed with. In his famous memoir *On the Dynamical Theory of Gases*, which appeared in 1866, Maxwell gave a beautiful mathematical account of the properties of such a system. The memoir inspired Boltzmann to a Wagnerian rapture. He compared Maxwell's theory to a musical drama: "At first are developed majestically the

simply did not reach — and a profound transformation of ideas had to take place before physics could rise to — a new level of understanding. Quantum theory — the far-reaching system of thought revolving about Planck's universal constant, h — was needed to deal with the phenomena broached by Maxwell and Boltzmann.* The behavior of microscopic particles eluded description by classical methods, classical concepts of mass, energy and the like; a finer mesh of imagination alone would serve in the small world of the atom. But neither quantum theory, nor relativity, nor the other modes of thought constituting the twentieth-century revolution in physics would have been possible had it not been for the brilliant labors of these natural philosophers in applying statistical methods to the study of gases.

Variations of the Velocities, then from one side enter the Equations of State, from the other the Equations of Motion in a Central Field; ever higher swoops the chaos of Formulae; suddenly are heard the four words: 'Put n = 5'. The evil spirit V (the relative velocity of two molecules) vanishes and the dominating figure in the bass is suddenly silent; that which had seemed insuperable being overcome as if by a magic stroke . . . result after result is given by the pliant formula till, as unexpected climax, comes the Heat Equilibrium of a heavy gas; the curtain then drops."

Unfortunately, however, the descent of the curtain did not, as Boltzmann had supposed, mark a happy ending. For as James Jeans points out, "Maxwell's belief that the viscosity of an actual gas varied directly as the absolute temperature proved to have been based on faulty arithmetic, and the conclusions he drew from his belief were vitiated by faulty algebra." [Jeans, *op. cit.*] It was, says Jeans, "a very human failing, which many of us will welcome as a bond of union between ourselves and a really great mathematician" — even though the results were disastrous.

* Explanation of the discrepancies they found had to await the development of quantum theory, which showed that the spin and vibration of molecules were restricted to certain values.

A fine example of the reach of a scientific field, from research lab to industrial plant to concert hall.

11   Frontiers of Physics Today: Acoustics

Leo L. Beranek

An excerpt from his book *Mr Tompkins in Paperback,* 1965.

AN INTELLECTUALLY VITAL and
stimulating field, acoustics is rich in
unsolved and intriguing research problems. Its areas of interest are per-
tinent to the activities of many traditional university departments:
mathematics, physics, electrical engineering, mechanical engineering, land
and naval architecture, behavioral
sciences and even biology, medicine
and music.

On opening a recent issue of the
*Journal of the Acoustical Society of
America,* a leading Boston neurosur-
geon exclaimed: "It's like Alice's Won-
derland. You find a parade of papers
on echoencephalograms, diagnostic
uses of ultrasound in obstetrics and
gynecology, acoustical effects of violin varnish, ultrasonic cleavage of cy-
clchexanol, vibration analysis by holographic interferometry, detection of
ocean acoustic signals, sounds of mi-
grating gray whales and nesting ori-
ental hornets, and sound absorption
in concert halls. Certainly no other
discipline could possibly be more varie-
gated."

Acoustics assumed its modern aspect
as a result of at least seven factors.
They are:
• a research program begun in 1914
at the Bell Telephone Laboratories
(on the recording, transmission, and
reproduction of sound and on hearing)
that flourished because of the triode
vacuum tube[1]
• the development of quantum
mechanics and field theory, which un-
derlay Philip M. Morse's classic text
of 1936[2]
• large government funding of research and development during and
since World War II, resulting in many
valuable acoustics texts[3-22] and,
since 1950, a five-fold increase in the
number of papers published annually
in the *Journal of the Acoustical Society of America*
• a growing public demand in the
last decade for quieter air and surface
transportation
• the tremendous growth of acoustics study in other countries[23]
• the reconstruction of European
dwellings, concert halls and opera
houses destroyed during World War
II, and the postwar construction of
new music centers in the US, UK,
Israel and Japan[24,25]
• development of the solid-state
digital computer.[26]

Instruction in acoustics has moved
steadily across departmental boundaries in the universities, beginning in
physics prior to the time of radio and
electronics and moving into electrical
engineering as the communication and
underwater-acoustics fields developed.
Then, more recently, it has reached
into mechanical engineering and fluid
mechanics as the nonlinear aspects of
wave propagation and noise generation in gases, liquids and solids have
become of prime interest. Also, because much of acoustics involves the
human being as a source, receiver and
processor of signals that impinge on

his ears and body, the subject has attained vital importance to departments of psychology and physiology.

In spite of its variety and its importance to other sciences, acoustics remains a part of physics. It involves all material media; it requires the mathematics of theoretical physics; and, as a tool, it plays a primary role in solving the mysteries of the solid, liquid and gaseous states of matter.

Frederick V. Hunt of Harvard suggests that the field of acoustics might be separated into the categories of sources, receivers, paths, tools and special topics. These are the categories I will use here. Scientists and engineers are active in all these groups, and each group promises exciting frontiers for those entering the field.

SOURCES OF SOUND

The sources that we must consider include speech, music, signals, and a variety of generators of noise.

Speech

One of the most challenging goals of

Leo L. Beranek, chief scientist of Bolt Beranek and Newman Inc of Cambridge, Mass., was its first president for 16 years and continues as director. He also has a continuous association with Massachusetts Institute of Technology dating from 1946. Beranek holds degrees from Cornell (Iowa) and Harvard and was Director of the Electro-Acoustics Laboratory at Harvard during World War II. He has served as vice-president (1949–50) and president (1954–55) of the Acoustical Society of America, and is a member of the National Academy of Engineering.

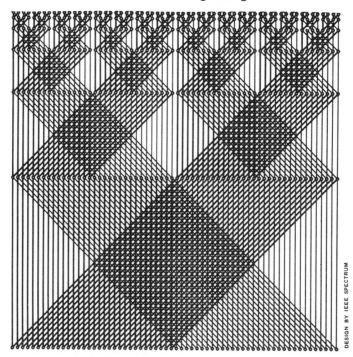

DESIGN BY IEEE SPECTRUM

FAST FOURIER TRANSFORM permits a spectral analysis of sounds in near-real time. This tree graph is used as an algorithm to obtain factored matrices in the computation of Fourier transforms. For further details see E. O. Brigham, R. E. Morrow, IEEE Spectrum, Dec. 1967, page 63. **—FIG. 1**

speech research is speech synthesis by rule ("talking computers"). At the simplest level we could assemble all the basic sounds (phonemes) of speech by cutting them from a tape

ELECTRONIC MUSIC. Robert A. Moog is here seen (left) at the keyboard of one of his "synthesizers" that generate and modify musical sounds. **—FIG. 2**

recording and calling them up for reproduction, thus producing connected speech according to a set of instructions. But this procedure works very poorly, because perceptually discrete phonemes, when combined by a person talking to produce syllables, have a modifying influence on each other. Thus stringing together phonemes to produce good speech would require a very large inventory of recorded units.

Workers at the Haskins Laboratories and at Bell Labs agree on these fundamentals, but have taken somewhat different approaches. Bell Labs uses the digital computer to assemble natural utterances by appropriate modification of pitch, stress and duration of words spoken in isolation. One of the Bell Labs methods applies

the principles of predictive coding. However, the basic problem remains: How does one structure the computer "brain" so that it will select, modify and present a sequence of sounds that can carry the desired meaning in easily interpretable form?

The geographers of speech have received new impetus with relatively recent, easy access to large computer power. A potent tool for this work is the fast Fourier transform, which allows spectral analyses of sounds with high resolution in near-real time (figure 1). Accompanying this process are new methods for three-dimensional display of speech spectra with continuously adjustable resolution in time and frequency. Thus deeper insights into the structure of speech signals and their spectra are slowly becoming possible. The problem is to select the meaningful parameters of the primary information-bearing parts of speech and to learn how they are superimposed on, or modulate, the secondary parameters that are associated with accent and individual style and voice quality.

Music

Currently, the availability of rich avant-garde sounds is stirring creative activity in acoustics and music. Solid-state devices are generally responsible for this incipient revolution, partly because they permit complex machines in small space (figure 2), but also because of their lower price.

The initial period of bizarre, experimental, musical sounds is passing; music critics speak more frequently of beauty and intellectual challenge. Soon a new version of musical form and sound will evolve and, as decreasing costs widen the availability of new instruments, recreational composing may eventually occupy the leisure time of many individuals. Hopefully these new sounds and compositions will excite educated people to an extent not observed since the 18th century.

The on-line computer will also play

its part, permitting traditional composers to perfect their compositions with an entire orchestra at their fingertips.[26]

Composers in all eras have had some specific hall-reverberation characteristics in mind for each of their works. Some modern composers now can see the exciting possibility of the expansion of artificial reverberation to permit reverberation times that change for different parts of a composition, and are different at low, medium and high frequencies.

Perhaps the greatest progress will be made by those trained from youth in both the musical arts and physics, so that the novel ideas of the two disciplines can be combined to produce results inconceivable to the classical composer. Early stages of this type of education are under way in universities in the Boston, New York and San Francisco areas.

Noise

Noise sources must be understood if they are to be controlled, but the study of them has often been neglected in the past. Many challenges appear in the understanding and control of high-level, nonlinear vibrations, including nonlinear distortion, harmonic and subharmonic generation, radiation forces and acoustic wind.

Aerodynamic noise looms large on the research frontier. For example, the periodic aerodynamic loads associated with noise from helicopter blades are not well understood, particularly as the stall point of the blades is approached. Multiple-rotor helicopters, in which one set of blades cuts through the vortices produced by the other set, offer important possibilities for theoretical investigation. For example the helicopter rotor must operate in unsteady air flow, but this condition produces uneven loadings,

JOHN M. JOHANSEN AND EVANS WOOLLEN, ASSOCIATED ARCHITECTS

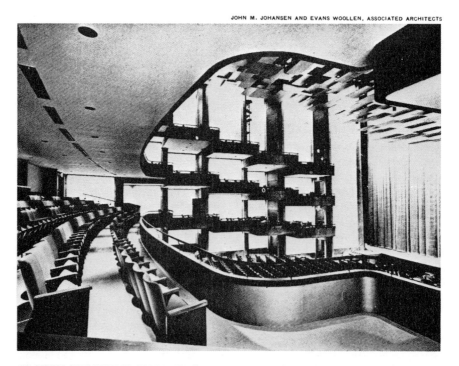

CLOWES MEMORIAL HALL, Butler University, Indianapolis. The acoustics of this hall (Johansen and Woollen, architects, and Bolt Beranek and Newman Inc, consultants) are acknowledged to be among the best of contemporary halls. Research is needed to explain why this hall is superior, to the ears of musicians and music critics, to Philharmonic Hall in New York. The same general principles were used in the design of the two halls, which opened at about the same time. —FIG. 3

random stresses on the blades and magnified vortex production. The fuselage of the helicopter also affects the noise produced.

Surprisingly, noise production by jet-engine exhausts is not yet well understood, although large sums of money have been spent on "cut-and-try" muffling.

Perhaps least understood of all mechanical sources of noise is the impact of one body on another. For example even the sound of a handclap has never been studied. The noise of engine blocks and industrial machinery is largely produced by impacts. The production of noise by hammers, punches, cutters, weaving shuttles, typewriter keys and wheels rolling on irregular surfaces is also largely unexplored.

RECEIVERS OF SOUND

The most important receivers of sound are people—those who use sound to aid them, as in listening and communication, and those who are bothered by the annoying or harmful aspects of noise. Much engineering effort is constantly expended to better the acoustic environment of people at home and at work. In some areas the basic understanding of noise problems is well developed, and engineering solutions are widely available. In others, such understanding is only beginning to emerge and engineering solutions are still uncertain.

Variety and complexity

The intellectually interesting questions related to human beings as receivers of sound derive in large part from the extraordinary variety in the physical stimuli and the complexity of human responses to them. The questions include: What are the few most important physical descriptions (dimensions) that will capture the essence of each complex psychophysical situation? How can the variety of stimuli be catalogued in a manageable way so that they can be related to the hu-

man responses of interest?

Many of the sources of sound are so complex (a symphony orchestra, for example) that simplified methods must be used to describe them and to arrive at the responses of things or people to them. The dangers in simplified approaches, such as statistical methods for handling room or structural responses, are that one may make wrong assumptions in arriving at the physical stimulus-response description, and that the description may not be related closely enough to the psychophysical responses. The process of threading one's way through these dangers is a large part of being on the research frontier. Good examples of the perils are found in architectural acoustics (figure 3).

Concert halls

In 1900, Wallace C. Sabine gave room acoustics its classical equation.[27,28] Sabine's statistically based equation for predicting reverberation time (that is, the time it takes for sound to decay 60 decibels) contains a single term directly proportional to the volume of a room and inversely proportional to the total absorbing power of the surfaces and contents. A controversy exists today as to its relevance to many types of enclosure. Research at Bell Labs, aided by ray-tracing studies on a digital computer,[26] shows that the influence of room shape is of major importance in determining reverberation time, a fact not recognized in the Sabine equation. A two- or three-term equation appears to be indicated, but until it is available there are many subtleties that confront the engineer in the application of published sound-absorption data on acoustical materials and objects.[29,30]

Reverberation time is only one of the factors contributing to acoustical quality in concert halls. A hall with *either* a short or a long reverberation time, may sound either dead or live.[26] Of greater importance, probably, is the detailed "signature" of the hall reverberation that is impressed on the music during the first 200 milliseconds after the direct sound from the orchestra is heard.[25]

It would be easy to simulate the reverberation signature of a hall by earphones or a loudspeaker, were it not that spatial factors are of primary importance to the listener's perception. Reflections that come from overhead surfaces are perceived differently from those that come from surfaces in front, and from surfaces to the right, left and behind the listener. A new approach suggests that with a number of loudspeakers, separated in space about a listener and excited by signals in precise relative phases, one can produce the direct analog of listening in an auditorium.

Frequency is a further dimension. To be optimum, both the 60-dB reverberation time and the 200-msec signature of the hall should probably be different at low, middle and high frequencies.

There are many other subjective attributes to musical-acoustical quality besides liveness (reverberation time). They include richness of bass, loudness, clarity, brilliance, diffusion, orchestral balance, tonal blend, echo, background noise, distortion and other related binaural-spatial effects.[25] Computer simulations may lead to the separation of a number of the variables involved, but analog experiments conducted in model and full-scale halls will most likely also be necessary to improve our understanding of the relative importance of the many factors. These studies would be very costly and would need Federal support. The prospect of greater certainty in design of concert halls makes this an exciting frontier for research.

Psychoacoustics

Traditional advances in psychoacoustics have resulted from investigation of the basic aspects of hearing: thresholds of audibility (both temporary and permanent), masking loudness, binaural localization, speech intelligibility, detectability of signals in noise, and the like.[6] Just as in the case of structures, humans exhibit a multiplicity of responses to different noise situations. Those on the forefront of research are attempting to find simplified statistical descriptions of the various physical stimuli that correlate well with several subjective responses, such as annoyance.

As an example, a recent means for rating the subjective nuisance value of noises[31] says that the nuisance value is greater as the average level of the noise is increased and is greater the less steady it is. In other words, the nuisance is related to the standard deviation of the instantaneous levels from the average; the background noise, if appreciable, is part of the average level. But there is no treatment of the "meaning" in the noise (the drip of a faucet would not be rated high, although it might be very annoying), or of special characteristics —such as a shrill or warbling tone, or a raucous character. Although this formulation is probably an improvement over previous attempts to relate annoyance to the level of certain types of noise, the whole subject of a person's reaction to unwanted sounds is still wide open for research.

Another forefront area of psychoacoustics is the response of the tactile senses to physical stimuli, both when the body is shaken without sound and when the body and the hearing sense are stimulated together. We know that discomfort in transportation is a function of both noise and body vibration. How the senses interact, and whether or how they mask each other, is not known. Neither do we understand the mechanism by which the hearing process takes place in humans beyond the point where the mechanical motions of the inner ear are translated into nerve impulses. We also do not know whether extended exposure to loud noise or to sonic booms has detrimental physiological or psychological effects, other than damage to the middle ear. We have not adequately analyzed the nonlinear behavior of the ear and its effect on enjoyment of music or understanding of speech.

UNDERWATER AND AIRBORNE PATHS

Several major problem areas exist in underwater and airborne sound propagation. One is prediction of acoustic propagation between two points in the ocean over distances up to several hundred times the depth of the water. Involved are many alternate paths of propagation, spatial distributions of pressure and temperature, spatial and temporal fluctuation resulting from waves, suspended particles, bubbles, deep-water currents and so on. Mathematical physics and the computer have proven that strictly deterministic thinking about sound propagation is frequently fruitless. The need is to characterize *statistically* the transmission between two points in both amplitude and phase. The ultimate value of this research is to distinguish information-bearing signals from all other sounds in which they are immersed.[32] Similar needs exist in air. In short, this area is an important element of the acoustical frontier.

Structural paths

When sound or vibration excites a structure, waves are propagated throughout it and sound is radiated to the surrounding medium. An understanding of the physics of these phenomena, adequate to quantitative prediction of the effect of changes in the structural design on them, is required for many applications. The response of buildings to sonic booms, including the noise generated by objects in the building set in vibration by the boom, is one example.[33] Many other examples arise in connection with buildings and transportation vehicles, including underground, ground, marine, air and space vehicles.

Structures and the noise and vibration fields in them are generally complex beyond description. Almost invariably, the vibrational properties of an existing structure cannot be determined in a way consistent with setting up the dynamical equations of motion and arriving at solutions to them on a computer. Furthermore, the real interest is in *predicting* response for a structure that has not been built. Again the problem is, in principle, *deterministic* (solvable on a computer) but one does not ever know the parameters to use. Progress is now resulting from the invention of a new language, a statistical mathematical approach, for describing what goes on.[34] But the dangers, as in room acoustics, are that the answer may be incomplete. It is necessary to go back repeatedly to the laboratory experiment and try to improve the language, the vocabulary of statistical assumptions, that is used to describe the physical situation. The added dimension of damping, nonhomogeneity of structures, and radiation into media of widely different properties (air and water) make this field rich in research topics.[20,35]

ACOUSTIC TOOLS

Satisfaction of the needs of tool seekers is a lush field for the acoustical inventor. Here is where the acoustic delay line is perfected for radar systems and process-control computers; where sound is used to help clean metals and fabrics; where vibration is used to process paints, candy, and soups; and where ultrasonics is used to test materials nondestructively. Transducers of all types, seismic, underwater, vibration, microphones, loudspeakers, and so forth are constantly being improved. The medical profession seeks help from ultrasonics as a means of detecting objects or growths imbedded in the body, or as a means for producing warming of body tissue. The whole field of spectrographic analysis of body sounds as an aid to medical diagnosis is largely unexplored. Special tools such as sonic anemometers and sonic

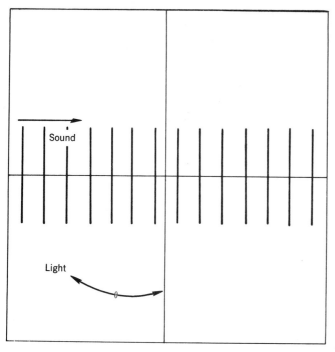

DEBYE-SEARS SCATTERING. A beam of light, passed through a fluid at an angle to the direction of a sound wave, diminishes in amplitude, and first-order diffracted waves appear. **—FIG. 4**

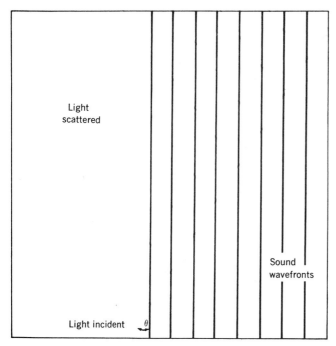

BRILLOUIN SCATTERING by a sound wave wide compared with the wavelength of the light, generates two new frequencies —that of the light plus and minus the acoustic frequency.**—FIG. 5**

temperature- and velocity-sensing devices, are just becoming available.

SPECIAL TOOLS

The *Physical Review Letters* attest to a renaissance of acoustics in physics during the past decade. High-frequency sound waves are being used in gases, liquids and solids as tools for analyzing the molecular, defect, domain-wall and other types of motions in these media. High-frequency sound waves interact in various media with electric fields and light waves at frequencies for which their wavelengths in the media become about alike (typically 10^8 to 10^{12} Hz). From these basic investigations, practical devices are emerging for signal processing, storage and amplification, for testing, measurement, inspection, medical diagnosis, surgery and therapy, and for ultrasonic cleaning, welding, soldering and homogenizing.[3,18]

Plasma acoustics

Plasma acoustics is concerned with the dynamics of a weakly ionized gas.[3] The electrons in the gas (with a temperature of 10^4 to 10^5 K, typically) will draw energy from the electric field that maintains the plasma. Because of the lower temperature of the neutral gas (500 K, typically), much of this energy is transferred to the neutral-gas particles through elastic collisions. If this transfer is made to vary with time, for example, by a varying external electric field, a sound wave is generated in the neutral gas. Alternatively, the electric field may be held constant and the electron density varied by an externally applied sound wave. When the frequency and other parameters are in proper relation, a coupling of the electron energy to the acoustic wave may create a positive feedback that results in sound amplification.

Current research involves examination of the acoustic instabilities that result from this amplification and in the determination of the conditions for spontaneous excitation of normal modes of vibration, such as in a tube. Because there is coupling between the neutral gas and the electrons, the sound-pressure field can be determined in terms of the electron-density field. Thus an ordinary Langmuir probe, arranged to measure fluctuations in the electron density, can be used as a microphone in the weakly ionized gas. This technique has proved useful in the determination of the speed of sound and the temperature, of the neutral-gas component in a plasma. It also appears to be a promising tool in the study of density fluctuations in jet and supersonic wind-tunnel flow.

In a fully ionized gas there exists a type of sound wave, called "plasma oscillation," in which there is charge separation. The speed of propagation of this ion–acoustic longitudinal wave is determined by the inertia of the ions and the "elasticity" of the electrons. In the presence of a magnetic field, the plasma becomes nonisotropic; the wave motion then becomes considerably more complicated, creating an interesting area for research.

Optical acoustics

The density fluctuations caused by a sound wave in a gas, liquid or solid, produce corresponding fluctuations in the index of refraction, and this leads to scattering and refraction of light. Conversely, under certain conditions, sound can be generated by light.[3]

To illustrate Debye–Sears scattering (figure 4), a beam of light is passed through a fluid at an angle with respect to the direction of travel of a narrow-beam sound wave. The sound wave acts somewhat like an optical transmission grating, except for its finite width and time and motion dependence. If the light penetrates at a right angle to the direction of propagation of the sound wave, the incident light beam diminishes in amplitude, and first-order diffracted waves appear at angles $\pm\theta$, where $\sin\theta$ equals the ratio of the wavelength of the light to that of the sound.

When the width of the sound wave is very large compared to the wavelength of light, the wavefronts of the sound in the medium form a succession of infinite partially-reflecting planes traveling at the speed of sound, and the scattered light occurs in only one direction. At very high frequencies (10^9 to 10^{10} Hz) the primary scattered wave is backward, and the effects of thermal motion of the medium on scattering are easily observed. Because thermal sound waves travel in all directions and have a wide frequency spectrum, frequency-shifted light beams are scattered from them at all angles. This phenomenon is called "Brillouin scattering" (figure 5). There are two Brillouin "lines" in the scattered light, equal in frequency to that of the light plus and minus the acoustic frequency. These lines are broadened by an amount of the order of the inverse of the "lifetimes" of the ordinary and transverse propagating sound waves.

A very active area of research is the determination of the acoustic dispersion relation for "hypersound" (frequencies above 10^9 Hz) in fluids, with lasers as the light sources and high-resolution spectroscopic techniques (for example heterodyne spectroscopy) for the frequency analysis.[3]

Other frontiers

Other areas of research are reported in *Physical Review Letters*, as already mentioned, and in the *Journal of the Acoustical Society of America* and elsewhere.

One such frontier involves the collective modes of vibration in liquid helium. In particular, the sound attenuation has been measured at temperatures very close to absolute zero with incredible accuracy, with and without porous materials present in the liquid.[36]

An interesting geophysical problem is the generation of seismic waves by sonic booms[37] from supersonic aircraft at high altitudes. When the seismic waves travel at the same speed as the phase velocity of the air wave, efficient and effective coupling of energy from the acoustic mode to the seismic mode takes place. One application of this coupling effect is as a tool to determine surficial earth structure.

Holographic imaging has attracted interest because it offers the possibility, first, of three-dimensional image presentation of objects in opaque gases or liquids, and, second, of recording and utilizing more of the information contained in coherent sound-field configurations than do the more conventional amplitude-detecting systems.[38] Holographic imaging has been done in an elementary way at both sonic and ultrasonic frequencies and in air and water. Figure 6 shows an example.

Much recent research in physical acoustics is concerned with ultrasonic absorption in solids, particularly crystals, explained in terms of attenuation by thermal photons.[18] An intrinsic mechanism for the attenuation of ultrasonic sound in solids is the interaction of the mechanical (coherent) sound wave with thermal (incoherent) phonons, where thermal phonons are described as the quantized thermal vibrations of the atoms in the crystal lattice of the solid. Because the relation between the applied force and the atomic displacements is nonlinear, a net "one-way" transfer of energy from the ultrasonic wave to the thermal phonons results. At very high frequencies and low temperatures, such interactions must be considered in terms of discrete events, namely, acoustic phonons interacting with thermal phonons.[18,39] Also in this field, light scattering has proven to be a useful diagnostic tool in the study of sound and crystal properties.[40]

Just as we may have interaction between sound waves and electrons in a gaseous plasma, sound and electrons may interact in certain semiconductors. In a semiconductor the tension and compressions of the acoustic wave create an electric field that moves along with the traveling wave. If an intense steady electric field is applied to the semiconductor, the free electrons will try to go somewhat faster than the sound wave, and the sound wave will increase in amplitude, provided the thermal losses in the crystal are not too great. This interaction requires extremely pure crystalline material.[41]

Attempts are underway to make ultrasonic delay lines adjustable, by drawing upon the interaction between acoustic waves and magnetic "spin waves." Fermi-surface studies for many metals can also be carried out by measuring attenuation in the presence of magnetic fields.

One application for surface (Rayleigh) waves on a crystalline solid is in signal processing. Surface waves are accessible along their entire wavelength and are compatible with integrated-circuit technology. Perhaps such waves at GHz frequencies can be used to build mixers, filters, couplers, amplifiers, frequency shifters, time compressors and expanders, and memory elements.[42]

In the study of high-frequency surface waves, laser light again proves to be a useful diagnostic tool. With it, the thermally excited surface waves in liquids have been studied by techniques quite similar to the Brillouin scattering from phonons.[43] One application is determination of surface tension through observation of the mean frequency and bandwidth of such waves.

Many more examples of modern physical acoustics could be cited, but these examples should prove my opening statement that acoustics is a vital, growing field.

* * *

I wish to thank Frederick V. Hunt, Manfred R. Schroeder, K. Uno Ingard, Preston W. Smith, Jr, Theodore J. Schultz and Richard H. Lyon for their helpful comments during the preparation of this paper.

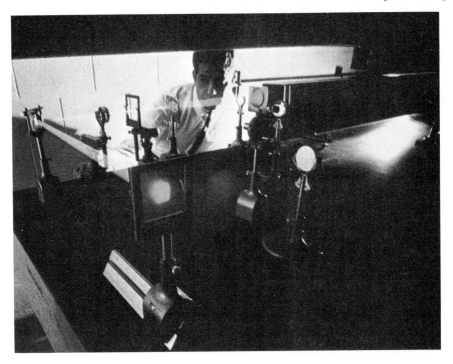

ACOUSTICAL HOLOGRAPHY. Acoustical wavefronts reflected from irregular surfaces can be recorded and reconstructed with coherent laser light. An advantage over conventional holography is that optically opaque gases and liquids can be penetrated. The experiment shown is in progress at the McDonnell Douglas Corp. **—FIG. 6**

References

1. I. B. Crandall, *Theory of Vibrating Systems and Sound,* D. Van Nostrand Co, New York (1926).
2. P. M. Morse, *Vibration and Sound,* McGraw-Hill Book Co, Inc, New York (1936) (1948, 2nd ed.).
3. P. M. Morse, U. Ingard, *Theoretical Acoustics,* McGraw-Hill Book Co, Inc, New York (1968).
4. S. S. Stevens, H. Davis, *Hearing,* John Wiley & Sons, Inc, New York (1938).
5. L. L. Beranek, *Acoustic Measurements,* John Wiley & Sons, Inc, New York (1949).
6. S. S. Stevens, ed., *Handbook of Experimental Psychology,* John Wiley & Sons, Inc, New York (1951).
7. I. J. Hirsh, *The Measurement of Hearing,* McGraw-Hill Book Co, Inc, New York (1952).
8. Y. Kikuchi, *Magnetostriction Vibration and Its Application to Ultrasonics,* Carona Ltd, Tokyo (1952).
9. E. G. Richardson, *Technical Aspects of Sound,* Elsevier Publishing Co, Vols. I–III, Amsterdam (1953–1962).
10. F. V. Hunt, *Electroacoustics.* Harvard University Press, Cambridge, Mass. (1954).
11. T. F. Hueter, R. H. Bolt, *Sonics,* John Wiley & Sons, Inc, New York (1955).
12. C. M. Harris, *Handbook of Noise Control,* McGraw-Hill Book Co, Inc, New York (1957).
13. H. F. Olson, *Acoustical Engineering,* D. Van Nostrand Co, Inc, Princeton, N.J. (1957).
14. L. L. Beranek, *Noise Reduction,* McGraw-Hill Book Co, Inc, New York (1960).
15. L. M. Brekhovskikh, *Waves in Layered Media,* Academic Press, New York (1960).
16. R. Lehmann, *Les Tranducteurs Electro et Mecano-Acoustiques,* Editions Chiron, Paris (1963).
17. G. Kurtze, *Physik und Technik der Lärmbekämpfung,* G. Braun Verlag, Karlsruhe, Germany (1964).
18. W. P. Mason, *Physical Acoustics,* Vols. 1–5, Academic Press, New York (1964–1968).
19. J. R. Frederick, *Ultrasonic Engineering,* John Wiley & Sons, Inc, New York (1965).

20. L. Cremer, M. Heckl, *Koerperschall*, Springer-Verlag, Berlin–New York (1967).
21. A. P. G. Peterson, E. E. Gross, *Handbook of Noise Measurement*, General Radio Company, W. Concord, Mass. (1967).
22. E. Skudrzyk, *Simple and Complex Vibrating Systems*, Pennsylvania State University Press, University Park, Pa. (1968).
23. Acoustical journals of the world: *Acoustics Abstracts* (British), *Acustica* (international), *Akustinen Aikakauslehti* (Engineering Society of Finland), *Applied Acoustics* (international), *Archiwum Akustyki* (Acoustical Committee of the Polish Academy), *Audiotechnica* (Italian), *B&K Technical Review* (US and Danish), *Electroacoustique* (Belgian), *IEEE Trans. on Audio and Electroacoustics, IEEE Trans. on Sonics and Ultrasonics, Journal of the Acoustical Society of America, Journal of the Acoustical Society of Japan, Journal of the Audio Engineering Society, Journal of Sound and Vibration* (British), *Journal of Speech and Hearing Research, Lärmbekämpfung* (German), *Review Brown Boveri* (Swiss), *Revue d'Acoustique* (French), *Schallschutz in Gebauden* (German), *Sound and Vibration* (S/V), *Soviet Physics-Acoustics* (Translation of *Akusticheskii Zhurnal*), *Ultrasonics*.
24. P. H. Parkin, H. R. Humphreys, *Acoustics, Noise and Buildings*, Faber and Faber Ltd, London (1958).
25. L. L. Beranek, *Music, Acoustics, and Architecture*, John Wiley & Sons, Inc, New York (1962).
26. M. R. Schroeder, "Computers in Acoustics: Symbiosis of an Old Science and a New Tool," *J. Acoust. Soc. Am.* **45**, 1077 (1969).
27. W. C. Sabine, *Collected Papers on Acoustics*, Harvard University Press, Cambridge, Mass. (1927).
28. W. C. Orcutt, *Biography of Wallace Clement Sabine*, published privately in 1932. Available from L. L. Beranek, 7 Ledgewood, Winchester, Mass. 01890.
29. R. W. Young, "Sabine Reverberation Equation and Sound Power Calculations," *J. Acous. Soc. Am.* **31**, 912 (1959).
30. L. L. Beranek, "Audience and Chair Absorption in Large Halls. II," *J. Acoust. Soc. Am.* **45**, 13 (1969).
31. D. W. Robinson, "The Concept of Noise Pollution Level," National Physical Laboratory Aero Report no. AC 38, March 1969, London.
32. P. W. Smith Jr, I. Dyer, "Reverberation in Shallow-water Sound Transmission," Proc. NATO Summer Study Institute, La Spezia, Italy (1961).
33. S. H. Crandall, L. Kurzweil, "Rattling of Windows by Sonic Booms," *J. Acoust. Soc. Am.* **44**, 464 (1968).
34. R. H. Lyon, "Statistical Analysis of Power Injection and Response in Structures and Rooms," *J. Acoust. Soc. Am.* **45**, 545 (1969).
35. E. E. Ungar, E. M. Kerwin Jr, "Loss Factors of Viscoelastic Systems in Terms of Energy Concepts," *J. Acoust. Soc. Am.* **34**, 954 (1962).
36. J. S. Imai, I. Rudnick, *Phys. Rev. Lett.* **22**, 694 (1969).
37. A. F. Espinosa, P. J. Sierra, W. V. Mickey, "Seismic Waves Generated by Sonic Booms—a Geo-acoustical Problem," *J. Acoust. Soc. Am.* **44**, 1074 (1968).
38. F. L. Thurstone, "Holographic Imaging with Ultrasound," *J. Acoust. Soc. Am.* **45**, 895 (1969).
39. C. Elbaum, "Ultrasonic Attenuation in Crystalline Solids—Intrinsic and Extrinsic Mechanisms," *Ultrasonics* **7**, 113 (April 1969).
40. C. Krischer, PhD thesis, physics department, Massachusetts Institute of Technology (1969).
41. A. Smith, R. W. Damon, "Beyond Ultrasonics," *Science and Technology* no. 77, 41 (May 1968).
42. A. P. Van der Heuvel, "Surface-wave Electronics," *Science and Technology* no. 85, 52 (Jan. 1969).
43. R. H. Katyl, U. Ingard, *Phys. Rev. Lett.* **20**, 248 (1968). □

The use of random elements is common today not only
in science, but also in music, art, and literature. One
influence was the success of kinetic theory in the
nineteenth century.

---

12   Randomness and The Twentieth Century

Alfred M. Bork

An article from *The Antioch Review*, 1967.

■ As I write this I have in front of me a book that may be unfamiliar to many. It is entitled *One Million Random Digits with
1,000 Normal Deviates* and was produced by the Rand Corporation
in 1955. As the title suggests, each page contains digits—numbers
from 1 to 9—arranged as nearly as possible in a completely random
fashion. An electronic roulette wheel generated the numbers in this
book, and afterwards the numbers were made even more random by
shuffling and other methods. There is a careful mathematical definition of randomness, and associated with it are many tests that one
can apply. These numbers were shuffled until they satisfied the tests.

    I want to use this book as a beginning theme for this paper. The
production of such a book is entirely of the twentieth century. It
could not have been produced in any other era. I do not mean to
stress that the mechanism for doing it was not available, although
that is also true. What is of more interest is that before the twentieth-
century no one would even have thought of the *possibility* of producing a book like this; no one would have seen any use for it.
A rational nineteenth-century man would have thought it the height
of folly to produce a book containing only random numbers. Yet
such a book is important, even though it is not on any of the usual
lists of one hundred great books.

That this book *is* strictly of the twentieth century is in itself of importance. I claim that it indicates a cardinal feature of our century: randomness, a feature permeating many different and apparently unrelated aspects of our culture. I do not claim that randomness is the only feature which characterizes and separates twentieth-century thought from earlier thought, or even that it is dominant, but I *will* argue, admittedly on a speculative basis, that it is an important aspect of the twentieth century.

Before I leave the book referred to above, you may be curious to know why a collection of random numbers is of any use. The Rand Corporation, a government-financed organization, is not likely to spend its money on pursuits having no possible application. The principal use today of a table of random numbers is in a calculational method commonly used on large digital computers. Because of its use of random numbers, it is called the Monte Carlo method, and it was developed primarily by Fermi, von Neumann, and Ulam at the end of the Second World War. The basic idea of the Monte Carlo method is to replace an exact problem which cannot be solved with a probabilistic one which can be approximated. Another area where a table of random numbers is of importance is in designing experiments, particularly those involving sampling. If one wants, for example, to investigate certain properties of wheat grown in a field, then one wants thoroughly random samplings of wheat; if all the samples came from one corner of the field, the properties found might be peculiar to that corner rather than to the whole field. Random sampling is critical in a wide variety of situations.

Actually, few computer calculations today use a table of random numbers; rather, a procedure suggested during the early days of computer development by John von Neumann is usually followed. Von Neumann's idea was to have the computer generate its own random numbers. In a sense numbers generated in this way are not "random," but they can be made to satisfy the same exacting tests applied to the Rand Table; randomness is a matter of degree. It is more generally convenient to let the computer produce random numbers than to store in the computer memory a table such as the Rand Table. Individual computer centers often have their own methods for generating random numbers.

I shall not give any careful definition of randomness, but shall rely on intuitive ideas of the term. A formal careful definition would be at odds with our purposes, since, as A. O. Lovejoy noted in *The Great Chain of Being*, it is the vagueness of the terms which allows them to have a life of their own in a number of different areas. The careful reader will notice the shifting meanings of the word "random," and of related words, in our material.

However, it may be useful to note some of the different ideas connected with randomness. D. M. Mackay, for example, distinguishes between "(a) the notion of *well-shuffledness* or impartiality of distribution; (b) the notion of *irrelevance* or absence of correlation; (c) the notion of '*I don't care*'; and (d) the notion of *chaos*"[1] Although this is not a complete, mutually exclusive classification— the editor of the volume in which it appears objects to it—the classification indicates the range of meaning that "random" has even in well-structured areas like information theory.

Let us, then, review the evidence of randomness in several areas of twentieth-century work, and then speculate on why this concept has become so pervasive, as compared with the limited use of randomness in the nineteenth century.

I begin with the evidence for randomness in twentieth-century physics. There is no need to search far, for the concept helps to separate our physics from the Newtonian physics of the last few centuries. Several events early in this century made randomness prominent in physics. The first was the explanation of Brownian motion. Brownian movement, the microscopically observed motion of small suspended particles in a liquid, had been known since the early 1800's. A variety of explanations had been proposed, all unsatisfactory. But Albert Einstein showed, in one of his three famous papers of 1905, that Brownian motion could be understood in terms of kinetic theory:

> . . . it will be shown that according to the molecular-kinetic theory of heat, bodies of microscopically visible size, suspended in a liquid, will perform movements of such magnitude that they can be easily observed

---

[1] Donald M. Mackay, "Theoretical Models of Space Perception—Appendix," in "Aspects of the Theory of Artificial Intelligence," *The Proceedings of the First International Symposium of Biosimulation*, edited by C. A. Muses (Plenium Press, New York, 1962), p. 240.

in a microscope on account of the molecular motions of heat. It is possible that the movements to be discussed here are identical with the so-called "Brownian molecular motion." . . . if the movement discussed here can actually be observed . . . then classical thermodynamics can no longer be looked on as applicable with precision to bodies even of dimensions distinguishable in a microscope. . . . On the other hand [if] the prediction of this movement proves to be incorrect, weighty argument would be provided against the molecular-kinetic theory of heat.[2]

It is the randomness of the process, often described as a "random walk," which is the characteristic feature of Brownian motion.

But an even more direct experimental situation focused attention on randomness. During the last years of the nineteenth century, physicists suddenly found many new and strange "rays" or "radiations," including those from radioactive substances. A series of experimental studies on alpha-rays from radioactive elements led Rutherford to say in 1912 that "The agreement between theory and experiment is excellent and indicates that the alpha particles are emitted at random and the variations accord with the laws of probability."[3] These radiations were associated with the core of the atom, the nucleus, so randomness was present in the heart of matter.

One of the two principal physical theories developed in the past forty years is the theory of atomic structure, quantum mechanics, developed during the period from 1926 to 1930. Wave mechanics, the form of quantum mechanics suggested by the Austrian physicist Erwin Schrödinger, predicted in its original form only the allowable energy levels and hence the spectroscopic lines for an atom of some particular element. Later, Max Born and Werner Heisenberg gave quantum theory a more extensive interpretation, today called the "Copenhagen Interpretation," which relinquishes the possibility of predicting *exactly* the outcome of an individual measurement of an atomic (or molecular) system. Instead, statistical predictions tell what, on the average, will happen if the same measurement is performed on a large number of identically prepared systems. Identical

---

[2]Albert Einstein, *Investigations on the Theory of Brownian Movement*, edited by R. Fürth, translated by A. A. Cowper (E. P. Dutton, New York).
[3]E. Rutherford, *Radioactive Substances and their Radiations* (Cambridge University Press, Cambridge, 1913), p. 191.

measurements on identically prepared systems, in this view, do not always give the same result. Statistical ideas had been used in the nineteenth-century physics, but then it was always assumed that the basic laws were completely deterministic. Statistical calculations were made when one lacked complete information or because of the complexity of the system involved. In the statistical interpretation of quantum mechanics I have just described, however, randomness is not accepted purely for calculational purposes. It is a fundamental aspect of the basic physical laws themselves. Although some physicists have resisted this randomness in atomic physics, it is very commonly maintained. A famous principle in contemporary quantum mechanics, the "uncertainty principle," is closely related to this statistical view of the laws governing atomic systems.

These examples illustrate randomness in physics; now we proceed to other areas. Randomness in art is particularly easy to discuss because it has been so consistently and tenaciously used. My first example is from graphic design. For hundreds of years books and other publications have been "justified" in the margins in order to have flush right margins in addition to flush left margins. This is done by hyphenation and by adding small spaces between letters and words. But recently there is a tendency toward books that are not "justified"; the right margins end just where they naturally end, with no attempt to make them even. This is a conscious design choice. Its effect in books with two columns of print is to randomize partially the white space between columns of print, instead of maintaining the usual constant width white strip.

In the fine arts, the random component of assemblages, such as those of Jean Tinguely, often lies in the use of "junk" in their composition. The automobile junkyard has proved to be a particularly fruitful source of material, and there is something of a random selection there. Random modes of organization, such as the scrap-metal press, have also been used.

In art, as elsewhere, one can sometimes distinguish two kinds of randomness, one involving the creative technique and another exploiting the aesthetic effects of randomness. We see examples of this second type, called "accident as a compositional principle" by Rudolf Arnheim, in three woodcuts by Jean Arp, entitled "Placed According to the Laws of Chance." We would perhaps not have understood the artist's intent if we did not have the titles. Arp, like other contemporary artists, has returned repeatedly to the exploration of such random arrangements. As James Thrall Soby says, "There can be no doubt that the occasional miracles of accident have particular meaning for him. . . . One assumes that he considers spontaneity a primary asset of art."[4]

An area which has been particularly responsive to the exploration of randomness for aesthetic purposes is "op art." Again the titles often identify this concept, as in "Random Field" by Wen-Yin Tsai.

Perhaps more common, however, is the former aspect, an artistic technique by which the artist intentionally employs some random element. The contemporary school of action painting is an example. Jackson Pollock often would place his canvas on the ground and walk above it allowing the paint to fall several feet from his brush to the canvas. Soby describes it as follows: "Pollock's detractors call his current painting the 'drip' or 'spatter' school, and it is true that he often spreads large canvases on the floor and at them flings or dribbles raw pigments of various colors."[5] With this method he did not have complete control of just where an individual bit of paint fell—this depended in a complicated way on the position of the brush, the velocity of the brush, and the consistency of the paint. Thus this technique had explicit chance elements, and its results have been compared to Brownian motion.

Similarly, J. R. Rierce, in *Symbols, Signals, and Noise*, discussing random elements in art, gives some examples of computer-generated art. He emphasizes the interplay of "both randomness and order" in art, using the kaliedoscope as an example.

I will comment even more briefly on music. In Percy Granger's "Random Round" each instrument has a given theme to play; the entrances are in sequence, but each player decides for himself just when he will enter. Thus each performance is a unique event, involving random choices. The most famous example of random musical composition is the work of John Cage. One of his best known works involves a group of radios on a stage, each

---

[4]James Thrall Soby, *Arp* (Museum of Modern Art, New York, 1958).
[5]James Thrall Soby, "Jackson Pollock," in *The New Art in America* (Frederick Praeger, Inc., Greenwich, Conn., 1957).

with a person manipulating the controls. They work independently, each altering things as he wishes, and the particular performance is further heavily dependent on what programs happen to be playing on the local radio stations at the time of the performance. There is no question that Cage furnishes the most extreme example of exploitation of techniques with a chance component.

Most evidence for randomness in literature is not as clear as in science, art, or music. The first example is clear, but perhaps some will not want to call it literature at all. In 1965 two senior students at Reed College saw some examples of computer-produced poetry and decided that they could do as well. As their model was symbolist poetry, they did not attempt rhyme or meter, although their program might be extended to cover either or both. The computer program is so organized that the resulting poem is based on a series of random choices. First, the computer chooses randomly a category—possibilities are such themes as "sea" or "rocks." The program then selects (again using a built-in random number generator) a sentence structure from among twenty possibilities. The sentence structure contains a series of parts of speech. The computer randomly puts words into it, keeping within the previously chosen vocabulary stored in the computer memory. Because of the limited memory capacity of the small computer available, only five words occur in a given thematic and grammatical category. There are occasionally some interesting products.

Turning from a student effort to a recently available commercial product, consider the novel *Composition I* by Marc Saporta, which comes in a box containing a large number of separate sheets. Each page concludes with the end of a paragraph. The reader is told to shuffle the pages before beginning to read. Almost no two readers will see the pages in the same order, and the ordering is determined in a random process. For some readers the girl is seduced before she is married, for other readers after she is married. A similar process has been used by William Burroughs in *The Naked Lunch* and elsewhere, except that in this case the shuffling is done by the writer himself. Burroughs writes on many separate pieces of paper and then orders them over and over in different ways until he is satisfied with the arrangement. He has suggested that his work can be read in other orders, and ends *The Naked Lunch* with an "Atrophied Preface."

P. Mayersburg[6] has pointed out elements of chance construction in several other writers' work. He says of Michel Botor: "*Mobile* is constructed around coincidence: coincidence of names, places, signs, and sounds. . . . Coincidence implies the destruction of traditional chronology. It replaces a pattern of cause and effect with one of chance and accident." He sees another chance aspect in these writers: they recognize that they cannot completely control the mind of the reader.

But can we find examples in the work of more important writers? The evidence is less direct. While contemporary artists have openly mentioned their use of randomness, contemporary writers and critics, with a few exceptions, have seldom been willing to admit publicly that randomness plays any role in their writings. But I will argue that randomness is nevertheless often there, although I am aware of the difficulty of establishing it firmly.

The cubist poets, perhaps because of their associations with artists, did experiment consciously with randomness. The story is told of how Apollinaire removed all the punctuation from the proofs of *Alcools* because of typesetting errors, and he continued to use random organization in his "conversation poems" and in other work.

> The "opposite of narration" defines the very quality Apollinaire finally grasped in following cubism into the experimental work of Delaunay, the quality he named simultanism. It represents an effort to retain a moment of experience without sacrificing its logically unrelated variety. In poetry it also means an effort to neutralize the passage of time involved in the act of reading. The fragments of a poem are deliberately kept in a random order to be reassembled in a single instant of consciousness.[7]

It can be argued that James Joyce used random elements in *Ulysses* and *Finnegans Wake*. Several minor stories at least indicate that Joyce was not unfriendly toward the use of random input. For example, when Joyce was dictating to Samuel Beckett, there was a knock at the door. Joyce said, "Come in," and Beckett wrote down, "Come in," thinking that it was part of the book. He immediately

---

[6]P. Mayersberg, "The Writer as Spaceman," *The Listener*, October 17, 1963, p. 607.

[7]Roger Shattuck, *The Banquet Years* (Harcourt, Brace, and Co., New York), p. 238.

realized that Joyce had not intended to dictate it; but when he started to erase it, Joyce insisted that it should stay. And it is still there in *Finnegans Wake*, because of a chance occurrence. A related comment is made by Budgin in *James Joyce and the Making of Ulysses*: "... he was a great believer in his luck. What he needed would come to him."

Proceeding from such stories to Joyce's books, I believe that there are random elements in the vocabulary itself. It is well known that much of the vocabulary of *Finnegans Wake* differs from the vocabulary of other English-language books. Some of the words are combinations of other better-known English words, and others are traceable to exotic sources. I do not think that Joyce constructed every new word carefully, but rather that he consciously explored randomly or partially randomly formed words. There is some slight tradition for this procedure in such works as "Jabberwocky."

Another aspect of Joyce's writing, shared with other works of contemporary literature, also has some connection with our theme, although this connection is not generally realized. I refer to the "stream of consciousness" organization. The Victorian novel was ordered in a linear time sequence; there were occasional flashbacks, but mostly the ordering of events in the novel was chronological. The stream of consciousness novel does not follow such an order, but instead the events are ordered as they might be in the mind of an individual. This psychological ordering has distinctly random elements. *Finnegans Wake* has been interpreted as one night in the mental life of an individual. I would not claim that our conscious processes are completely random, but I think it is not impossible to see *some* random elements in them

We mentioned that it has not been customary to admit that randomness is a factor in contemporary literature. Much of the critical literature concerning Joyce exemplifies this. But at least one study sees Joyce as using random components: R. M. Adams' *Surface and Symbol—the Consistency of James Joyce's Ulysses*.[8] Adams relates the story of the "come in" in *Finnegans Wake*, and he tells of Joyce's requesting "any God dam drivel you may remember" of

---

[8]R. M. Adams, *Surface and Symbol—The Consistency of James Joyce's Ulysses* (Oxford University Press, New York, 1952).

his aunt. Adams points out that artists and musicians of the period were also using chance components: "Bits of rope, match or newspaper began to be attached to paintings, holes were cut in their surfaces, toilet bowls and spark plugs appeared unadorned on pedestals as works of original sculpture. . . ." Adams calls *Ulysses* a collage, and in his conclusion he cautions against trying to define the symbolism of every tiny detail in *Ulysses*: "The novel is, in part at least, a gambler's act of throwing his whole personality—his accidents, his skills, his weaknesses, his luck—against the world."

My final example of randomness is lighter. I am reliably informed that several years ago a group of students at Harvard formed a random number society for propagating interest in random numbers. Among other activities they chose each week a random number of the week, and persuaded a local radio station to announce it!

Although the reader may not accept my thesis, I continue with the assumption that our culture differs from the culture of the previous few centuries partly because of an increased concern with and conscious use of elements which are random in some sense of the word. We have seen this use in seemingly unrelated areas, and in ways previously very uncommon. Now we will enter on an even more difficult problem: assuming that the twentieth century consciously seeks out randomness, can we find any historical reasons for its permeating different fields?

I need hardly remind you of the difficulty of this problem. Theorizing in history has generally seemed unreasonable, except to the theorist himself and to a small group of devoted followers. The present problem is not general history but the even more difficult area of intellectual history. Despite vigorous attempts to understand cultural evolution, or particular aspects of it such as the development of scientific knowledge, I believe it is fair to say that we know far less than we would like to know about how ideas develop. It would, therefore, be unreasonable for me to expect to give a rich theory of how humans modify ideas. Instead I shall grope toward a small piece of such a theory, basing my attempt on the evidence presented on randomness as a twentieth-century theme.

The rough idea I shall bring to your attention might be crudely called the "splash in the puddle" theory. If a stone is dropped in a pond, waves travel out from the disturbance in all directions; a big splash may rock small boats a good bit away from the initial point of impact. Without claiming that this "mechanism" is complete, I shall argue that cultural evolution bears some analogy to the splash in the puddle. Even though the nineteenth century rejected the theme of fundamental randomness, cultural events then created new waves of interest in randomness, which eventually, through the traveling of the wave, affected areas at a distance from the source. Probably one source is not enough; often one needs reinforcement from several disturbances to create a revolution. And the sources themselves must be powerful if the effects are to be felt at great distances in the cultural plane.

I shall note two nineteenth-century events which were powerful sources, and so may have contributed to a new interest in randomness. Both are from science, but this may reflect my own specialization in history of science; I am likely to find examples from the area I know best. My two examples are of unequal weight. The minor one certainly affected profoundly the physicist's attitude toward randomness, but how widespread its effect was is not clear. The second example, however, was the major intellectual event of the century.

The first example is the development of kinetic theory and statistical thermodynamics in the last half of the century, involving Rudolf Clausius, James Clerk Maxwell, Ludwig Boltzmann, Willard Gibbs, and others. Because physicists believed that Newtonian mechanics was the fundamental theory, they thought that all other theories should "reduce" to it, in the same sense that all terms could be defined using only the terms of mechanics, and that the fundamental principles of other areas could be deduced logically from the principles of mechanics. This attitude, applied to thermodynamics, led to kinetic theory and statistical thermodynamics.

In kinetic theory a gas (a word which may originally have meant "chaos"[9]) was viewed as a very large number of separate particles, each obeying the Newtonian laws of motion, exerting

---

[9]Pointed out to me by Steven Brush. See J. R. Partington, "Joan Baptist von Helmont," *Annals of Science*, I, 359-384 (1936).

forces on each other and on the walls of the container. To know the positions and velocities of all the particles was impossible because of the multitude of particles; ordinary quantities of gas contained 10^{24}—one followed by twenty-four zeros—particles. This lack of complete information made it necessary to use general properties such as energy conservation in connection with probability considerations. One could not predict where each particle would be, but one could predict average behavior and relate this behavior to observed thermodynamical quantities. Thus statistical thermodynamics introduced statistical modes of thought to the physicist; but the underlying laws were still considered to be deterministic.

A fundamental quantity in thermodynamics, entropy, was found to have a simple statistical interpretation: it was the measure of the degree of randomness in a collection of particles. Entropy could be used as the basis of the most elegant formulation of the second law of thermodynamics: in a closed system the entropy always increases, or the degree of randomness tends to increase.

A special series of technical problems developed over the two kinds of averaging used in statistical considerations: time-averaging, inherently involved in all measurements; and averaging over many different systems, the ensemble averaging of Gibbs used in the calculations. The "ergodic theorems" that were extensively developed to show that these two averages were the same again forced careful and repeated attention on probabilistic considerations.

My second example is the theory of evolution, almost universally acknowledged as the major intellectual event of the last century. Charles Darwin and Alfred Russell Wallace developed the theory independently, using clues from Malthus' essay on population. The basic ideas are well known. Organisms vary, organisms having the fittest variations survive, and these successful variations are passed on to the progeny. The random element of evolution is in the "numerous successive, slight favorable variations"; the offspring differ slightly from the parents. Darwin, lacking an acceptable theory of heredity, had little conception of how these variations come about; he tended to believe, parallel to the developers of statistical thermodynamics, that there *were* exact laws, but that they were unknown.

I have hitherto sometimes spoken as if the variations . . . had been due to chance. This, of course, is a wholly incorrect expression, but it seems to acknowledge plainly our ignorance of the cause of each particular variation.[10]

But others were particularly disturbed by the chance factors apparently at work in variations. This was one of the factors that led Samuel Butler from his initial praise to a later critical view of Darwin. Sir John Herschel was very emphatic:

> We can no more accept the principle of arbitrary and casual variation and natural selection as a sufficient account, *per se*, of the past and present organic world, than we can receive the Laputian method of composing books . . . as a sufficient one of Shakespeare and the *Principia*.[11]

When a usable theory of heredity was developed during the next half century, randomness played a major role, both in the occurrence of mutations in genes and in the genetic inheritence of the offspring. So, almost in spite of Darwin, chance became increasingly important in evolutionary theory. ". . . The law that makes and loses fortunes at Monte Carlo is the same as that of Evolution."[12]

The theory of evolution roused almost every thinking man in the late nineteenth century. Frederick Pollock, writing about the important British mathematician William Kingdon Clifford, says:

> For two or three years the knot of Cambridge friends of whom Clifford was a leading spirit were carried away by a wave of Darwinian enthusiasm: we seemed to ride triumphant on an ocean of new life and boundless possibilities. Natural selection was to be the master-key of the universe; we expected it to solve all riddles and reconcile all contradictions.[13]

This is only one account outside biology, but it illustrates how evolution affected even those *not* directly concerned with it as a scientific theory. It does not seem unreasonable, then, that at the same time evolution contributed to the new attitude toward randomness. I

---

[10]C. Darwin, *Origin of the Species* (first edition), p. 114.

[11]Sir Herschel, *Physical Geography of the Globe* (Edinburgh, 1861), quoted in John C. Green, *The Death of Adam* (New American Library, New York), p. 296.

[12]M. Hopkins, *Chance and Error—The Theory of Evolution* (Kegan Paul, Trench, Truber & Co., London, 1923).

[13]W. K. Clifford, *Lectures and Essays* (Macmillan, London, 1886), Introduction.

might also mention two other books that are particularly interesting in showing the influence of evolution outside the sciences, offering details we cannot reproduce here. One is Leo J. Henkin's *Darwinism in the English Novel 1860-1910*; the other is Alvar Ellegård's *Darwin and the General Reader*.

There were of course other things happening in the nineteenth century, but these two developments were important and had far-reaching implications outside of their immediate areas. Alfred North Whitehead, in *Science and the Modern World*, claims that in the nineteenth century "four great novel ideas were introduced into theoretical science." Two of these ideas were energy, whose rise in importance was related to thermodynamics, and evolution. It was consistent with established tradition, however, to believe that the use of chance in these areas was not essential. Other non-scientific factors were also important; for example, Lord Kelvin's attitude toward chance was colored by religious considerations. In S. P. Thomson's *Life* we find a speech of his in the *Times* of 1903 arguing that "There is nothing between absolute scientific belief in Creative Power and the acceptance of the theory of a fortuitous concourse of atoms."

According to our splash in the puddle theory, we should be able to point out evidence that two nineteenth-century developments, statistical mechanics and evolution, had very far-reaching effects in areas quite different from their points of origin, effects reflecting interest in randomness. This is a big task, but we will attempt to give some minimal evidence by looking at the writings of two important American intellectuals near the turn of the century, both of whom were consciously influenced by statistical mechanics and Darwinian evolution. The two are Henry Adams and Charles Sanders Peirce.

We have Adams' account of his development in *The Education of Henry Adams*. Even a casual glance shows how much of the language of physics and biology occurs in the book, and how often references are made to those areas. Chapter 15 is entitled "Darwinism," and early in the chapter he says:

> The atomic theory; the correlation and conservation of energy; the mechanical theory of the universe; the kinetic theory of gases; and **Darwin's law of natural selection** were examples of what a young man had to take on trust.

Adams had to accept these because he was not in a position to argue against them. Somewhat later in the book Adams comments, in his usual third person:

> He was led to think that the final synthesis of science and its ultimate triumph was the kinetic theory of gases. . . . so far as he understood it, the theory asserted that any portion of space is occupied by molecules of gas, flying in right lines at velocities varying up to a mile a second, and colliding with each other at intervals varying up to seventeen million seven hundred and fifty thousand times a second. To this analysis—if one understood it right—all matter whatever was reducible and the only difference of opinion in science regarded the doubt whether a still deeper analysis would reduce the atom of gas to pure motion.

And a few pages later, commenting on Karl Pearson's "Grammar of Science":

> The kinetic theory of gases is an assertion of ultimate chaos. In plain, chaos was the law of nature; order was the dream of man.

Later, "Chaos was a primary fact even in Paris," this in reference to Henri Poincare's position that all knowledge involves conventional elements.

Of all Henry Adams' writings, "A Letter to American Teachers of History" is most consistently saturated with thermodynamical ideas. This 1910 paper[14] begins with thermodynamics. It first mentions the mechanical theory of the universe, and then says:

> Toward the middle of the Nineteenth Century—that is, about 1850—a new school of physicists appeared in Europe . . . made famous by the names of William Thomson, Lord Kelvin, in England, and of Clausius and Helmholtz in Germany, who announced a second law of thermodynamics.

He quotes the second law of thermodynamics in both the Thomson and the Clausius forms. It is not always clear how seriously one is to take this thermodynamical model of history.

About fifteen pages into "A Letter," Darwin is presented as contradicting the thermodynamical ideas of Thomson. He sees Darwin's contribution not in the theory of natural selection, but in that the evolutionary method shows how to bring "all vital processes under the law of development." It is this that is to furnish a lesson to the study of history. This apparent conflict is one of the major subjects of the early part of the "Letter."

---

[14]Henry Adams, *The Degradation of the Democratic Dogma* (Macmillan and Co., New York, 1920), pp. 137-366.

Thus, at the same moment, three contradictory ideas of energy were in force, all equally useful to science:

1. The Law of Conservation
2. The Law of Dissipation
3. The Law of Evolution

The contrast Adams is making is between Darwin's ideas and Kelvin's ideas.

We find other similar references in Henry Adams, but this should be enough to show his interest in Darwin and kinetic theory. Other aspects of contemporary science also very much influenced him; he often refers to the enormous change produced by the discovery of new kinds of radiation at the turn of the century. He seems to be a particularly rewarding individual to study for an understanding of the intellectual currents at the beginning of the century, as Harold G. Cassidy has pointed out:

> Henry Adams was an epitome of the non-scientist faced with science that he could not understand, and deeply disturbed by the technological changes of the time. He was a man with leisure, with the wealth to travel. With his enquiring mind he sensed, and with his eyes he saw a great ferment at work in the World. He called it a force, and tried to weigh it along with the other forces that moved mankind. The education he had received left him inadequate from a technical point of view to understand, much less cope with, these new forces. Yet his insights were often remarkable ones, and instructive to us who look at our own period from so close at hand.[15]

As final evidence we consider the work of the seminal American philosopher Charles Sanders Peirce. Peirce, although seldom holding an academic position, played an important role in American philosophy, particularly in the development of pragmatism. He was the leader of the informal "Metaphysical Club" in Cambridge during the last decades of the century. The history and views of the group, much influenced by evolutionary ideas, are discussed by Philip Weiner in *Evolution and the Founders of Pragmatism*.

Peirce was familiar with the development of both statistical thermodynamics and evolution, and both played an enormous role in the development of his thought. Peirce was a scientist by occupation, so his active interest in science is not surprising. We find his awareness of these theories (some of which he did not fully accept) evidenced by many passages in his work, such as these comments in "On the Fixation of Belief":

---

[15]Harold G. Cassidy, "The Muse and the Axiom," *American Scientist* 51, 315 (1963).

Mr. Darwin has purposed to apply the statistical method to biology. The same thing has been done in a widely different branch of science, the theory of gases. We are unable to say what the movements of any particular molecule of gas would be on a certain hypothesis concerning the constitution of this class of bodies. Clausius and Maxwell were yet able, eight years before the publication of Darwin's immortal work, by the application of the doctrine of probabilities, to predict that in the long run such and such a proportion of the molecules would under given circumstances, acquire such and such velocities; that there would take place, every second, such and such a relative number of collisions, etc., and from these propositions were able to deduce certain properties of gases especially in regard to the heat relations. In like manner, Darwin, while unable to say what the operation of variation and natural selection in any individual case will be, demonstrates that, in the long run, they will, or would, adopt animals to their circumstances.[16] [5.362]

A second example in which Peirce links the two theories is in "Evolutionary Lore":

> The Origin of the Species was published toward the end of the year 1859. The preceding years since 1846 had been one of the most productive seasons—or if extended so as to cover the book we are considering, *the* most productive period in the history of science from its beginnings until now. The idea that chance begets order, which is one of the cornerstones of modern physics . . . was at that time put into its clearest light. [6.297]

He goes on to mention Quetelet and Buckle, and then begins a discussion of the kinetic theory:

> Meanwhile, the statistical method had, under that very name, been applied with brilliant success to molecular physics. . . . In the very summer preceding Darwin's publication, Maxwell had read before the British Association the first and most important of his researches on the subject. The consequence was that the idea that fortuitous events may result in physical law and further that this is the way in which these laws which appear to conflict with the principle of conservation of energy are to be explained had taken a strong hold upon the minds of all who are abreast of the leaders of thought. [6.297]

Peirce is not reflecting the historical attitude of the physicists who developed statistical thermodynamics but is reading his own views back into this work.

---

[16]C. S. Peirce, *Collected Papers* ed. C. Hartshorn and P. Weiss (Harvard University Press, Cambridge, Mass.). References are to section numbers.

So it is not surprising that chance plays a fundamental role in Peirce's metaphysics. Peirce generalized these ideas into a general philosophy of three categories, Firstness, Secondness, and Thirdness. These three terms have various meanings in his work, but a frequent meaning of Firstness is chance. He was one of the first to emphasize that chance was not merely for mathematical convenience but was fundamental to the universe. He used the word "Tychism," from the Greek for "chance," the "doctrine that absolute chance is a factor in the universe." [6.2000]

This view of the essential role of chance he opposed to the view that universal necessity determined everything by fixed mechanical laws, in which most philosophers of science in the late nineteenth century still believed. In a long debate between Peirce and Carus concerning this issue, Peirce says:

> The first and most fundamental element that we have to assume is a Freedom, or Chance, or Spontaneity, by virtue of which the general vague nothing-in-particular-ness that preceded the chaos took on a thousand definite qualities.

In "The Doctrine of Necessity" Peirce stages a small debate between a believer in his position and a believer in necessity, to show that the usual arguments for absolute law are weak. Everyday experiences make the presence of chance in the universe almost obvious:

> The endless variety in the world has not been created by law. It is not of the nature of uniformity to originate variation nor of law to beget circumstance. When we gaze on the multifariousness of nature we are looking straight into the face of a living spontaneity. A day's ramble in the country ought to bring this home to us. [6.553]
>
> A man in China bought a cow and three days and five minutes later a Greenlander sneezed. Is that abstract circumstance connected with any regularity whatever? And are not such relations infinitely more frequent than those which are regular? [5.342]

The necessity of initial conditions in solving the equations of mechanics is another indication to Peirce of the essential part played by chance. Modern scientists have also stressed the "randomness" of initial conditions: E. P. Wigner writes, "There are . . . aspects of the world concerning which we do not believe in the existence of any accurate regularities. We call these initial conditions."

Peirce tells us we must remember that "Three elements are active in the world: first, chance; second, law; and third, habit taking." [1.409] He imagines what a completely chance world would be like, and comments, "Certainly nothing could be imagined more systematic." For Peirce the universe begins as a state of complete randomness. The interesting problem is to account for the regularity in the universe; law must evolve out of chaos. This evolutionary process is far from complete even now, and presents a continuing process still:

> We are brought, then, to this: Conformity to law exists only within a limited range of events and even there is not perfect, for an element of pure spontaneity or lawless originality mingles, or at least must be supposed to mingle, with law everywhere. [1.407]

Thus Peirce's scheme starts with chaos and out of this by habit orderliness comes, but only as a partial state.

What is of interest to us is the fundamental role of chance or randomness in Peirce's cosmology, and the connection of that role with statistical mechanics and Darwinism, rather than the details of his metaphysics.

The two examples of Henry Adams and C. S. Peirce do not establish the splash in the puddle, but they do serve at least to indicate the influence of the Darwinian and kinetic theory ideas, and they show the rising importance of chance.

Although I have concentrated on the relatively increased attention focused upon randomness in the twentieth century as compared with the nineteenth century, randomness attracted some interest before our century. One can find many earlier examples of the order-randomness dichotomy, and there have been periods when, even before the nineteenth century, random concepts acquired some status. One example containing elements of our present dichotomy is the continuing battle between classicism and romanticism in the arts and in literature. But the twentieth-century interest, as we have indicated, is more intense and of different quality. The chance component has never been totally absent; even the most careful artist in the last century could not be precisely sure of the result of his meticulously controlled brush stroke. The classical painter resisted chance—the goal of his years of training was to gain ever greater control over the brush. By contrast the contemporary painter often welcomes this random element and may even increase it. It is this contrast that I intend to stress. Although I point to this one element, the reader should not falsely conclude that I am not aware of nonrandom elements. Even now randomness is seldom the sole factor. When Pollock painted, the random component was far from the only element in his technique. He chose the colors, he chose his hand motions, and he chose the place on the canvas where he wanted to work. Further, he could, and often did, reject the total product at any time and begin over. Except in the most extreme examples, randomness is not used *alone* anywhere; it is almost always part of a larger situation. This is J. R. Pierce's emphasis on order.

The persistence of chance elements in highly ordered societies suggests a human need for these elements. Perhaps no society ever described was more completely organized than Arthur C. Clarke's fictional city of Diaspar, described in *The City and the Stars*. Diaspar, with its past, and even to some extent its future, stored in the memory banks of the central computer, has existed with its determined social structure for over a billion years. But the original planners of the city realized that perfect order was too much for man to bear:

> "Stability, however, is not enough. It leads too easily to stagnation, and thence to decadence. The designers of the city took elaborate steps to avoid this. . . . I, Khedron the Jester, am part of that plan. A very small part, perhaps. I like to think otherwise, but I can never be sure. . . . Let us say that I introduce calculated amounts of disorder into the city."[17]

But our present situation confronts us with something more than a simple dichotomy between order and disorder, as suggested in both of the following passages, one from L. L. Whyte and one from Erwin Schrödinger:

> In his long pursuit of order in nature, the scientist has turned a corner. He is now after *order and disorder* without prejudice, having discovered that complexity usually involves both.[18]

> The judicious elimination of detail, which the statistical system has taught us, has brought about a complete transformation of our knowledge of the heavens. . . . It is manifest on all sides that this statistical method is a dominant feature of our epoch, an important instrument of progress in almost every sphere of public life.[19]

---

[17]A. C. Clarke, *The City and the Stars* (Harcourt, Brace and Co., New York, 1953), pp. 47-53.

[18]L. L. Whyte, "Atomism, Structure, and Form," in *Structure in Art and in Science*, ed. G. Kepes (G. Braziller, New York, 1965) p. 20.

[19]E. Schrödinger, *Science and Human Temperament*, trans. J. Murphy and W. H. Johnston (W. W. Norton, Inc., New York), p. 128.

Although the use of random methods in physics and biology at the end of the last century originally assumed that one was dealing with areas that could not be treated exactly, but where exact laws did exist, a subtle change of view has come about, so that now random elements are seen as having a validity of their own. Both Whyte and Schrödinger see the current situation as something more than a choice between two possibilities. Whyte thinks both are essential for something he calls "complexity." But I prefer Schrödinger's suggestion that the two are not necessarily opposed, and that randomness can be a tool for increasing order. Perhaps we have a situation resembling a Hegelian synthesis, combining two themes which had been considered in direct opposition.

Finally I note an important twentieth century reaction to randomness: Joy. The persistence of games of chance through the ages shows that men have always derived some pleasure from randomness; they are important in Clarke's Diaspar, for example:

> In a world of order and stability, which in its broad outlines had not changed for a billion years, it was perhaps not surprising to find an absorbing interest in games of chance. Humanity had always been fascinated by the mystery of the falling dice, the turn of a card, the spin of the pointer . . . however, the purely intellectual fascination of chance remained to seduce the most sophisticated minds. Machines that behaved in a purely random way—events whose outcome could never be predicted, no matter how much information one had—from these philosopher and gambler could derive equal enjoyment.

But the present joy exceeds even this. Contemporary man often feels excitement in the presence of randomness, welcoming it in a way that would have seemed very strange in the immediate past. In some areas (literature, perhaps) this excitement still seems not quite proper, so it is not expressed openly. But in other places randomness is clearly acknowledged. We noted that the artist is particularly willing to admit the use of randomness, so it is not surprising to see an artist, Ben Shahn, admitting his pleasure: "I love chaos. It is a mysterious, unknown road with unexpected turnings. It is the way out. It is freedom, man's best hope."[20]

---

[20]Quoted in *Industrial Design* 13, 16 (1966).

A survey of the chief properties of wave motion, using simple mathematics in clear, step-by-step development.

13 Waves

Richard Stevenson and R. B. Moore

From their book *Theory of Physics*, 1967.

As we all know, energy can be localized in space and time. But the place where energy is localized may be different from the place where its use is desired, and thus mechanisms of transport of energy are of the greatest interest.

The transport of energy is achieved in only two ways. The first involves the transport of matter; as matter is moved its kinetic energy and internal energy move with it. The second method is more complicated and more interesting; it involves a wave process. The wave carries energy and momentum, but there is no net transfer of mass. There are many different types of waves, but the general nature of the events by which energy is carried by a wave is always the same. A succession of oscillatory processes is always involved. The wave is created by an oscillation in the emitting body; the motion of the wave through space is by means of oscillations; and the wave is absorbed by an oscillatory process in the receiving body.

Most waves are complex. In this chapter we study the most simple types of waves, those for which the amplitude varies sinusoidally.

17.1 PULSES

Suppose that you are holding the end of a relatively long rope or coil spring and that the other end is fixed to the wall.* If you raise your hand suddenly and bring it back to its original position, you will create a pulse which moves down the rope and is reflected back. The sequence of events is indicated in Figure 17.1.

Any individual point on the rope simply moves up and down as the pulse passes by. It is obvious that the pulse moves with a certain velocity, and we might imagine that there is a certain energy and momentum associated with it, even though there is no transfer of mass. Keep in mind the observation that the pulse is inverted after reflection from the wall.

Consider now another experiment with two ropes, one light

---

* It is best, of course, to hang the rope from the ceiling or lay it on a smooth table so that the rope does not sag under the action of gravity. We will draw the diagrams with the rope horizontal, as if there were no gravitational force.

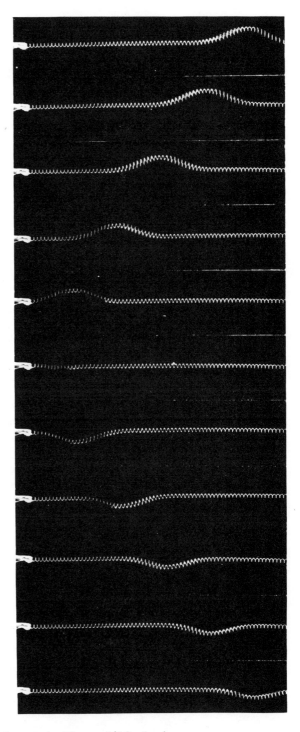

FIGURE 17.1 This sequence of photographs shows a pulse traveling to the left on a long coil spring. The pulse is reflected by the fixed end of the spring and the reflected pulse is inverted. (From Physical Science Study Committee: Physics. Boston, D. C. Heath & Co., 1960. Copyright, Educational Services Inc.)

and one heavy, attached to each other as in Figure 17.2. An incident pulse is sent along the light rope, and when it arrives at the junction or interface it is partially transmitted and partially re-

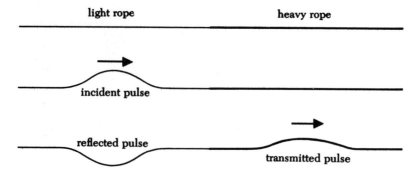

FIGURE 17.2 An incident pulse is sent along the light rope toward the attached heavy rope. The pulse is partially transmitted and partially reflected. The reflected pulse is inverted as in Figure 17.1.

flected. The transmitted pulse is upright, and the reflected pulse is inverted.

We can vary the two-rope experiment by sending the incident pulse along the heavy rope. Part is transmitted and part reflected, but the reflected part is *not* inverted. This is different from the case shown in Figure 17.3, and we conclude that the type of reflection depends on the nature of the interface at which reflection occurs.

What happens when two pulses are sent along a rope and pass over each other? If two equivalent pulses inverted with respect to each other are sent from opposite ends of the rope, they will seem to cancel each other when they meet, and at that instant the rope appears to be at rest. A moment later the pulses have passed by each other with no evident change in shape. Evidently one pulse can move along the rope quite independently of another, and when they meet the pulses are superimposed one on the other.

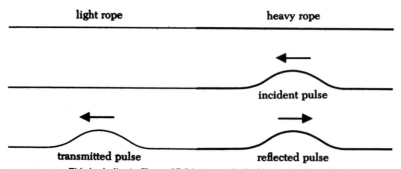

FIGURE 17.3 This is similar to Figure 17.2 but now the incident pulse is on the heavy rope. Again the pulse is partially reflected and partially transmitted. However the reflected pulse is *not* inverted. The nature of the reflected pulse will depend on the boundary which caused the reflection.

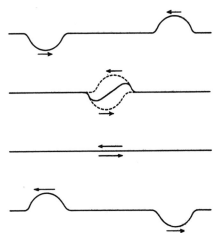

FIGURE 17.4 Superposition implies that waves or pulses pass through one another with no interaction. The diagram shows a rope carrying two pulses. In (a) the pulses approach each other. In (b) they begin to cross, and the resultant rope shape is found by the addition of pulse displacements at each point along the rope. At the instant of time shown in (c) there will be no net displacement of the rope; if the pulse shapes are the same and their amplitudes are opposite there will be an instantaneous cancellation. In (d) the pulses move along with no change in shape or diminution of amplitude, just as if the other pulse had not existed.

17.2 RUNNING WAVES

Let us supply a succession of pulses to our long rope, as in Figure 17.5. This is easily enough done by jerking the end of the rope up and down at regular intervals. If the interval is long enough we would have a succession of separate pulses traveling along the rope. Eventually, of course, these pulses will be reflected and will complicate the picture, but for the moment we can assume that no reflection has occurred.

Problem 2

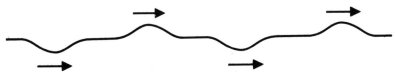

FIGURE 17.5 We can send a succession of pulses along a long rope by jerking one end up and down.

Now suppose that we apply the pulses to the rope so that there is no interval between pulses. The result is shown in Figure 17.6. This is obviously a special case, and we give it a special name. We say that a wave is moving along the rope, and it is clear that the wave is composed of a specially applied sequence of pulses. Such a wave is called a running or traveling wave.

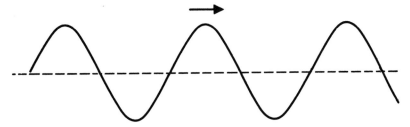

FIGURE 17.6 Instead of sending isolated pulses along the rope as in Figure 17.5, we move our hand up and down continuously. Now there is no interval of time between individual pulses, and we say that the rope is carrying a wave. The wave velocity is identical to the velocity of the individual pulses which make up the wave.

A simple type of wave can be created by causing the end of the rope to move up and down in simple harmonic motion. The sequence of events by which the wave was established is shown in Figure 17.7. The motion of the end of the rope causes the wave pulse to move along the rope with velocity c. As the wave pulse moves along, a point on the rope a distance l from the end of the

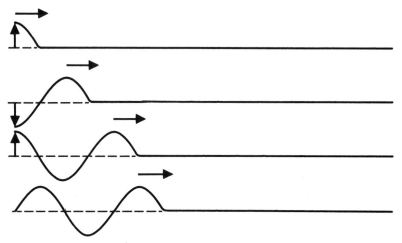

FIGURE 17.7 This sequence of drawings shows the means by which a wave is established along a rope. The left hand end moves up and down in simple harmonic motion. This causes the wave pulse to move along the rope with velocity c. The frequency of the wave will be the same as the frequency of the event which started the wave.

rope will also start into simple harmonic motion, but it will start at a time l/c later than that of the end of the rope.

Consider Figure 17.8. Point A has just completed one cycle of simple harmonic motion. It started at $t = 0$ and finished at $t = T$,

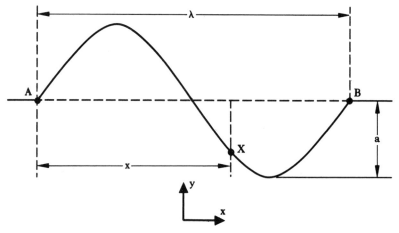

FIGURE 17.8 This shows the wave form for one complete cycle of simple harmonic motion of the source. The wave moves in the x-direction, and individual points on the rope move in the $\pm y$-directions. The wavelength λ is the distance the wave travels for one complete cycle of the source. The wave amplitude is a.

where T is the period. If the amplitude of motion is a, then the displacement in the y direction of point A can be represented by

$$y_A = a \sin 2\pi f t \qquad (17\text{--}1)$$

where f is the frequency of the motion. Now as point A is just finishing one cycle and starting another, point B is starting its first cycle. If it is a distance λ away from A, it starts at time

$$t_B = \frac{\lambda}{c}$$

Another point on the curve, such as X, had started at a time

$$t_X = \frac{x}{c}$$

With respect to point A, the motion of point X is delayed by a time t_X. We can see that the displacements of points B and X can be represented by

$$y_B = a \sin 2\pi f \left(t - \frac{\lambda}{c} \right)$$
$$\qquad (17\text{--}2)$$
$$y_X = a \sin 2\pi f \left(t - \frac{x}{c} \right)$$

Let us return for a moment to Figure 17.8. The distance $AB = \lambda$, for one complete wave form, is called the wavelength. If the wave has velocity c, the time required for the wave to travel from A to B is λ/c, and this will just equal the period of the simple harmonic motion associated with the wave. That is,

$$T = \frac{\lambda}{c}$$

However

$$T = \frac{1}{f}$$
$$= \frac{\lambda}{c}$$

Thus

$$\lambda f = c \qquad (17\text{--}3)$$

This very important relationship between wavelength, frequency and wave velocity holds for any type of wave.

We also have developed an equation which represents the wave. For the wave moving in the positive x-direction, the displacement of any point a distance x from the origin is given by (17–2).

$$y = a \sin 2\pi f \left(t - \frac{x}{c} \right)$$

We can simplify this by noting that

$$\omega = 2\pi f$$

and

$$ft = \frac{t}{T} \quad \text{and} \quad \frac{fx}{c} = \frac{x}{\lambda}$$

Thus we have

$$y = a \sin \omega\left(t - \frac{x}{c}\right)$$

$$= a \sin 2\pi\left(\frac{t}{T} - \frac{x}{\lambda}\right) \tag{17-4}$$

Example. Two sources separated by 10 m vibrate according to the equations $y_1 = 0.03 \sin \pi t$ and $y_2 = 0.01 \sin \pi t$. They send out simple waves of velocity 1.5 m/sec. What is the equation of motion of a particle 6 m from the first source and 4 m from the second?

We suppose that source 1 sends out waves in the +*x*-direction,

$$y_1 = a_1 \sin 2\pi f_1\left(t - \frac{x_1}{c}\right)$$

and that source 2 sends out waves in the −*x*-direction,

$$y_2 = a_2 \sin 2\pi f_2\left(t + \frac{x_2}{c}\right)$$

Then

$$
\begin{array}{ll}
a_1 = 0.03 \text{ m} & a_2 = 0.01 \text{ m} \\
x_1 = 6 \text{ m} & x_2 = -4 \text{ m} \\
f_1 = f_2 = \frac{1}{2} \text{ sec}^{-1} \\
c = 1.5 \text{ m/sec}
\end{array}
$$

Thus

$$
\begin{aligned}
y_1 &= 0.03 \sin \pi(t - 4) \\
&= 0.03 \sin \pi t \cos 4\pi - \cos \pi t \sin 4\pi \\
&= 0.03 \sin \pi t
\end{aligned}
$$

$$
\begin{aligned}
y_2 &= 0.01 \sin \pi(t - 8/3) \\
&= 0.01 \ (\sin \pi t \cos 8\pi/3 - \cos \pi t \sin 8\pi/3) \\
&= 0.01 \ (\sin \pi t(-1/2) - \cos \pi t \ \sqrt{3}/2) \\
&= -0.005 \sin \pi t - 0.00866 \cos \pi t
\end{aligned}
$$

The resultant wave motion is

$$
\begin{aligned}
y &= y_1 + y_2 \\
&= 0.03 \sin \pi t - 0.005 \sin \pi t - 0.00866 \cos \pi t \\
&= 0.025 \sin \pi t - 0.00866 \cos \pi t
\end{aligned}
$$

We will write this in the form

$$
\begin{aligned}
y &= A \sin (\pi t + \phi) \\
&= A \sin \pi t \cos \phi + A \cos \pi t \sin \phi
\end{aligned}
$$

Thus

$$A^2 = 0.025^2 + 0.00866^2 \qquad A = 0.0264 \text{ m}$$
$$- \tan \phi = \frac{0.00866}{0.025} = 0.346$$
$$- \phi = 19.1°$$

17.3 STANDING WAVES

Suppose that we have a long rope with one wave train of angular frequency ω traveling in the +x-direction and another of the same frequency traveling in the −x-direction. Both wave trains have the same amplitude, and we can write the general displacements as

$$y_+ = a \sin \omega\left(t - \frac{x}{c}\right)$$
$$y_- = a \sin \omega\left(t + \frac{x}{c}\right) \qquad (17\text{-}5)$$

These two wave trains are superimposed, so the net displacement is

$$y = y_+ + y_-$$
$$= a \sin \omega\left(t - \frac{x}{c}\right) + a \sin \omega\left(t + \frac{x}{c}\right) \qquad (17\text{-}6)$$

To simplify this we use the trigonometric relations

$$\sin(\theta + \phi) = \sin \theta \cos \phi + \cos \theta \sin \phi$$
$$\sin(\theta - \phi) = \sin \theta \cos \phi - \cos \theta \sin \phi$$

Thus (17-6) is transformed to

$$y = (2a \sin \omega t) \cos \frac{\omega x}{c} \qquad (17\text{-}7)$$

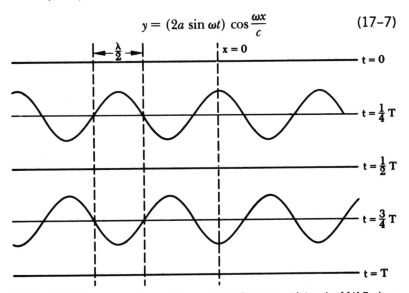

FIGURE 17.9 This sequence shows pictures of standing waves at intervals of 1/4 T, where $T = 1/f$ is the period. At $t = 0$, 1/2 T, T the displacement at all points is instantaneously zero. At intervals of $\lambda/2$ along the wave there are points called nodes for which the displacement is zero at all times.

This is called a standing wave. The amplitude is $2a \sin \omega t$, which varies with time and is zero at $t = 0$, $t = \frac{1}{2} T$, and so forth. The displacement on the rope will be zero for distances x, where

$$\frac{\omega x}{c} = (2n - 1) \frac{\pi}{2} \qquad (17\text{-}8)$$
$$n = 0, \pm 1, \pm 2, \ldots$$

Since $\omega = 2\pi f$, from (17–7), these points of zero displacement or nodes are located at

$$x = (2n - 1) \frac{c}{\omega} \frac{\pi}{2}$$
$$= (2n - 1) \frac{c}{2\pi f} \frac{\pi}{2} \qquad (17\text{-}9)$$
$$= (2n - 1) \frac{\lambda}{4}$$

The distance between two nodes will be, therefore, $n\lambda/2$ where $n = 1, 2, 3$, and so forth.

It is easy to see how standing waves can be created on a string which is fixed at one or at both ends. One wave train is caused by

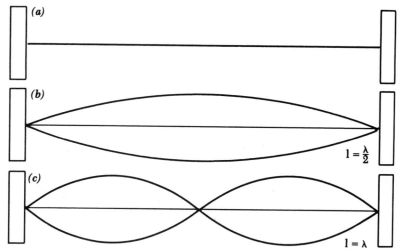

FIGURE 17.10 A string of length l, such as a violin string, is clamped at both ends. Both ends must be nodes if a standing wave is to be set up on the string. The maximum wavelength of the standing wave will be $\lambda = 2\,l$. The next possible standing wave will have a wavelength $\lambda = l$. Vibrations with wavelengths different from those of the standing waves will die out quickly.

the agency which causes the vibration, and the other wave train arises from a reflection at the fixed end. Consider a string fixed at both ends. Both ends must be nodes, so that if the length of the string is l, then by (17–9)

$$l = \frac{n\lambda}{2} \qquad (17\text{-}10)$$

The string can vibrate with wavelengths $2l$, l, $2l/3$, and so forth. Vibrations with other wavelengths can be set up of course, but these die out very quickly. The string will resonate to the wavelengths given by (17–10).

It is very important that the distinction between a running wave and a standing wave be kept in mind. The running wave is illustrated in Figures 17.6 and 17.7. The wave disturbance moves in one direction only and each particle through which the wave passes suffers a sinusoidal variation of amplitude with time. The standing wave, on the other hand, is a superposition of two running waves of the same frequency and amplitude, moving in opposite directions. Certain points on the standing waves, the nodes, have a constant zero amplitude even though the two running waves are continually passing through these points. Usually a standing wave is made by the superposition of an incident wave and the reflected wave from some boundary.

Example. Standing waves are produced by the superposition of two waves

$$y_1 = 15 \sin (3\pi t - 5x)$$
$$y_2 = 15 \sin (3\pi t + 5x)$$

Find the amplitude of motion at $x = 21$.

We use the relationships

$$\sin (\alpha \pm \beta) = \sin \alpha \cos \beta \pm \cos \alpha \sin \beta$$
$$\sin (\alpha + \beta) + \sin (\alpha - \beta) = 2 \sin \alpha \cos \beta$$

Thus

$$y = y_1 + y_2 = 30 \sin 3\pi t \cos 5x$$

With

$$x = 21, \, 5x = 105 \text{ radians}$$
$$= 38.4\pi \text{ radians}$$

Now $\cos 38.4\pi = \cos 0.4\pi = \cos 72° = 0.309$.

Thus the amplitude at $x = 21$ is

$$30 \cos 38.4\pi = 30 \times 0.309$$
$$= 9.27$$

17.4 THE DOPPLER EFFECT

We wish now to study what happens when waves from a point source S, which moves with velocity u, are detected by an observer O who moves with velocity v.

Let the situation be as in Figure 17.11. The velocities u and v are in the positive x-direction. The velocity of the waves emitted by S is c, and we can imagine two points A and B fixed in space

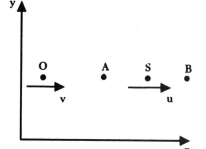

FIGURE 17.11 Waves are emitted by a point source S moving with velocity u, and detected by an observer O moving with velocity v. At $t = 0$, points A and B are equidistant from S. A spherical wave emitted from S at $t = 0$ will just reach A and B at time $t = \tau$.

equidistant from S at $t = 0$ such that a wave emitted at $t = 0$ will just reach A and B at time τ. Thus at $t = 0$

$$\text{dist } AS = c\tau \qquad t = 0$$
$$\text{dist } BS = c\tau$$

But by time τ, S will have moved a distance $u\tau$, and then

$$\text{dist } AS = c\tau + u\tau \qquad t = \tau$$
$$\text{dist } BS = c\tau - u\tau$$

If the frequency of the source is f_0, it will have emitted f_0 wavefronts between $t = 0$ and $t = \tau$. Since the first wavefront reaches A and B at $t = \tau$, then f_0 wavefronts are contained in the distances AS and BS. Thus the apparent wavelength in front of the source is

$$\lambda = \frac{BS}{f_0 \tau} = \frac{c - u}{f_0} \qquad (17\text{--}11)$$

and the wavelength behind the source is

$$\lambda' = \frac{AS}{f_0 \tau} = \frac{c + u}{f_0} \qquad (17\text{--}12)$$

Now the observer O moves with velocity v, and the speed of the waves relative to him is $c + v$. Since he is behind the source he experiences waves of wavelength λ' at an apparent frequency f given by

$$f = \frac{c + v}{\lambda'}$$
$$= \frac{c + v}{c + u} f_0 \qquad (17\text{--}13)$$

The various expressions can easily be altered if the source is moving in a direction opposite to that of the detector.

Most of us will have noticed the Doppler effect in the change in pitch of a horn or siren as it passes by. The Doppler effect is a property of any wave motion, and is used, for example, by the police in the radar sets that are employed to apprehend speeding motorists.

Example. A proposed police radar is designed to work by the Doppler effect using electromagnetic radiation of 30 cm wave-

length. The radar beam is reflected from a moving car; the motion causes a change in frequency, which is compared with the original frequency to compute the speed.

A car moves toward the radar at 65 mph (31 m/sec). The wavelength of the beam emitted by the radar is

$$\lambda_0 = \frac{c}{f_0}$$

On time τ the source emits f_0 wavefronts, and these travel a distance $c\tau - v\tau$ before reflection. Thus the wavelength of the reflected beam as seen by the car is

$$\lambda' = \frac{c\tau - v\tau}{f_0\tau} = \frac{c - v}{f_0}$$

As seen by the stationary radar set this wave λ' reflected by the moving car has wavelength λ'' and frequency f''.

$$f'' = \frac{c}{\lambda''}$$

$$= f_0 \frac{c - 2v}{c}$$

The fractional change in frequency is

$$\frac{\Delta f}{f_0} = \frac{f_0 - f''}{f_0} = 1 - \frac{c - 2v}{c} = \frac{2v}{c} = \frac{62}{3 \times 10^8}$$
$$= 2.06 \times 10^{-7}$$

The frequency of 30 cm radiation is

$$f_0 = \frac{c}{\lambda_0} = \frac{3 \times 10^8}{0.3} = 10^9 \text{ sec}^{-1}$$

Thus the change in frequency would be

$$\Delta f = 2.06 \times 10^{-7} \times 10^9$$
$$= 206 \text{ cps}$$

17.5 SOUND WAVES

Waves on a string are called transverse waves because the motion of the individual particles is perpendicular or transverse to the direction of motion of the wave. Another type of wave is the longitudinal wave, where the motion of the particle is along the same line as the direction of motion of the wave.

Sound is a longitudinal wave which involves very small changes in density of the medium through which it is propagated. That is, a sound is a train of pressure variations in a substance. At any one point there is an oscillatory variation in pressure or density.

In a solid the velocity of sound is given by

$$c = \sqrt{\frac{E}{d}} \qquad (17\text{--}14)$$

where d is the density and E is Young's modulus (the ratio of stress to strain in the elastic region).*

In a perfect gas the velocity of sound is given by

$$c = \sqrt{\frac{c_p p}{c_v d}} \qquad (17\text{--}15)$$

where again $d = m/v$ is the density of the gas. Since $pV = RT$, we can see from (17–15) that $c \propto T^{1/2}$.

Very interesting effects occur with sound waves when the source emitting the wave is moving faster than the velocity of sound. For example, in Figure 17.12, consider a source moving with speed $v > c$. It moves from A to B in time Δt and from B to C in an equal time Δt. When the body is at C the wave emitted at B has spread out as a sphere of radius $c\Delta t$. Similarly the wave emitted

---

* See Section 27.5.

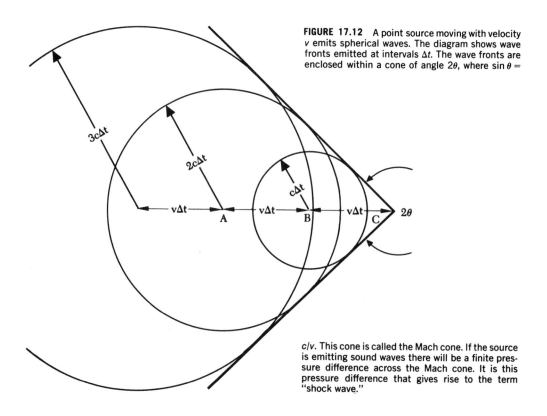

FIGURE 17.12 A point source moving with velocity v emits spherical waves. The diagram shows wave fronts emitted at intervals Δt. The wave fronts are enclosed within a cone of angle 2θ, where $\sin \theta =$ c/v. This cone is called the Mach cone. If the source is emitting sound waves there will be a finite pressure difference across the Mach cone. It is this pressure difference that gives rise to the term "shock wave."

at A has spread out as a sphere of radius $2c\Delta t$. All the waves emitted at previous times are enclosed within a cone, called the Mach cone, of angle 2θ, where $\sin \theta = c/v$. The wave along this cone is called a shock wave because there is a finite difference of pressure across the front. The ratio v/c is called the Mach number, after the scientist who first proposed its use. The cone of shock waves is called the Mach cone.

Example. The index of refraction n of a substance is the ratio of the velocity of light in a vacuum to the velocity of light in the substance, $n = c/v$. If a high speed charged particle is sent with velocity u through the substance, the ratio (the Mach number, as it were) u/v can be greater than unity. Then any radiation emitted by the particle is enclosed within a cone of angle 2θ where

$$\sin \theta = \frac{v}{u} = \frac{c}{nu}$$

The velocity of the particle can be greater than the velocity of light in the medium (but never greater than the velocity of light in a vacuum).

The radiation emitted by the particle is known as Cherenkov radiation. By measuring θ, this phenomena finds useful application in the measurement of the velocities of charged particles.

17.6 ENERGY OF WAVES

Let us return to the wave moving along a string. The displacement of point x at time t is

$$y = a \sin \omega\left(t - \frac{x}{c}\right) \tag{17-16}$$

The velocity v of this point is

$$v = \frac{\Delta y}{\Delta t} = a\omega \cos \omega\left(t - \frac{x}{c}\right) \tag{17-17}$$

Now we suppose that the mass of a small element of the string at this point is m; thus, the kinetic energy is

$$\begin{aligned} T &= \tfrac{1}{2}\, mv^2 \\ &= \tfrac{1}{2}\, ma^2\omega^2 \cos^2 \omega\left(t - \frac{x}{c}\right) \end{aligned} \tag{17-18}$$

The time average of the kinetic energy is

$$T = \tfrac{1}{4}\, ma^2\omega^2 \tag{17-19}$$

And finally we define an energy density as being the average kinetic energy per unit mass.

$$\text{kinetic energy density} = \tfrac{1}{4}\, a^2\omega^2 \tag{17-20}$$

Since the energy of the system is being transformed from kinetic to potential and back again, and since $T_{max} = V_{max}$ we can see that

$$\text{potential energy density} = \tfrac{1}{4}\, a^2\omega^2 \qquad (17\text{--}21)$$

Thus

$$\text{total energy density} = \tfrac{1}{2}\, a^2\omega^2 \qquad (17\text{--}22)$$

The energy density is proportional to the square of the amplitude and the square of the frequency.

The same expression (17–22) holds for a sound wave. The density d gives the mass per unit volume; thus, the total energy per unit volume is

$$\tfrac{1}{2}\, da^2\omega^2 \qquad (17\text{--}23)$$

We can now begin to perceive how energy is transported by waves. By expending energy a source can cause a harmonic disturbance in a medium. This disturbance is propagated through the medium by the influence that an individual particle has on other particles immediately adjacent to it. The motion of the particle means that it has a certain amount of energy, part kinetic and part potential at any instant of time. At some point energy is removed from the wave and presumably dissipated. And to sustain the wave motion along the wave train, energy must be supplied by the source.

17.7 DISPERSION OF WAVES

We have discussed only the simplest type of waves, sinusoidal in form, and in the remainder of the book we will never have occasion to talk about more complicated waves.

In a simple wave, at a point in space there is a simple harmonic motion of mass or a sinusoidal variation of a field vector. This local event may be parallel or perpendicular to the direction of the wave, from which arises the terms "longitudinal" or "transverse" waves. The wave has a frequency f and a wavelength λ. The wave velocity c is related to these by $c = f\lambda$.

Strictly speaking, we should call this velocity the phase velocity, and give it another symbol v_ϕ.

$$v_\phi = f\lambda \qquad (17\text{--}24)$$

This is because v_ϕ gives the velocity at which an event of constant phase is propagated along the wave. For later use we will define another quantity, the wave vector modulus k.

$$k = \frac{1}{2\pi\lambda}$$

Thus

$$v_\phi = \frac{\omega}{k} \qquad (17\text{--}25)$$

As might be expected, real waves are liable to be more complicated than the simple waves, and we might suppose that the real wave is a result of the superposition of many simple waves. If the velocities of the simple waves vary with wavelength, what then is the velocity of the resultant wave and how is it related to wavelength?

For an example consider two simple waves of slightly different wavelengths λ and λ' and velocities v and v', but with the same amplitude. For the resultant wave the displacement x at time t is

$$y = a \sin (\omega t - kx) + a \sin (\omega' t - k'x) \qquad (17\text{-}26)$$

We can use the trigonometric identity

$$\sin \alpha + \sin \beta = 2 \sin \frac{\alpha + \beta}{2} \cos \frac{\alpha - \beta}{2}$$

Thus the displacement of y becomes

$$y = 2a \sin \left[\left(\frac{\omega + \omega'}{2} \right) t - \left(\frac{k + k'}{2} \right) x \right] \cos \left[\left(\frac{\omega - \omega'}{2} \right) t - \left(\frac{k - k'}{2} \right) x \right] \quad (17\text{-}27)$$

We will rewrite (17-27) as

$$y = 2a \sin (\omega_\phi t - k_\phi x) \cos (\omega_g t - k_g x) \qquad (17\text{-}28)$$

The individual waves correspond to the sine factor in (17-27) and (17-28) and the phase velocity is

$$v_\phi = \frac{\omega_\phi}{k_\phi} = \frac{\omega + \omega'}{k + k'} \cong \frac{\omega}{k} \qquad (17\text{-}29)$$

The cosine factor in (17-27) and (17-28) indicates that another wave is present with velocity

$$v_g = \frac{\omega_g}{k_g} = \frac{\omega - \omega'}{k - k'}$$
$$= \frac{\Delta \omega}{\Delta k} \qquad (17\text{-}30)$$

This is called the group velocity, using the terminology that the real wave is made up of a group of individual waves.

We know that $\omega = v_\phi k$, thus

$$\Delta \omega = (\omega + \Delta \omega) - \omega$$
$$= (v_\phi + \Delta v_\phi)(k + \Delta k) - v_\phi k$$
$$= v_\phi \Delta k + k \Delta v_\phi$$

Therefore

$$v_g = \frac{\Delta \omega}{\Delta k}$$
$$= v_\phi + k \frac{\Delta v_\phi}{\Delta k} \qquad (17\text{-}31)$$

The significance of this is that the group velocity is the velocity at which energy flows, and it is normally the only velocity that can be observed for a wave train. Dispersion is said to occur when the phase velocity varies with wavelength, that is when $\Delta v_\phi / \Delta k \neq 0$. If there is no dispersion the phase velocity is identical to the group velocity.

Example. An atom emits a photon of green light $\lambda = 5200$ Å in $\tau = 2 \times 10^{-10}$ sec. Estimate the spread of wavelengths in the photon.

We will consider the photon to be composed of a train of waves. The length of the wave train is $c\tau = 3 \times 10^8 \times 2 \times 10^{-10} = 0.06$ m.

To make the estimate we can suppose that the wave train is made up of waves with slightly different frequencies and wavelengths.

$$y = a \sin (\omega t - kx) + a \sin (\omega' t - k'x)$$
$$= 2a \sin \tfrac{1}{2}[(\omega + \omega')t - (k + k')x] \cos \tfrac{1}{2}[(\omega - \omega')t - (k - k')x]$$

The resultant wave has an overall frequency $\tfrac{1}{2}(\omega - \omega')$ and an overall wave vector $\tfrac{1}{2}(k - k')$. Thus the length of the wave train is approximated by

$$2l = \frac{1}{2\pi \cdot \tfrac{1}{2}(k - k')}$$

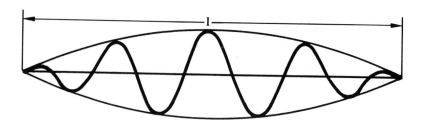

Since $k = \dfrac{1}{2\pi\lambda}$, $k' = \dfrac{1}{2\pi\lambda'}$. This length is given by

$$l = \frac{\lambda\lambda'}{\lambda - \lambda'}$$

We can write $\lambda' = \lambda + \Delta\lambda$, thus

$$l = \frac{\lambda^2}{\Delta\lambda}$$

and we calculated $l = 0.06$ m. Therefore

$$\Delta\lambda = \frac{\lambda^2}{l} = \frac{(0.52 \times 10^{-6})^2}{0.06}$$
$$= 4.5 \times 10^{-12} \text{ m}$$
$$= 4.5 \times 10^{-2} \text{ Å}$$

A similar estimate of $\Delta\lambda$ can be made using the uncertainty principle in the following way. We use $\Delta E \Delta t \sim h$, and $E = hf$; thus

$$h\Delta f \Delta t \sim h$$
$$\Delta f \sim \frac{1}{\Delta t}$$

Now $\lambda f = c$, therefore

$$(\lambda + \Delta\lambda)(f + \Delta f) - \lambda f = 0$$

which gives, in absolute values,

$$\frac{\Delta\lambda}{\lambda} = \frac{\Delta f}{f}$$

Thus $\Delta f \sim \frac{1}{\Delta t}$ reduces to

$$\Delta\lambda = \frac{\lambda}{f\Delta t} = \frac{\lambda^2}{c\Delta t}$$

which is the same as the expression used in the previous calculation.

17.8 SPHERICAL WAVES

So far we have talked about only waves on a rope, and clearly the rope was the medium which carried the wave. Many waves are associated with a medium, but the existence of a medium is not essential to the existence of a wave; all we need is something that vibrates in simple harmonic motion.

Perhaps the most important types of waves are sound waves and electromagnetic waves. A sound wave needs a medium to be transmitted, and the vibration consists of small oscillations in the density of the medium in the direction of propagation of the wave. Thus a sound wave is classified as a longitudinal wave. On the other hand, an electromagnetic wave needs no medium and con-

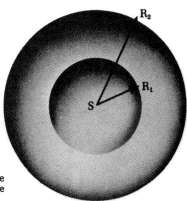

FIGURE 17.13 A point source S emits spherical waves. At time t_1 the wavefront is a sphere of radius R_1; at time t_2 the wavefront is a sphere of radius R_2.

sists of oscillation of electric and magnetic field vectors perpendicular to the direction of propagation. It is classified, therefore, as a transverse wave.

For a rope the medium extends only along a rope; thus, the wave can be propagated only in that direction. But a sound wave or an electromagnetic wave can be propagated in all directions at once. Consider, as in Figure 17.13, a small source S of wave motion. The wave front travels out in every direction from S, and we can consider it to be spherical since no direction of propagation is preferred over another.

Suppose that the energy associated with the wavefront is E. This energy is distributed over the spherical wavefront of radius R. Thus the intensity* or energy density at a point is

$$I = \frac{E}{4\pi R^2} \tag{17-32}$$

We can measure the intensity at two distances R_1 and R_2 from the source. They will be

$$I_1 = \frac{E}{4\pi R_1^2}$$

$$I_2 = \frac{E}{4\pi R_2^2}$$

Thus

$$\frac{I_2}{I_1} = \frac{R_1^2}{R_2^2} \tag{17-33}$$

That is, the intensity of a spherical wave varies inversely as the square of the distance from the wave source. This inverse square law applies only to spherical waves, but can be used in an approximate way to estimate the variation in intensity of waves which are only approximately spherical.

17.9 HUYGENS' PRINCIPLE

In the last few sections we have talked about wavefronts without defining them carefully. A small source S of frequency f can emit waves of wavelength λ and velocity c. We can suppose that the source sends out wavefronts at time intervals $1/f$, and that these wavefronts are separated by a distance λ.

If we know the position of a wavefront at time t, how do we find its position at time $t + \Delta t$? This problem is solved by Huygens' principle, which states that every point on the wavefront at time t can be considered to be the source of secondary spherical waves

---

* Keep in mind that the intensity of the wave is proportional to the square of the amplitude; see Section 17.6.

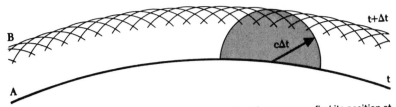

FIGURE 17.14 If we know the position of a wavefront at time t, we can find its position at time $t + \Delta t$ by Huygens' principle. Each point on the original wavefront is thought to emit a secondary spherical wavelet. In time Δt the wavelet will have a radius $c\Delta t$, where c is the wave velocity. The wavefront at time $t + \Delta t$ will be the envelope of all the secondary wavelets.

which have the same velocity as the original wave. The wavefront at time $t + \Delta t$ is the envelope of these secondary waves.

This is a geometric principle, of course, and is best illustrated by a diagram. In Figure 17.14, AB is a wavefront at time t. If the wave velocity is c, then in time Δt a secondary wave will travel a distance $c\Delta t$. The envelope of the secondary waves is AB, which is therefore the position of the wavefront at time $t + \Delta t$.

Two masters of physics introduce the wave concept in this section from a well-known popular book.

14   What is a Wave?

Albert Einstein and Leopold Infeld

An excerpt from their book *The Evolution of Physics*, 1961.

A bit of gossip starting in Washington reaches New York very quickly, even though not a single individual who takes part in spreading it travels between these two cities. There are two quite different motions involved, that of the rumor, Washington to New York, and that of the persons who spread the rumor. The wind, passing over a field of grain, sets up a wave which spreads out across the whole field. Here again we must distinguish between the motion of the wave and the motion of the separate plants, which undergo only small oscillations. We have all seen the waves that spread in wider and wider circles when a stone is thrown into a pool of water. The motion of the wave is very different from that of the particles of water. The particles merely go up and down. The observed motion of the wave is that of a state of matter and not of matter itself. A cork floating on the wave shows this clearly, for it moves up and down in imitation of the actual motion of the water, instead of being carried along by the wave.

In order to understand better the mechanism of the wave let us again consider an idealized experiment. Suppose that a large space is filled quite uniformly with water, or air, or some other "medium." Somewhere in the center there is a sphere. At the beginning of the experiment there is no motion at all. Suddenly the sphere begins to "breathe" rhythmically, expanding and contracting in volume, although retaining its spherical shape. What will happen in the medium? Let us begin our examination at the moment the sphere begins to expand. The particles of the medium in the immediate vicinity of the sphere are pushed out, so that the density of a spherical shell of water, or air, as the case may be, is increased above its normal value. Similarly, when the sphere contracts, the density of that part of the medium immediately surrounding it will be decreased. These changes of density are propagated' throughout the entire medium. The particles constituting the medium perform only small vibrations, but the whole motion is that of a progressive wave. The essentially new thing here is that for the first time we consider the motion of something which is not matter, but energy propagated through matter.

Using the example of the pulsating sphere, we may introduce two general physical concepts, important for the characterization of waves. The first is the velocity with which the wave spreads. This will depend on the medium, being different for water and air, for example. The second concept is that of *wave-length*. In the case of waves on a sea or river it is the distance from the trough of one wave to that of the next, or from the crest of one wave to that of the next. Thus sea waves have greater wave-length than river waves. In the case of our waves set up by a pulsating sphere the wave-length is the distance, at some definite time, between two neighboring spherical shells showing maxima or minima of density. It is evident that this distance will not depend on the medium alone. The rate of pulsation of the sphere will certainly have a great effect, making the wave-length shorter if the pulsation becomes more rapid, longer if the pulsation becomes slower.

This concept of a wave proved very successful in physics. It is definitely a mechanical concept. The phenomenon is reduced to the motion of particles which, according to the kinetic theory, are constituents of matter. Thus every theory which uses the concept of wave can, in general, be regarded as a mechanical theory. For example, the explanation of acoustical phenomena is based essentially on this concept. Vibrating bodies, such as vocal cords and violin strings, are sources of sound waves which are propagated through the air in the manner explained for the pulsating sphere. It is thus possible to reduce all acoustical phenomena to mechanics by means of the wave concept.

It has been emphasized that we must distinguish between the motion of the particles and that of the wave itself, which is a state of the medium. The two are very different but it is apparent that in our example of the pulsating sphere both motions take place in the

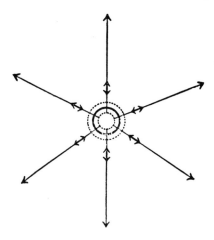

same straight line. The particles of the medium oscillate along short line segments, and the density increases and decreases periodically in accordance with this motion. The direction in which the wave spreads and the line on which the oscillations lie are the same. This type of wave is called *longitudinal*. But is this the only kind of wave? It is important for our further considerations to realize the possibility of a different kind of wave, called *transverse*.

Let us change our previous example. We still have the sphere, but it is immersed in a medium of a different kind, a sort of jelly instead of air or water. Furthermore, the sphere no longer pulsates but rotates in one direction through a small angle and then back again,

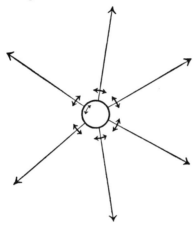

always in the same rhythmical way and about a definite axis. The jelly adheres to the sphere and thus the adhering portions are forced to imitate the motion. These portions force those situated a little further away to imitate the same motion, and so on, so that a wave is set up in the medium. If we keep in mind the distinction between the motion of the medium and the motion of the wave we see that here they do not lie on the same line. The wave is propagated in the direction of the radius of the sphere, while the parts of the medium move perpendicularly to this direction. We have thus created a transverse wave.

Waves spreading on the surface of water are transverse. A floating cork only bobs up and down, but the wave spreads along a horizontal plane. Sound waves, on the other hand, furnish the most familiar example of longitudinal waves.

One more remark: the wave produced by a pulsating or oscillating sphere in a homogeneous medium is a *spherical* wave. It is called so because at any given moment all points on any sphere surrounding the source behave in the same way. Let us consider a portion of such a sphere at a great distance from the source. The farther away the portion is, and the smaller we take it, the more it resembles a plane. We can say, without trying to be too rigorous, that there is no essential difference between a part of a plane and

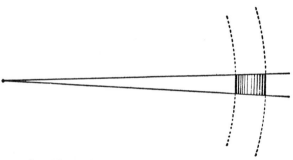

a part of a sphere whose radius is sufficiently large. We very often speak of small portions of a spherical wave far removed from the source as *plane waves*. The farther we place the shaded portion of our drawing from the center of the spheres and the smaller the angle between the two radii, the better our representation of a plane wave. The concept of a plane wave, like many other physical concepts, is no more than a fiction which can be realized with only a certain degree of accuracy. It is, however, a useful concept which we shall need later.

Many aspects of the music produced by instruments, such as tone, consonance, dissonance, and scales, are closely related to physical laws.

15 Musical Instruments and Scales

Harvey E. White

A chapter from his book *Classical and Modern Physics*, 1940.

MUSICAL instruments are often classified under one of the following heads: *strings, winds, rods, plates,* and *bells.* One who is more or less familiar with instruments will realize that most of these terms apply to the material part of each instrument set into vibration when the instrument is played. It is the purpose of the first half of this chapter to consider these vibrating sources and the various factors governing the frequencies of their musical notes, and in the second part to take up in some detail the science of the musical scale.

16.1. Stringed Instruments. Under the classification of *strings* we find such instruments as the *violin, cello, viola, double bass, harp, guitar,* and *piano.* There are two principal reasons why these instruments do not sound alike as regards *tone quality*; first, the design of the instrument, and second, the method by which the strings are set into vibration. The violin and cello are bowed with long strands of tightly stretched horsehair, the harp and guitar are plucked with the fingers or picks, and the piano is hammered with light felt mallets.

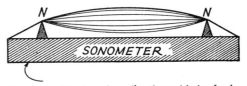

Fig. 16A—Single string vibrating with its fundamental frequency.

Under very special conditions a string may be made to vibrate with nodes at either end as shown in Fig. 16A. In this state of motion the string gives rise to its lowest possible note, and it is said to be vibrating with its *fundamental* frequency.

Every musician knows that a thick heavy string has a lower natural pitch than a thin one, that a short strong string has a higher pitch than a long one, and that the tighter a string is stretched the higher is its pitch. The *G* string of a violin, for example, is thicker and heavier than the high pitched *E* string, and the *bass* strings of the piano are longer and heavier than the strings of the *treble.*

Accurate measurements with vibrating strings, as well as theory, show that the frequency n is given by the following formula:

$$n = \frac{1}{2L} \sqrt{F/m},$$ (16a)

where L is the distance in centimeters between two consecutive nodes, F is the tension on the string in dynes, and m the mass in grams of one centimeter length of string. The equation gives the exact pitch of a string or the change in pitch due to a change in *length, mass*, or *tension*. If the length L is doubled the frequency is halved, i.e., the pitch is lowered one octave. If m is increased n decreases, and if the tension F is increased n increases. The formula shows that to double the frequency by tightening a string the tension must be increased fourfold.

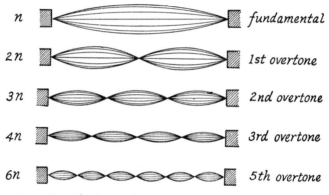

FIG. 16B—Vibration modes for strings of musical instruments.

16.2. Harmonics and Overtones. When a professional violinist plays *"in harmonics"* he touches the strings lightly at various points and sets each one vibrating in two or more segments as shown in Fig. 16B. If a string is touched at the center a node is formed at that point and the vibration frequency, as shown by Eq. (16a), becomes just double that of the fundamental. If the string is touched lightly at a point just one-third the distance from the end it will vibrate in three sections and have a frequency three times that of the fundamental. These higher vibration modes as shown in the figures, which always have frequencies equal to whole number multiples of the fundamental frequency n, are called *overtones*.

It is a simple matter to set a string vibrating with its fundamental frequency and several overtones simultaneously. This is accomplished by plucking or bowing the string vigorously. To illustrate this, a diagram of a string vibrating with its fundamental and first overtone is shown in Fig. 16C. As the string vibrates with a node at the center and a frequency $2n$, it also moves up and down as a whole with the fundamental frequency n and a node at each end.

It should be pointed out that a string set into vibration with nodes and loops is but an example of *standing waves*, see Figs. 14K and 14L. Vibrations produced at one end of a string send a continuous train of waves along the string to be reflected back from the other end. This is true not only for transverse

FIG. 16C—String vibrating with its fundamental and first overtone simultaneously.

waves but for longitudinal or torsional waves as well. Standing waves of the latter two types can be demonstrated by stroking or twisting one end of the string of a sonometer or violin with a rosined cloth.

16.3. Wind Instruments. Musical instruments often classified as "wind instruments" are usually divided into two subclasses, "wood-winds" and "brasses." Under the heading of wood-winds we find such instruments as the *flute, piccolo, clarinet, bass clarinet, saxophone, bassoon*, and *contra bassoon*, and under the brasses such instruments as the *French horn, cornet, trumpet, tenor trombone, bass trombone*, and *tuba* (or *bombardon*).

In practically all wind instruments the source of sound is a vibrating air column, set into and maintained in a state of vibration by one of several different principles. In instruments like the saxophone, clarinet, and bassoon, air is blown against a thin strip of wood called a reed, setting it into vibration. In most of the brasses the musician's lips are made to vibrate with certain required frequencies, while in certain wood-winds like the flute and piccolo air is blown across the sharp edge of an opening near one end of the instrument setting the air into vibration.

The fundamental principles involved in the vibration of an air column are demonstrated by means of an experiment shown in Fig. 16D. A vibrating tuning fork acting as a source of sound waves is held over the open end of several long hollow tubes. Traveling down the tube with the velocity of sound in air, each train of sound waves is reflected from the bottom back toward the top. If the tube is adjusted to the proper length, standing waves will be set up and the air column will resonate to the frequency of the tuning fork. In this experiment the proper length of the tube for the closed pipes is obtained by slowly pouring water into the cylinder and listening for the loudest response. Experimentally, this occurs at several points as indicated by the first three diagrams; the first resonance occurs at a distance of one and one-quarter wave-lengths, the second at three-quarters of a wave-length, and the third at one-quarter of a wave-length. The reason for these

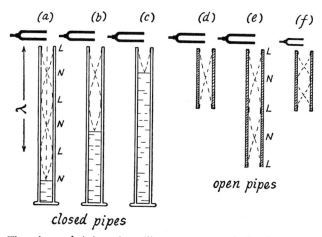

FIG. 16D—The column of air in a pipe will resonate to sound of a given pitch if the length of the pipe is properly adjusted.

odd fractions is that only a node can form at the closed end of a pipe and a loop at an open end. This is true of all wind instruments.

For open pipes a loop forms at both ends with one or more nodes in between. The first five pipes in Fig. 16D are shown responding to a tuning fork of the same frequency. The sixth pipe, diagram (f), is the same length as (d) but is responding to a fork of twice the frequency of the others. This note is one octave higher in pitch. In other words, a pipe of given length can be made to resonate to various frequencies. Closed pipe (a), for example, will respond to other forks whose waves are of the right length to form a node at the bottom, a loop at the top and any number of nodes in between.

The existence of standing waves in a resonating air column may be demonstrated by a long hollow tube filled with illuminating gas as shown in Fig. 16E. Entering through an adjustable plunger at the left the gas escapes through tiny holes spaced at regular intervals in a row along the top. Sound waves from an organ pipe enter the gas column by setting into vibration a thin rubber sheet stretched over the right-hand end. When resonance is attained by sliding the plunger to the correct position, the small gas flames will appear as shown. Where the nodes occur in the vibrating gas column the air molecules are not moving, see Fig. 14L (b); at these points the pressure is high and the flames are tallest. Half way between are the loops; regions where the molecules vibrate back and forth with large amplitudes, and the flames are low. Bernoulli's principle is chiefly responsible for the pressure

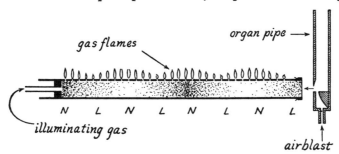

Fig. 16E—Standing waves in a long tube containing illuminating gas.

differences, see Sec. 10.8, for where the velocity of the molecules is high the pressure is low, and where the velocity is low the pressure is high.

The various notes produced by most wind instruments are brought about by varying the length of the vibrating air column. This is illustrated by the organ pipes in Fig. 16F. The longer the air column the lower the frequency or pitch of the note. In a regular concert organ the pipes vary in length from about six inches for the highest note to almost sixteen feet for the lowest. For the middle octave of the musical scale the open-ended pipes vary from two feet for *middle* C to one foot for C^1 one octave higher. In the wood-winds like the flute the length of the column is varied by openings in the side of the instrument and in many of the brasses like the trumpet, by means of valves. A valve is a piston which on being pressed down throws in an additional length of tube.

The frequency of a vibrating air column is given by the following formula,

$$n = \frac{1}{2L} \sqrt{K \frac{p}{d}},$$

where L is the length of the air column, K is a number representing the compressibility of the gas, p is the pressure of the gas, and d is its

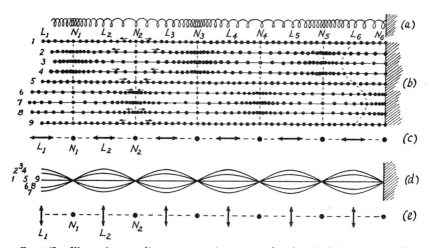

FIG. 14L—Illustrating standing waves as they are produced with (*a*) the longitudinal waves of a spring, (*b*) the longitudinal waves of sound in the air, and (*d*) the transverse waves of a rope. (*c*) and (*e*) indicate the direction of vibration at the loops.

density. The function of each factor in this equation has been verified by numerous experiments. The effect of the length L is illustrated in Fig. 16F. To lower the frequency to half-value the length must be doubled. The effect of the density of a gas on the pitch of a note may be demonstrated by a very interesting experiment with the human

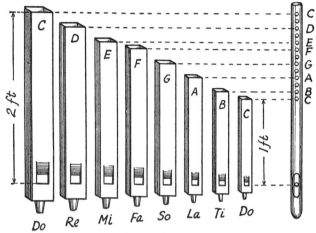

FIG. 16F—Organ pipes arranged in a musical scale. The longer the pipe the lower is its fundamental frequency and pitch. The vibrating air column of the flute is terminated at various points by openings along the tube.

voice. Voice sounds originate in the vibrations of the vocal cords in the larynx. The pitch of this source of vibration is controlled by muscular tension on the cords, while the quality is determined by the size and shape of the throat and mouth cavities. If a gas lighter than air is breathed into the lungs and vocal cavities, the above equation shows that the voice should have a higher pitch. The demonstration can be best and most safely performed by breathing helium gas, whose effect is to raise the voice about two and one-half octaves. The experiment must be performed to be fully appreciated.

16.4. Edge Tones. When wind or a blast of air encounters a small obstacle, little whirlwinds are formed in the air stream behind the obstacle. This is illustrated by the cross-section of a flue organ pipe in Fig. 16G. Whether the obstacle is long, or a small round object, the whirlwinds are formed alternately on the two sides as shown. The air stream at B waves back and forth, sending a pulse of air first up one side and then the other. Although the wind blows through the opening A as a continuous stream, the separate whirlwinds going up each side of the obstacle become periodic shocks to the surrounding air. Coming at perfectly regular intervals these pulses give rise to a musical note often described as the whistling of the wind. These notes are called "edge tones."

The number of whirlwinds formed per second, and therefore the pitch of the edge tone, increases with the wind velocity. When the wind howls through the trees the pitch of the note rises and falls, its frequency at any time denoting the velocity of the wind. For a given wind velocity smaller objects give rise to higher pitched notes than large objects. A fine stretched wire or rubber band when placed in an open window or in the wind will be set into vibration and give out a musical note. Each whirlwind shock to the air reacts on the obstacle (the wire or rubber band), pushing it first to one side and then the other. These are the pushes that cause the reed of a musical instrument to vibrate and the rope of a flagpole to flap periodically in the breeze, while the waving of the flag at the top of a pole shows the whirlwinds that follow each other along each side.

These motions are all "forced vibrations" in that they are forced by the wind. A stretched string or the air column in an organ pipe has its own natural frequency of vibration which may or may not coincide with the frequency of the edge tone. If they do coincide, resonance will occur, the string or air column will vibrate with a large amplitude, and a loud sound will result. If the edge tone has a different frequency than the fundamental of the string, or air column, vibrations will be set up but not as intensely as before. If the frequency of the edge tone of an organ pipe, for example, becomes double that of the fundamental, and this can be obtained by a stronger blast of air, the pipe will resonate to double its fundamental frequency and give out a note one octave higher.

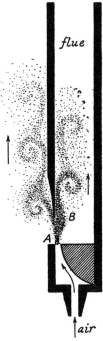

FIG. 16G—A steady stream of air blown across the lip of an organ pipe sets up whirlwinds along both sides of the partition.

16.5. Vibrating Rods. If a number of small sticks are dropped upon the floor the sound that is heard is described as a *noise*. If one stick alone is dropped one would also describe the sound as a noise, unless, of course, a set of sticks of varying lengths are arranged in order of length and each one dropped in its order. If this is done, one notices that each stick gives rise to a rather definite musical note and the set of sticks to a musical scale. The use of vibrating rods in the design of a musical instrument is to be found in the *xylophone*, the *marimba*, and the *triangle*. Standing waves in a rod, like those in a stretched string, may be any one of three different kinds, transverse, longitudinal, and torsional. Only the first two of these modes of vibration will be treated here.

Transverse waves in a rod are usually set up by supporting the rod at points near each end and striking it a blow at or near the center. As

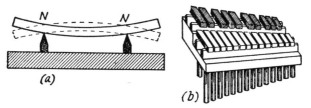

FIG. 16H—The bars of the marimba or xylophone vibrate transversely with nodes near each end.

illustrated in Fig. 16H(a) the center and ends of the rod move up and down, forming nodes at the two supports. Like a stretched string of a musical instrument, the shorter the rod the higher is its pitch, and the longer and heavier the rod the lower is its frequency of vibration and pitch.

The *xylophone* is a musical instrument based upon the transverse vibrations of wooden rods of different lengths. Mounted as shown in Fig. 16H(b) the longer rods produce the low notes and the shorter ones the higher notes. The *marimba* is essentially a xylophone with a long, straight hollow tube suspended vertically under each rod. Each tube is cut to such a length that the enclosed air column will resonate to the sound waves sent out by the rod directly above. Each resonator tube, being open at both ends, forms a node at its center.

Longitudinal vibrations in a rod may be set up by clamping a rod at one end or near the center and stroking it with a rosined cloth. Clamped in the middle as shown in Fig. 16I the free ends of the rod move back and forth while the middle is held motionless, maintaining a node at that point. Since the vibrations are too small to be seen with the eye a small ivory ball is suspended near the end as shown. The bouncing of this ball is indicative of the strong longitudinal vibrations. This type of vibration in a rod is not used in musical instruments.

16.6. Vibrating Plates. Although the *drum* or the *cymbals* should hardly be called musical instruments

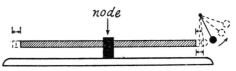

FIG. 16I—Diagram of a rod vibrating longitudinally with a node at the center.

they are classified as such and made use of in nearly all large orchestras and bands. The noise given out by a vibrating drumhead or cymbal plate is in general due to the high intensity of certain characteristic overtones. These overtones in turn are due to the very complicated modes of vibration of the source.

Cymbals consist of two thin metal disks with handles at the centers. Upon being struck together their edges are set into vibration with a clang. A drumhead, on the other hand, is a stretched membrane of

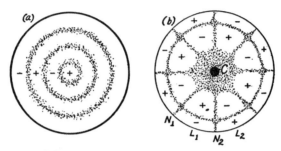

FIG. 16J—Chladni's sand figures showing the nodes and loops of (*a*) a vibrating drumhead (clamped at the edge) and (*b*) a vibrating cymbal plate (clamped at the center).

leather held tight at the periphery and is set into vibration by being struck a blow at or near the center.

To illustrate the complexity of the vibrations of a circular plate, two typical *sand patterns* are shown in Fig. 16J. The sand pattern method of studying the motions of plates was invented in the 18th century by Chladni, a German physicist. A thin circular metal plate is clamped at the center C and sand sprinkled over the top surface. Then while touching the rim of the plate at two points N_1 and N_2 a violin bow is drawn down over the edge at a point L. Nodes are formed at the stationary points N_1 and N_2 and loops in the regions of L_1 and L_2. The grains of sand bounce away from the loops and into the nodes, the regions of no motion. At one instant the regions marked with a $+$ sign all move up, while the regions marked with a $-$ sign all move down. Half a vibration later the $+$ regions are moving down and the $-$ regions up. Such diagrams are called *Chladni's sand figures*.

With cymbal plates held tightly at the center by means of handles a node is always formed there, and loops are always formed at the periphery. With a drumhead, on the other hand, the periphery is always a node and the center is sometimes but not always a loop.

16.7. Bells. In some respects a bell is like a cymbal plate, for when it is struck a blow by the clapper, the rim in particular is set

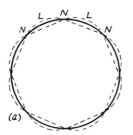
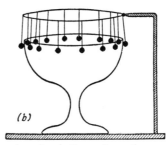

FIG. 16K—Experiment illustrating that the rim of a bell or glass vibrates with nodes and loops.

vibrating with nodes and loops distributed in a symmetrical pattern over the whole surface. The vibration of the rim is illustrated by a diagram in Fig. 16K(a) and by an experiment in diagram (b). Small cork balls are suspended by threads around and just touching the outside rim of a large glass bowl. A violin bow drawn across the edge of the bowl will set the rim into vibration with nodes at some points and loops at others. The nodes are always even in number just as they are in cymbal plates and drumheads, and alternate loops move *in* while the others move *out*.

Strictly speaking, a bell is not a very musical instrument. This is due to the very complex vibrations of the bell surface giving rise to so many loud overtones. Some of these overtones harmonize with the fundamental while others are discordant.

16.8. The Musical Scale. The musical scale is based upon the relative frequencies of different sound waves. The frequencies are so chosen that they produce the greatest amount of *harmony*. Two notes are said to be harmonious if they are pleasant to hear. If they are not pleasant to hear they are discordant.

The general form of the musical scale is illustrated by the symbols, letters, terms, and simple fractions given in Fig. 16L.

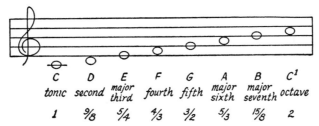

FIG. 16L—Diagram giving the names, and fractional ratios of the frequencies, of the different tone intervals on the diatonic musical scale.

The numbers indicate that whatever the frequency of the *tonic C*, the frequency of the octave C^1 will be twice as great, that G will be three halves as great, F four thirds as great, etc. These fractions below each note are proportional to their frequencies in whatever octave of the musical scale the notes are located.

The musical pitch of an orchestral scale is usually determined by specifying the frequency of the A string of the *first violin*, although sometimes it is given by *middle C* on the piano. In the history of modern music the standard of pitch has varied so widely and changed so frequently that no set pitch can universally be called standard.* For many scientific purposes the A string of the violin is tuned to a frequency of 440 vib/sec, while in a few cases the slightly different scale of 256 vib/sec is used for the *tonic*, sometimes called *middle C*.

16.9. The Diatonic Scale. The middle octave of the diatonic musical scale is given in Fig. 16M assuming as a standard of pitch $A = 440$. The *vocal notes* usually sung in practicing music are given in the second row. The *ratio numbers* are the smallest whole numbers proportional to the *scale ratios* and to the actual *frequencies*.

The *tone ratios* given at the bottom of the scale indicate the ratio between the frequencies of two consecutive notes. *Major tones* have a ratio of 8 : 9, *minor tones* a ratio of 9 : 10, and diatonic semitones a ratio 15 : 16. (The major and minor tones on a piano are called *whole tones* and the semitones are called *half tones*.)

Other tone intervals of interest to the musician are the following:

Interval	Frequency Ratio	Examples
Octave	1 : 2	CC^1, DD^1, EE^1
Fifth	2 : 3	CG, EB, GD^1
Fourth	3 : 4	CF, EA, GC^1
Major third	4 : 5	CE, FA, GB
Minor third	5 : 6	EG, AC^1
Major sixth	3 : 5	CA, DB, GE^1
Minor sixth	5 : 8	EC^1, AF^1

A scientific study of musical notes and *tone intervals* shows that harmony is based upon the frequency ratios between notes. The smaller the whole numbers giving the ratio between the frequencies of

* For a brief historical discussion of normal standards of pitch the student is referred to the book "The Science of Musical Sounds" by D. C. Miller. For other treatments of the science of music see "Sound" by Capstick, "Science and Music" by James Jeans, and "Sound and Music" by J. A. Zahn.

	major tone	minor tone	semitone	major tone	minor tone	major tone	semitone	majortone	
scale notes	C	D	E	F	G	A	B	C^1	D^1
vocal notes	Do	Re	Mi	Fa	So	La	Ti	Do	Re
ratio numbers	24	27	30	32	36	40	45	48	54
frequencies	264	297	330	352	396	440	495	528	594
scale ratios	1	9/8	5/4	4/3	3/2	5/3	15/8	2	9/4
tone ratios		8:9	9:10	15:16	8:9	9:10	8:9	15:16	8:9

FIG. 16M—The diatonic musical scale illustrated by the middle octave with C as the tonic and $A = 440$ as the standard pitch.

two notes the more *harmonious*, or *consonant*, is the resultant. Under this definition of harmony the octave, with a frequency ratio of 1 : 2, is the most harmonious. Next in line comes the fifth with a ratio 2 : 3, followed by the fourth with 3 : 4, etc. The larger the whole numbers the more *discordant*, or *dissonant*, is the interval.

Helmholtz was the first to give a physical explanation of the various degrees of consonance and harmony of these different intervals. It is based in part upon the beat notes produced by two notes of the interval.

As shown by Eq. (15a) the *beat frequency* between two notes is equal to their frequency difference. Consider, for example, the two notes C and G of the middle octave in Fig. 16M. Having frequencies of 264 and 396, the beat frequency is the difference, or 132. This is a frequency fast enough to be heard by the ear as a separate note, and in pitch is one octave below *middle C*. Thus in sounding the *fifth*, C and G, three harmonious notes are heard, 132, 264, 396. They are harmonious because they have ratios given by the smallest whole numbers 1 : 2 : 3.

Harmonious *triads* or *chords* are formed by three separate notes each of which forms a harmonious interval with the other two, while the highest and lowest notes are less than an octave apart. Since there are but six such triads they are shown below.

Harmonic Triads or Chords	*Frequency Ratio*	*Example*
Major third followed by minor third.....	4 : 5 : 6	C E G
" " " " fourth..........	3 : 4 : 5	C F A
Minor third " " major third.....	5 : 6, 4 : 5	E G B
Minor third " " fourth..........	5 : 6, 3 : 4	E G C^1
Fourth " " major third.....	4 : 5, 3 : 4	C E A
Fourth " " minor third.....	3 : 4, 5 : 6	E A C^1

Consider the *beat notes* or *difference tones* between the various pairs of notes in the second triad above. The notes themselves have frequencies $C = 264$, $F = 352$, and $A = 440$. The difference tones F-$C = 88$, A-$F = 88$, and A-$C = 176$. Being exactly one and two octaves below C, one of the notes of the triad, they are in harmony with each other. Grouping the first two beat frequencies as a single note, all the frequencies heard by the ear have the frequencies 88, 176, 264, 352, and 440. The frequency ratios of these notes are $1 : 2 : 3 : 4 : 5$, the first five positive whole numbers.

16.10. The Chromatic Scale. Contrary to the belief of many people the *sharp* of one note and the *flat* of the next higher major or minor tone are not of the same pitch. The reason for this false impression is that on the piano the black keys represent a compromise. The piano is not tuned to the *diatonic scale* but to an *equal tempered scale*. Experiments with eminent musicians, and particularly violinists, have shown that they play in what is called *pure intonation*, that is, to a *chromatic scale* and not according to equal temperament as will be described in the next section.

On the *chromatic scale* of the musician the ratio between the frequency of one note and the frequency of its sharp or flat is $25 : 24$. This ratio is just the difference between a *diatonic semitone* and a *minor tone*, i.e., $^{15}\!/_{16} \div ^{9}\!/_{10} = ^{25}\!/_{24}$. The actual frequencies of the various sharps and flats for the middle octave of the chromatic scale, based upon $A = 440$, are shown above in Fig. 16N. $C^\sharp$ for example has

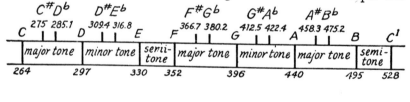

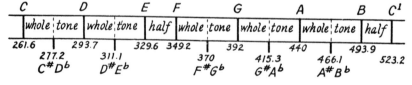

FIG. 16N—Scale diagrams showing the diatonic and chromatic scale above and the equal tempered scale below.

a frequency of 275 whereas $D^\flat$ is 285.1. This is a difference of 10 vib/sec, an interval easily recognized at this pitch by most everyone. (The sharps and flats of the semitone intervals are not shown.)

16.11. The Equal Tempered Scale. The white keys of the piano are not tuned to the exact frequency ratios of the diatonic scale; they are tuned to an equal tempered scale. Each octave is divided into twelve equal ratio intervals as illustrated below in Fig. 16N. The *whole tone* and *half tone* intervals shown represent the white keys of the piano, as indicated in Fig. 16O, and the sharps and flats represent the black keys. Including the black keys, all twelve tone intervals in every octave are exactly the same.

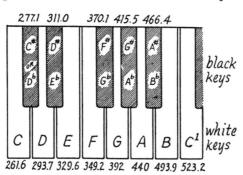

FIG. 16O—The equal tempered scale of the piano illustrating the frequencies of the middle octave based upon $A = 440$ as the standard pitch.

The frequency of any note in the equal tempered scale turns out to be 6 percent higher than the one preceding it. More accurately, the frequency of any one note multiplied by the decimal 1.05946 gives the frequency of the note one-half tone higher. For example, $A = 440$ multiplied by 1.05946 gives $A^{\#}$ or $B^{\flat}$ as 466.1 vib/sec. Similarly, 466.1 $\times$ 1.05946 gives 493.9.

The reason for tuning the piano to an equal tempered scale is to enable the pianist to play in any key and yet stay within a given pitch range. In so doing, any given composition can be played within the range of a given person's voice. In other words, any single note can be taken as the *tonic* of the musical scale.

Although the notes of the piano are not quite as harmonious as if they were tuned to a diatonic scale, they are not far out of tune. This can be seen by a comparison of the actual frequencies of the notes of the two scales in Fig. 16N. The maximum differences amount to about 1 percent, which for many people is not noticeable, particularly in a modern dance orchestra. To the average musician, however, the difference is too great to be tolerated, and this is the reason most symphony orchestras do not include a piano. The orchestral instruments are usually tuned to the A string of the *first violin* and played according to the chromatic and diatonic scale.

16.12. Quality of Musical Notes. Although two musical notes have the same pitch and intensity they may differ widely in tone quality. Tone quality is determined by the number and intensity of the overtones present. This is illustrated by an examination either of the vibrating source or of the sound waves emerging from the source. There are numerous experimental methods by which this is accomplished.

A relatively convenient and simple demonstration is given in Fig. 16P, where the vibrating source of sound is a stretched piano string. Light from an arc lamp is passed over the central section of the string which, except for a small vertical slot, is masked by a screen. As the string vibrates up and down the only visible image of the string is a very short section as shown at the right, and this appears blurred. By reflecting the light in a rotating mirror the section of wire draws out a wave W on a distant screen.

If a string is made to vibrate with its fundamental alone, its own motion or that of the emitted sound waves have the form shown in diagram (a) of Fig. 16Q. If it vibrates in two segments or six segments (see Fig. 16B) the wave forms will be like those in diagrams (b) and (c) respectively. Should the string be set vibrating with its fundamental and first overtone simultaneously, the wave form will appear something like diagram (d). This curve is the sum of (a) and (b) and is obtained graphically by adding the displacement of corresponding points. If in addition to the fundamental a string vibrates with

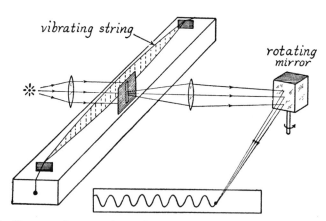

FIG. 16P—Diagram of an experiment demonstrating the vibratory motion of a stretched string.

the first and fifth overtones the wave will look like diagram (e). This is like diagram (d) with the fifth overtone added to it.

It is difficult to make a string vibrate with its fundamental alone. As a rule there are many overtones present. Some of these overtones harmonize with the fundamental and some do not. Those which harmonize are called *harmonic overtones*, and those which do not are called *anharmonic overtones*. If middle $C = 264$ is sounded with its

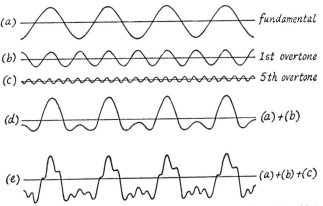

(a) ——————— *fundamental*

(b) ——————— *1st overtone*

(c) ——————— *5th overtone*

(d) ——————— *(a)+(b)*

(e) ——————— *(a)+(b)+(c)*

FIG. 16Q—Illustrating the form of the sound waves resulting from the addition of overtones to the fundamental.

first eight overtones, they will have 2, 3, 4, 5, 6, 7, and 8 times 264 vib/sec. These on the diatonic scale will correspond to notes C^1, G^1, C^2, E^2, G^2, X, and C^3. All of these except X, the sixth overtone, belongs to some harmonic triad. This sixth overtone is anharmonic and should be suppressed. In a piano this is accomplished by striking the string one-seventh of its length from one end, thus preventing a node at that point.

16.13. The Ranges of Musical Instruments. The various octaves above the middle of the musical scale are often labeled with numerical superscripts as already illustrated, while the octaves below the middle are labeled with numerical subscripts.

The top curve in Fig. 16Q is typical of the sound wave from a tuning fork, whereas the lower one is more like that from a violin. The strings of a violin are tuned to intervals of the *fifth*, $G_1 = 198$, $D = 297$, $A = 440$, and $E^1 = 660$. The various notes of the musical scale are obtained by touching a string at various points, thus shortening the section which vibrates. The lowest note reached is with the untouched G_1 string and the highest notes by the E^1 string fingered about two-thirds of the way up toward the *bridge*. This gives the violin a playing range, or compass, of $3\frac{1}{2}$ octaves, from $G_1 = 198$ to $C^3 = 2112$.

The *viola* is slightly larger in size than the violin but has the same shape and is played with slightly lower pitch and more sombre tone quality. Reaching from C_1 to C^2, it has a range of three octaves.

The *cello* is a light bass violin which rests on the floor, is played with a bow, has four strings pitched one octave lower than the viola, C_2, G_2, D_1, and A_1, and has a heavy rich tone quality. The *double bass* is the largest of the violin family, rests on the floor and is played with a bow. The strings are tuned to two octaves below the viola and one octave below the cello. In modern dance orchestras the bow is often discarded and the strings are plucked with the fingers.

Of the wood-wind instruments the *flute* is nearest to the human voice. It consists essentially (see Fig. 16R) of a straight narrow tube about 2 feet long and is played by blowing air from between the lips across a small hole near the closed end. The openings along the tube are for the purpose of terminating the vibrating air column at various points. See Fig. 16F. With all holes closed a loop forms at both ends with a node in the middle. See Fig. 16D(d). As each hole is opened one after the other, starting from the open end, the vibrating air column with a loop at the opening grows shorter and shorter, giving out higher and higher notes. To play the scale one octave higher, one blows harder to increase the frequency of the *edge tones* and set the air column vibrating, as in Fig. 16D(e), with three loops and two nodes. Starting at *middle C* the flute can be extended in pitch for two octaves, up to C^2. The *piccolo* is a small flute, 1 foot long, and sings one octave higher. The tone is shrill and piercing and the compass iis C^1 to A^2.

The *oboe* is a melodic double-reed keyed instrument, straight and about 2 feet long. It has a reedy yet beautiful quality, and starting at B_1 has a range of about two octaves. The *clarinet*, sometimes called

Fig. 16R—Musical instruments. Brasses: (*a*) horn, (*b*) bugle, (*c*) cornet, (*d*) trombone. Wood-winds: (*e*) flute, (*f*) oboe, and (*g*) clarinet.

the violin of the military band (see Fig. 16R), is a single-reed instrument about 3 feet long. It has a range of over three octaves starting at E_1. The *bass clarinet* is larger than the clarinet, but has the same shape and plays one octave lower in pitch.

The *bassoon* is a bass double-reed keyed instrument about 4 feet long. The tone is nasal and the range is about two octaves starting at B^b_3.

The *horn* is a coiled brass tube about 12 feet in length (see Fig. 16R) but interchangeable according to the number of crooks used. It has a soft mellow tone and starting at C_2 has a range of three octaves. The *cornet*, not usually used in symphony orchestras (see Fig. 16R), is a coiled conical tube about 4½ feet long with three valves. It has a mellow tone starting at *middle C* and extends for two octaves. The trumpet is a brass instrument having a similar shape as, and slightly larger than, the cornet. Having three valves, it extends to two octaves above *middle C*. The purpose of the valves is to vary the length of the vibrating air column.

The *trombone* is a brass instrument played with a slide, is a conical tube about 9 feet long when straightened (see Fig. 16R), and has a tone range from F_2 to C^1. Since the length of the vibrating air column can be varied at will it is easily played to the chromatic scale. The *tuba* is the largest of the saxhorns and has a range from F_3 to F_1.

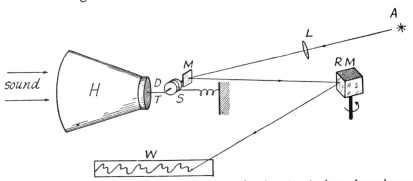

FIG. 16S—Diagram of a phonodeik. An instrument for observing the form of sound waves.

The *bugle* (see Fig. 16R) is not capable of playing to the musical scale but sounds only certain notes. These notes are the harmonic overtones of a fundamental frequency of about 66 vibrations per second. With a loop at the mouthpiece, a node in the center, and a loop at the flared end, this requires a tube 8 feet long. The second, third, fourth, and fifth overtones have the frequencies $66 \times 3 = 198$, $66 \times 4 = 264$, $66 \times 5 = 330$, and $66 \times 6 = 396$ corresponding to G_1,

C, E, and G, the notes of the bugle. By making the lips vibrate to near these frequencies the air column is set resonating with 3, 4, 5, or 6 nodes between the two open ends.

16.14. The Phonodeik. The phonodeik is an instrument designed by D. C. Miller for photographing the minute details and wave forms of all audible sounds. The instrument consists of a sensitive diaphragm D (see Fig. 16S), against which the sound waves to be studied are allowed to fall. As the diaphragm vibrates back and forth under the impulses of the sound waves the thread T winds and unwinds on the spindle S, turning the tiny mirror M up and down. A beam of light from an arc lamp A and lens L is reflected from this mirror onto a rotating mirror RM. As RM spins around the light sweeps across a distant screen, tracing out the sound wave. The trace may be either photographed or observed directly on the screen. Persistence of vision enables the whole curve to be seen for a fraction of a second.

Several sound curves photographed by Miller are redrawn in Fig. 16T. In every graph except the one of the piano, the sound is

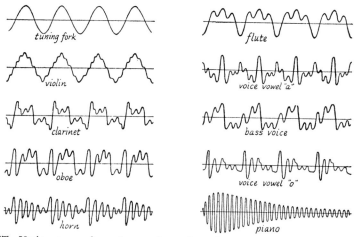

Fig. 16T—Various types of sound waves in music as observed with a phonodeik or cathode ray oscillograph.

maintained at the same frequency so that the form of each wave, no matter how complex, is repeated the same number of times. The tuning fork is the one instrument which is readily set vibrating with its fundamental alone and none of its harmonics. Although each different instrument may sound out with the same note, that is, the same fundamental, the various overtones present and their relative loudness determines the quality of the note identified with that instrument.

The four members of the violin family have changed very little in hundreds of years. Recently, a group of musicians and scientists have constructed a "new" string family.

16   Founding a Family of Fiddles

Carleen M. Hutchins

An article from *Physics Today*, 1967.

New measurement techniques combined with recent acoustics research enable us to make violin-type instruments in all frequency ranges with the properties built into the violin itself by the masters of three centuries ago. Thus for the first time we have a whole family of instruments made according to a consistent acoustical theory. Beyond a doubt they are musically successful.

by Carleen Maley Hutchins

FOR THREE OR FOUR centuries string quartets as well as orchestras both large and small, have used violins, violas, cellos and contrabasses of classical design. These wooden instruments were brought to near perfection by violin makers of the 17th and 18th centuries. Only recently, though, has testing equipment been good enough to find out just how they work, and only recently have scientific methods of manufacture been good enough to produce consistently instruments with the qualities one wants to design into them. Now, for the first time, we have eight instruments of the violin family constructed on principles of proper resonance for desired tone quality. They represent the first successful application of a consistent acoustical theory to a whole family of musical instruments.

The idea for such a gamut of violins is not new. It can be found in Michael Praetorius's *Syntagma Musicum* published in 1619. But incomplete understanding and technological ob-

stacles have stood in the way of practical accomplishment. That we can now routinely make fine violins in a variety of frequency ranges is the result of a fortuitous combination: violin acoustics research—showing a resurgence after a lapse of 100 years—and the new testing equipment capable of responding to the sensitivities of wooden instruments.

As is shown in figure 1, our new instruments are tuned in alternate intervals of a musical fourth and fifth over the range of the piano keyboard. Moreover each one has its two main resonances within a semitone of the tuning of its middle strings. The result seems beyond a doubt successful musically. Over and over again we hear the comment, "One must hear the new instruments to believe such sounds are possible from strings."

Catgut Acoustical Society

Groundwork in the scientific investigation of the violin was laid by such men as Marin Mersenne (1636), Ernst Chladni (1802), Felix Savart (1819) and Hermann L. F. Helmholtz (1860). Savart, who can rightly be considered the grandfather of violin research, used many ingenious devices to explore the vibrational characteristics of the violin. But he was unable to gain sufficient knowledge of its complicated resonances to apply his ideas successfully to development and construction of new instruments. Recent research that has led to our new fiddle family is largely the work of Hermann Backhaus, Herman Meinel, Gioacchino Pasqualini, Ernst Rohloff, Werner Lottermoser and Frieder Eggers in Europe and of the late Frederick A. Saunders, John C. Schelleng, William Harvey Fletcher and myself in the United States.

Saunders, widely known for his work on Russell-Saunders coupling, pioneered violin research on this side of the Atlantic. He was a former chairman of the physics department of Harvard University, a fellow of the National Academy of Sciences and president of the Acoustical Society of America. In his work on violin acoustics, Saunders gradually became associated with colleagues who were highly competent in various scientific and musical disciplines. These associates greatly furthered the development of his work and contributed valuable technical knowledge, but they had little time for experimentation. Some were skillful musicians living under

the pressure of heavy teaching and concert schedules. Nevertheless some were able to find time for the testing, designing and craftsmanship needed in the development of experimental instruments. In 1963 about 30 persons associated with Saunders in this project labeled themselves the "Catgut Acoustical Society." This informal society now has more than 100 members (see box on page 26), publishes a semiannual newsletter and holds one or two meetings each year. Among its members are acousticians, physicists, chemists, engineers, instrument makers, composers, performing musicians, musicologists, patrons and others who believe that insufficient attention has been paid to the inherent potentialities of bowed string instruments. They are making a coördinated effort to discover and develop these potentialities and are encouraged that many members of the violin fraternity share their aims.

Among other accomplishments of our Catgut Acoustical Society is a concert played at Harvard last summer during the meeting of the Acoustical Society of America. It was dedicated to Saunders and the instruments were our eight new fiddles, which are the outgrowth of research he began. I write about the concert and about the instruments as a member of the society and as one who worked with Saunders from 1948 until his death in 1963. My activities include reconciliation of the wisdom of experienced musicians

and violin makers, coördination of much technical information from widely separated sources, and design, construction and testing of experimental instruments. In 1937 Saunders reported[1] in the *Journal of the Acoustical Society of America* what later proved to be basic to the development of the new violin family, namely the position of the main body resonance as well as the main cavity resonance in a series of excellent violins. (The main body resonance is the lowest fundamental resonance of the wood structure; the cavity resonance is that of the air in the instrument cavity.) But the necessary knowledge of how to place these resonances with any degree of predictability in instruments of good tone quality was not evolved and reported until 1960.[2] The tonal effect of this placement of the two main resonances for each instrument and the necessary scaling theory was not reported until 1962.[3]

Between 1950 and 1958 Saunders and I undertook a long series of experiments to test various features of violin construction one at a time. We determined effect of variations in length, shape and placement of the f holes, position of the bass bar and sound post, significance of the inlay of purfling around the edges of top and back plates and frequency of the cavity resonance as a function of rib height and f hole areas (see figure 2). Because many of these experiments needed definitive testing equipment not then available, most of the results are still unpublished in Saunders's notebooks.

One sobering conclusion we reached was that with many alterations in such features as size and shape of f holes, position of the bass bar and sound post, the best tonal qualities resulted when conventional violin-making rules were followed. In other words, the early violin makers, working empirically by slow trial and error, had evolved a system that produced practically optimal relationships in violin construction.

In 1958, during a long series of experiments to test the effect of moving violin and viola resonances up and down scale, the composer in residence at Bennington College, Henry Brant, and the cellist, Sterling Hunkins, proposed development of eight violin-type instruments in a series of tunings

In addition to nurturing her fiddle family, the author shows interest in children. After graduating from Cornell she taught for 15 years in New York schools, acquiring an MA from New York University meanwhile. She also acquired a chemist husband and two children, all of whom live in Montclair, N. J.

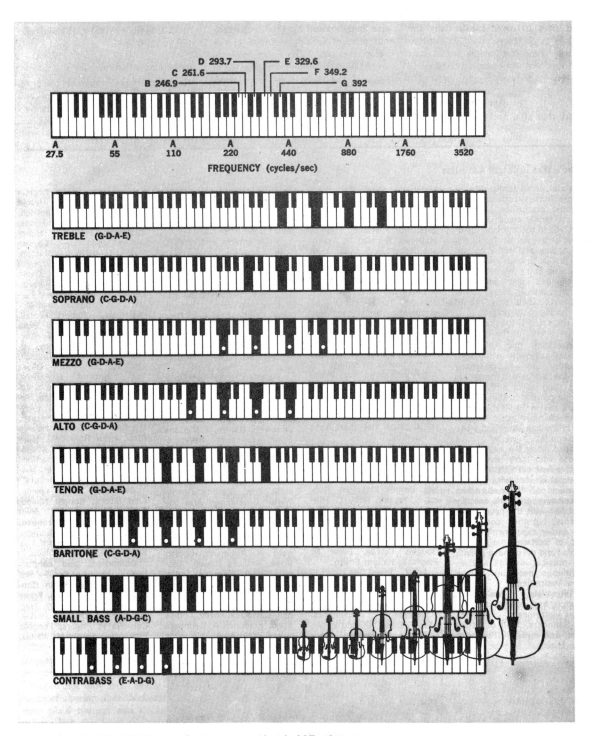

NEW INSTRUMENT TUNING spans the piano range with eight fiddles that range in size from 210-cm contrabass to a 27-cm treble. The conventional violin is the mezzo of the new series. Colored keys show tuning of new instruments and white dots that of conventional instruments. —FIG. 1

and sizes to cover substantially the whole pitch range used in written music; these instruments would start with an oversize contrabass and go to a tiny instrument tuned an octave above the violin. Their request was so closely related to our experimental work that after half an hour's discussion Saunders and I agreed that a serious attempt would be made to develop the set. The main problem would be to produce an instrument in each of the eight frequency ranges having the dynamics, the expressive qualities and overall power that are characteristic of the violin itself, in contrast to the conventional viola, cello and string bass.

Research and new fiddles

The problem of applying basic research results to actual design and construction of new instruments now faced us. From the previous ten

---

Who's Who in Catgut Acoustics

Without cross fertilization of ideas from experts in many related disciplines our new fiddle family could not have evolved in the short period of nine or ten years. No listing of names and activities can do justice to each one whose thinking and skills have been challenged and who has given time, energy and money. Their only reward is sharing in the project.

The spirit of the group has been likened to the informal cooperation that flourished among scientists in the 18th century. In addition many of the active experimenters are themselves enthusiastic string players so that a technical session is likely to end with chamber-music playing.

In the following list I try to include all those who have helped along the way, listing those who have been most active first even though they are not all members of CAS. Some of the numerous musicians are not actually familiar with the new instruments, but their comments on earlier experimental models of conventional violins, violas and cellos have provided musical insights and information necessary to the new instruments.

Physicists. Basic research and scaling for the new instruments: Frederick A. Saunders, John C. Schelleng and myself. Theory of vibrations, elasticity, shear and damping in the instruments and their parts: Arthur H. Benade, Frieder Eggers, Roger Kerlin, Max V. Mathews, Bernard W. Robinson, Robert H. Scanlan, John C. Schelleng, Eugen J. Skudrzyk, Thomas W. W. Stewart, Sam Zaslavski.

Chemists. Effects of varnish and humidity on the instruments; varnish research: Robert E. Fryxell, Morton A. Hutchins, Louis M. Condax.

Architect. Basic design and development of patterns for the new violin family, and maker of bows for them: Maxwell Kimball.

Electronic engineers. Norman Dooley, Francis L. Fielding, Sterling W. Gorrill, A. Stuart Hegeman, Alvin S. Hopping.

Translators. Mildred Allen, Edith L. R. Corliss, Donald Fletcher.

Editors. Harriet M. Bartlett, Dennis Flanagan, Robert E. Fryxell, Mary L. Harbold, Martha Taylor, Alice Torrey, Howard Van Sickle.

Photographers. Louis M. Condax, Russell B. Kingman, Douglas Ogawa, Peter N. Pruyn, J. Kellum Smith.

Artist. Irving Geis.

Lawyers. Harvey W. Mortimer, J. Kellum Smith, Robert M. Vorsanger.

General consultants. Alice T. Baker, Donald Engle, Cushman Haagensen, Mary W. Hinckley, Ellis Kellert, Henry Allen Moe, Ethel and William R. Scott.

Secretaries. Lorraine Elliott, Belle Magram.

Violin experts and makers. Karl A. Berger, René Morel, Simone F. Sacconi, Rembert Wurlitzer, myself—and Virginia Apgar, Armand Bartos, William W. Bishop, Donald L. Blatter, William Carboni, Louis M. Condax, Fred Dautrich, Jean L. Dautrich, Louis Dunham, Jay C. Freeman, Louis Grand, Jerry Juzek, Otto Kaplan, Gordon McDonald, William E. Slaby.

Violinists. Charles F. Aue, Broadus Erle, William Kroll, Sonya Monosoff, Helen Rice, Louis E. Zerbe—and Samuel Applebaum, Catherine Drinker Bowen, Marjorie Bram, Ernestine Briemeister, Alan Branigan, Nicos Cambourakis, Roy B. Chamberlin Jr., Frank Clough, Louis M. Condax, Yoko Matsuda Erle, Sterling Gorrill, Walter Grueninger, Ann Haworth, H. T. E. Hertzberg, Carol Lieberman, Max Mandel, Max V. Mathews, David Montagu, Max Pollikoff, Bernard W. Robinson, Booker Rowe, Frances Rowell, Robert Rudie, Florence DuVal Smith, Jay C. Rosenfeld.

Violists. Robert Courte, Lilla Kalman, Maxwell Kimball, David Mankovitz, Louise Rood, Frederick A. Saunders—and John A. Abbott, Alice Schradieck Aue, Virginia Apgar, Emil Bloch, Harold Coletta, Helene Dautrich, John D'Janni, Lillian Fuchs, Raphael Hillyer, Henry James, Boris Kroyt, Eugene Lehner, Rustin McIntosh, John Montgomery, Elizabeth Payne, Werner Rose, David Schwartz, Emanuel Vardi, Eunice Wheeler, Bernard Zaslav, Sam Zaslavski, myself.

Cellists. Robert Fryxell, John C. Schelleng, India Zerbe—and Charles F. Aue, Joan Brockway, Roy B. Chamberlin, Frank Church, Elwood Culbreath, Oliver Edel, Maurice Eisenberg, George Finckel, Marie Goldman, Barbara Hendrian, Arnold Kvam, Russell B. Kingman, Charles McCracken, Stephen McGee, George Ricci, Peter Rosenfeld, Mary Lou Rylands, True Sackrison, Mischa Schneider, Sanford Schwartz, Joseph Stein, Mischa Slatkin, Joseph Tekula.

Bassists. Julius Levine, Alan Moore, Ronald Naspo, David Walter—and Alvin Brehm, John Castronovo, Garry Karr, Stuart Sankey, Charel Traeger, Howard Van Sickle, Ellery Lewis Wilson.

Composers and conductors. Henry Brant—and Marjorie Bram, Justin Connolly, Herbert Haslam, Frank Lewin, Marc Mostovoy, Harold Oliver, Quincy Porter, Cornelia P. Rogers, Leopold Stokowski, Arnold M. Walter.

REHEARSAL for a concert with Henry Brant conducting an octet of fiddles.

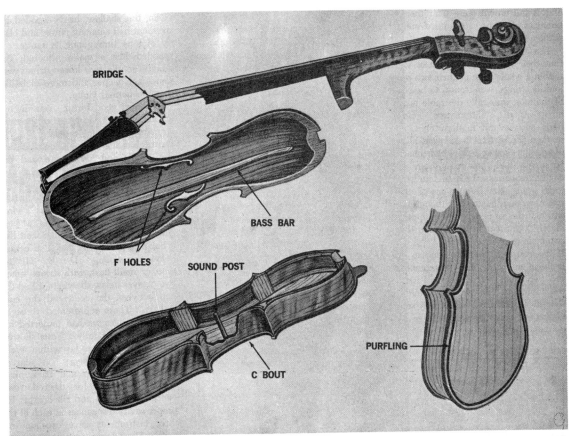

BRIDGE

BASS BAR

F HOLES

SOUND POST

C BOUT

PURFLING

INSTRUMENT PARTS, except for scaling, have remained the same since master makers brought the violin to near perfection about three centuries ago. —**FIG. 2**

years' experimentation, the following four working guides were at hand:

1. location of the main body and main cavity resonances of several hundred conventional violins, violas and cellos tested by Saunders and others,[1, 4-9]

2. the desirable relation between main resonances of free top and back plates of a given instrument, developed from 400 tests on 35 violins and violas during their construction, [2,10,11]

3. knowledge of how to change frequencies of main body and cavity resonances within certain limits (learned not only from many experiments of altering plate thicknesses, relative plate tunings and enclosed air volume but also from construction of experimental instruments with varying body lengths, plate archings and rib heights) and of resultant resonance placements and effects on tone quality in the finished instruments,[2,4,11]

4. observation that the main body

resonance of a completed violin or viola is approximately seven semitones above the average of the main free-plate resonances, usually one in the top and one in the back plate of a given instrument.[2] This observation came from electronic plate testing of free top and back plates of 45 violins and violas under construction. It should not be inferred that the relation implies a *shift* of free-plate resonances to those of the finished instrument. The change from two free plates to a pair of plates coupled at their edges through intricately constructed ribs and through an off-center soundpost, the whole under varying stresses and loading from fittings and string tension, is far too complicated to test directly or calculate.[12]

What is good?

In developing the new instruments our main problem was finding a measurable physical characteristic of the violin

itself that would set it apart from its cousins, the viola, cello and contrabass. The search for this controlling characteristic, unique to the violin, led us through several hundred response and loudness curves of violins, violas and cellos. The picture was at first confusing because many variations were found in the placement of the two main resonances. However, Saunders's tests on Jasha Heifetz's Guarnerius violin[13] showed the main-body resonance was near the frequency of the unstopped A 440-cycles-per-second string and the main cavity resonance at the unstopped D 294 string. Thus the two main resonances of this instrument were near the frequencies of its *two unstopped middle strings.*

Ten violins, selected on the basis that their two main resonances were within a whole tone of their two open middle strings, were found to be some of the most musically desirable instruments—Amatis, Stradivaris, Guarneris and several modern ones. In marked contrast to these were all violas and cellos tested, which characteristically had their main body and cavity resonances three to four semitones *above* the frequencies of their two open middle strings although they still had the same separation, approximately a musical fifth, between these two main resonances.

We reasoned that the clue to our problem might be this placement of the two main resonances relative to the tuning of the two open middle strings. A search through many small violins and cellos, as well as large and small violas, showed enormous variation in the placement of these two resonances. We hoped to find some instrument in which even one of these resonances would approximate what we wanted for the new instruments.

In one quarter-size cello the body resonance was right for viola tuning, D 294, but the cavity resonance was too low at D 147. We bought this chubby little cello and reduced the rib height nearly 4 in. (10 cm), thereby raising the frequency of the cavity resonance to the desired G 196. When it was put back together, it looked very thin and strange with ribs only 1.5 in. (3.8 cm) high and a body length of over 20 in. (51 cm), but strung as a viola it had tone quality satisfactory beyond expectations!

An experimental small viola that I had made for Saunders proved to have its two main resonances just a semitone below the desired frequency for violin tone range. When strung as a violin, this shallow, heavy-wooded instrument had amazing power and clarity of tone throughout its range. It sounded like a violin although the quality on the two lower strings was somewhat deeper and more viola-like that the normal violin.

The next good fortune was discovery and acquisition of a set of three instruments made by the late Fred L. Dautrich of Torrington, Conn., during the 1920's and '30's. He had described them in a booklet called *Bridging the Gaps in the Violin Family.*[14] His *vilonia,* with a body length of 20 in. (51 cm) was tuned as a viola and played cello-fashion on a peg. The *vilon,* or tenor, which looked like a half-size cello, was tuned an octave below the violin, G-D-A-E. His *vilono,* or small bass, with strings tuned two octaves below the violin, filled the gap between the cello and the contrabass. These represented three of the tone ranges we had projected for the new violin family. Tests showed that their resonances lay within working range of our theory. A year of work, adjusting top and back plate wood thicknesses for desired resonance frequencies and rib heights for proper cavity resonances in each of the three instruments gave excellent results. The vilono proved to have exactly the resonance frequencies projected for the enlarged cello, or baritone. So it was moved up a notch in the series and tuned as a cello with extra long strings.

Dautrich's pioneering work had saved years of cut and try. We now had four of the new instruments in playing condition; mezzo, alto (verti-

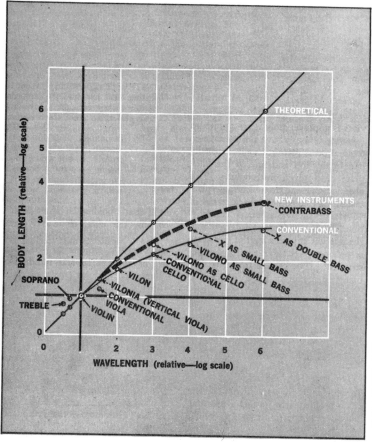

BODY LENGTHS for new instruments were determined by plotting lengths of known instruments against wavelength, then extending data in a smooth curve to include treble at one end and contrabass at the other. Identified points show where old and new instruments fall. —FIG. 3

cal viola), tenor and baritone. I was able to add a fifth by making a soprano, using information gained from many tests on three-quarter- and half-size violins.

With five of the new instruments developed experimentally and in playing condition, we decided to explore their musical possibilities and evaluate the overall results of our hypothesis of resonance placement. In October 1961 the working group gathered at the home of Helen Rice in Stockbridge, Mass., where Saunders and his associates had, for some years, met frequently to discuss violin acoustics and play chamber music. Short pieces of music were composed for the five in-

struments, and the musicians gave the new family of fiddles its first workout. The consensus was that our hypothesis was working even better than we had dared to hope! Apparently the violin-type placement of the two main resonances on the two open middle strings of each instrument was enabling us to project the desirable qualities of the violin into higher and lower tone ranges.

The next step was to explore the resonances of various size basses to help in developing the small bass and the contrabass. A small three-quarter-size bass with arched top and back proved to have just about proper resonances for the small bass. With re-

moval of its low E 41 string and the addition of a high C 131 string to bring the tuning to A-D-G-C (basses are tuned in musical fourths for ease of fingering) it fitted quite well into the series as the small bass. But as yet no prototype for the contrabass could be located. This final addition to the series was to come later.

First musical success

By January 1962 we were ready for a real test in which experts could hear our six new instruments and compare them with good conventional violins, violas and cellos. Composers arranged special music, and professional players had a chance to practice on the new instruments.

Ensemble results exceeded all our expectations. We had violin-like quality and brilliance through the entire range of tones. Our soprano produced a high clear quality that carried well over the other instruments although the high positions on its two lower strings were weak. The mezzo tone was powerful and clear although somewhat viola-like on the two lower strings. The alto (vertical viola) was judged a fine instrument even with inadequate strings. The unique tone of the tenor excited all who heard it. The baritone produced such powerful and clear tones throughout its range that the cellist playing it in a Brahms sonata commented, "This is the first time I have been able to hold my own with the piano!" The small bass was adequate but needed more work. General comments told us that the new instruments were ready to stand on their own, musically, although much more work was to be done on adjustments, strings and proper bows.

End-of-scale problems

With the helpful criticisms and suggestions that came from the first musical test we were encouraged to

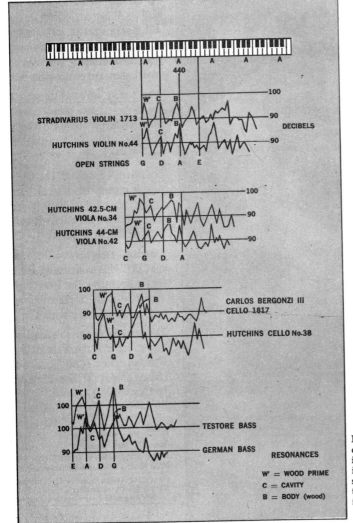

STRADIVARIUS VIOLIN 1713

HUTCHINS VIOLIN No.44

OPEN STRINGS   G   D   A   E

DECIBELS

HUTCHINS 42.5-CM VIOLA No.34

HUTCHINS 44-CM VIOLA No.42

C   G   D   A

CARLOS BERGONZI III CELLO 1817

HUTCHINS CELLO No.38

C   G   D   A

TESTORE BASS

GERMAN BASS

RESONANCES

W' = WOOD PRIME
C = CAVITY
B = BODY (wood)

E   A   D   G

LOUDNESS CURVES are useful evaluations of instrument characteristics. Each is made by bowing an instrument to maximal loudness at 14 semitones on each string and plotting the resulting loudness ceiling against frequency of sound.   —FIG. 4

tackle the problems of the largest and smallest instruments. No existing instruments could be adapted experimentally. We had to design and build them.

The largest bass available for testing was a huge Abraham Prescott, with a 48-in. (122-cm) body length, made in Concord, N.H., in the early 1800's but even that was not big enough! A tiny pochette, or pocket fiddle, from the Wurlitzer collection, with a body length of 7 in. (18 cm) had the right cavity resonance, but its body resonance was much too low.

The body length of each of the new instruments has been one of the controlling factors in all of our experiments. Thus it was decided that the best way to arrive at the dimensions for the largest and smallest would be to plot a curve of body lengths of known instruments, to check against their resonance placement and string tuning. This working chart is shown in figure 3 in which linear body length is plotted against the logarithm of wavelength. The curve for the new instruments was extended in a smooth arc to include the contrabass frequency at the low end and the treble frequency at the upper end, an octave above the normal violin. This procedure gave a projected body length of 51 in. (130 cm) for the contrabass and 10.5 in. (26.5 cm) for the treble. Of course rib height and enclosed air volume were separately determined by other considerations.

Current design practice

From all of this experience we have developed what we might call a "design philosophy." It depends mainly on resonance placement and loudness curves.

Our resonance principle, according to which each member of the new violin family has been made, can be stated as follows: The main body resonance of each of the instruments tuned in fifths is placed at the frequency of the open third string, and the main cavity resonance at the frequency of the open second string. Another way of stating the principle, and one that includes the instruments tuned in fourths as well as those tuned in fifths, is this: Wood prime is placed two semitones above the lowest tone, and the cavity resonance is a fourth above that. (Wood prime is the strengthened frequency one octave below the main body—"wood"—resonance.) These conditions are exemplified in Heifetz's Guarnerius violin and many other good ones, but they are not found in all good violins.

The loudness curve developed by Saunders is one of our most useful measures for evaluating overall instrument characteristics. We make such a curve by bowing an instrument as loudly as possible at 14 semitones on each string and plotting maximal loudness against frequency. Despite unavoidable variations in any test that requires a musician to bow an instrument, the loudness curve is significant because there is a fairly definite limit to the momentary volume an experienced player can produce with a short rapid bow stroke.

As you will see in figure 4, the loudness ceiling varies for each semitone on a given instrument. The curves of this figure were made by bowing each instrument without vibrato at a constant distance from a sound meter. From them you can see the placement of main body and cavity resonances in eight conventional instruments—two violins, two violas, two cellos and two basses. You can see that in the violins the wood prime adds power to the low range of the G string. In the violas, cellos and basses the two main resonances, which are higher in frequency relative to string tuning, create

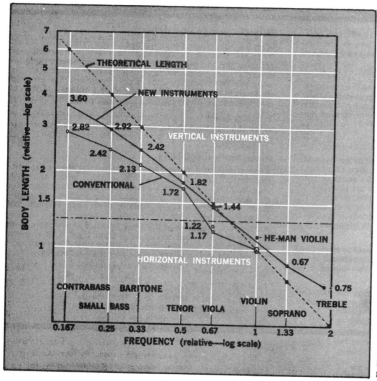

SCALING FACTORS for old and new instruments are a useful reference guide for designers. —FIG. 5

a condition of somewhat weaker response on the lowest four or five semitones.

Fitting fiddles to players

After you decide what kind of acoustics you want, you still have another problem: You have to make fiddles that people can play. For years we worked toward design of an acoustically good instrument with genuine viola tone. Meanwhile we had to keep in mind such conflicting requirements as large radiating areas in the plates and adequate bow clearance in the C bouts (figure 2). Relation of string length to other dimensions that define tone spacing on the fingerboard —the violin maker's "mensure"—is another consideration important to the player. With our acoustic pattern as a model we undertook enlarging, scaling and redesigning all our new instruments, always keeping violin placement of resonances in each tone range.

From our set of experimentally adapted instruments, which represent a variety of styles and designs in violin making, we had learned many things. The vertical viola was about right in body dimensions, but its strings were too long for viola fingering and too short for cello fingering. The tenor was too small, and the cellists were asking for it to have strings as long as possible. The baritone was right for body size, but it had much too long strings. The bass players were asking for a long neck on the small bass and a short one on the large bass with string lengths as close as possible to conventional.

From such comments we realized that there were two basic designs for ease of playing in relation to string lengths and overall mensure of each instrument. Controlling factor in the instrument mensure is placement of the notches of the f holes because a line drawn between these two points dictates the position of the bridge and the highest part of the arch of the top plate. Mensure for the tenor and small bass would need to be as great as possible and for the vertical viola and baritone it would need to be as small as possible. Since the relative areas of the upper and lower bouts are critical factors in plate tuning, adjustment of these mensures posed quite a set of problems.

We developed a series of scaling factors[3] based on relative body length, relative resonance placement and relative string tuning that could be used as a reference guide in actual instrument construction. Figure 5 shows the set which has proved most useful in making the eight new instruments as well as those of conventional instruments.

We had a problem in measuring responses of plates of many sizes—all the way from the 10.5-in. (26-cm) one of the treble violin to the 51-in. (130-cm) one of the contrabass. We solved it by redesigning our transducer from a magnet-armature to a moving-coil type. Then the wooden fiddle plate, suspended at its corners by elastic bands, was made to vibrate as the cone of a loudspeaker (figure 6).

Using the know-how developed in making and testing several hundred violin, viola and cello plates, I could tune the plates of new instruments so that not only did each pair of top and back plates have the desired frequency relation,[2] but it also had its wood thicknesses adjusted to give a reasonable approach to what would be an optimal response.[15]

As a starting guide in adjusting plate frequencies I used the finding that a seven-semitone interval should separate the main body resonance of the finished violin from the average of the two frequencies of the free plates. It was soon obvious, however, that this relationship was not going to hold as the instruments increased in size. As the instrument gets larger the interval becomes smaller, but we do not have enough data yet to make a precise statement about it.

We used scaling theory and the three basic acoustical tools of scientific violin making: (a) frequency relationship between free top and back plates, (b) optimal response in each plate and (c) interval between body resonance and average of free-plate frequencies. We are able not only to create new instruments of the violin family but also to improve the present members. But we have to combine the acoustical tools with the highest art of violin making.

Traits of family members

Any family has its resemblances and its differences. So it is with our violins. They make a family (figure 7) with basic traits in common. But they also have their own personalities.

Treble (G-D-A-E). The main problem with our treble has been to get the frequencies of body and cavity resonances high enough and still keep the mensure long enough for a player to finger consecutive semitones without having to slide his fingers around. We projected a theoretical body length of 10.5 in. (26.7 cm) and a string length of 10 in. (25.4 cm), but to have the proper cavity resonance in this size body, the ribs would be only 3 mm high—a potentially dangerous structural condition! Besides we knew of no string material that could be tuned to E 1320 at a length of 25.4 cm without breaking. At one point we thought we might have to resort to a three-stringed instrument in this range as was indicated by Michael Praetorius in 1619.[16]

The cavity-resonance problem was solved by making six appropriately sized holes in the ribs to raise its frequency to the desired D 587. A string material of requisite tensile strength to reach the high E 1320 was finally found in carbon rocket wire, made by National Standard Company. This proved suitable not only for the high E string but for a number of others on the new instruments. As a temporary measure the ribs were made of soft aluminum to prevent the holes from unduly weakening the structure. Redesign should eliminate the nasal quality found on the lower strings and improve the upper ones. Despite this nasal quality many musicians are pleased with the degree in which the upper strings surpass the normal violin in the same high range.

Plans are to redesign this instrument in several different ways in an effort to discover the best method of achieving desired tone quality throughout its entire range.

Soprano (C-G-D-A). The soprano was designed to have as large a plate area as possible, with resulting shallow ribs and fairly large f holes to raise the cavity resonance to the desired G 392. The overall tone has been judged good and is most satisfactory on the three upper strings. The instrument needs redesign, however, for a better quality on the lower strings. The mensure is as long as possible for playing convenience. J. S. Bach wrote for an in-

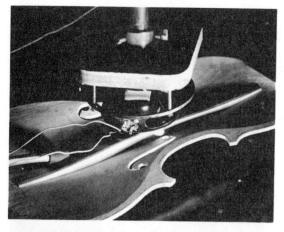
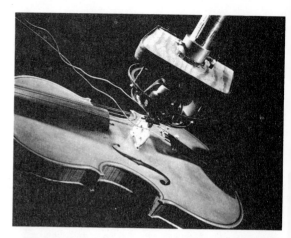
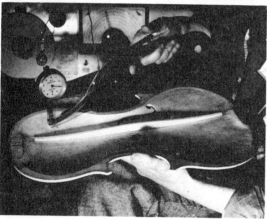
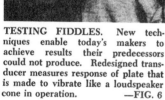

PHOTOS BY PETER PRUYN

TESTING FIDDLES. New techniques enable today's makers to achieve results their predecessors could not produce. Redesigned transducer measures response of plate that is made to vibrate like a loudspeaker cone in operation. —FIG. 6

strument in this tuning, which Sir George Grove describes in Grove's dictionary:[17] "The violino piccolo is a small violin, with strings of a length suitable to be tuned a fourth above the ordinary violin. It existed in its own right for playing notes in a high compass. . . . It survives as the 'three-quarter violin' for children. Tuned like a violin, it sounds wretched, but in its proper pitch it has a pure tone color of its own, for which the high positions on the ordinary violin gave no substitute."

Mezzo (G-D-A-E). The present mezzo with a body length of 16 in. (40.5 cm) was added to the new violin family when musicians found

that even an excellent concert violin did not have the power of the other members of the group. According to scaling theory[18] this instrument, which is 1.14 times as long as the violin, has somewhat more power than necessary to match that of the others. So a second instrument has been developed that is 1.07 times as long as the violin. It has violin placement of resonances yet is adjusted to have conventional violin mensure for the player.[19] It has more power than the normal violin and seems most satisfactory. In fact several musicians have indicated that it may be the violin of the future.

Alto (vertical viola) (C-G-D-A). The greatest difficulty with the alto is that it puts the trained viola player at a distinct disadvantage by taking the viola from under his chin and setting it on a peg, cello fashion on the

floor. Even with an unusual body length of 20 in., its mensure has been adjusted to that of a normal 17.5-in. (44.5-cm) viola, and some violists with large enough physique have been able to play it under the chin. Cello teachers have been impressed by its usefulness in starting young children on an instrument that they can handle readily as well as one they can continue to follow for a career. The greatest advantage is the increase in power and overall tone quality.[20] Leopold Stokowski said when he heard this instrument in concert, "That is the sound I have always wanted from the violas in my orchestra. No viola has ever sounded like that before. It fills the whole hall."

Tenor (G-D-A-E). The body length of the tenor was redeveloped from the Dautrich vilon which had a length ratio of 1.72 to the violin. The pres-

PHOTOS BY J. KELLUM SMITH

THE WHOLE FAMILY poses for pictures with performers trying them out. —FIG. 7

MAX POLLIKOFF	ERNESTINE BREIMEISTER	LILLA KALMAN
treble	soprano	mezzo

ent tenor has a ratio of 1.82 with other factors adjusted accordingly, and the strings as long as possible for convenience in cello fingering. Many musicians have been impressed with its potential in ensemble as well as solo work. They are amazed to find that it is not a small cello, musically, but a large octave violin.

The main problem for this instrument is that there is little or no music for it as yet. Early polyphonic music, where the tenor's counterpart in the viol family had a voice, has been rearranged for either cello or viola. It has no part in classical string or orchestral literature, and only a few contemporary compositions include it. Grove[17] has this to say: "The gradual suppression of the tenor instrument in the 18th century was a disaster; neither the lower register of the viola nor the upper register of the violoncello can give its effect. It is as though all vocal part music were sung without any tenors, whose parts were distributed between the basses and contraltos! It is essential for 17th century concerted music for violins and also for some works by Handel and Bach and even later part-writing. In Purcell's *Fantasy on One Note* the true tenor holds the sustained C. . . The need for a real tenor voice in the 19th century is evidenced by the many abortive attempts to create a substitute."

Baritone (C-G-D-A). The body res-

onance of our baritone is nearly three semitones lower than projected, and this departure probably accounts for the somewhat bass-like quality on the low C 65.4 string. Its strings are 0.75 in. (1.8 cm) longer than those of the average cello. One concert cellist said after playing it for half an hour, "You have solved all the problems of the cello at once. But I would like a conventional cello string length." Thus a redesign of this instrument is desirable by shortening the body length a little. This redesign would raise the frequency of the body resonance and at the same time make possible a shorter string.

Small bass (A-D-G-C). Our first newly constructed instrument in the bass range is shaped like a bass viol with sloping shoulders, but has both top and back plates arched and other features comparable to violin construction. This form was adopted partly to discover the effect of the sloping shoulders of the viol and partly because a set of half-finished bass plates was available. The next small bass is being made on violin shape with other features as nearly like the first one as possible. Bass players have found the present instrument has a most desirable singing quality and extreme playing ease. They particularly like the bass-viol shape. It has proved most satisfactory in both concert and recording sessions.

Contrabass (E-A-D-G). Our con-

trabass[21] is 7 ft (210 cm) high overall; yet it has been possible to get the string length well within conventional bass mensure at 43 in. (110 cm) so that a player of moderate height has no trouble playing it except when he reaches into the higher positions near the bridge. For sheer size and weight it is hard to hold through a 10-hr recording session as one bassist did. When it was first strung up, the player felt that only part of its potential was being realized. The one constructional feature that had not gone according to plan was rib thickness. Ribs were 3 mm thick, whereas violin making indicated they needed to be only 2 mm thick. So the big fiddle was opened; the lining stripes cut out, and the ribs planed down on the inside to an even 2 mm all over—a job that took 10 days. But when the contrabass was put together and strung up, its ease of playing and depth of tone delighted all who played or heard it. Henry Brant commented, "I have waited all my life to hear such sounds from a bass."

How good are they really?

All who have worked on the new instruments are aware of the present lack of objective tests on them—aside from musician and audience comments. In the near future we plan to compare comments with adequate tonal analyses and response curves of these present instruments as well as new ones when they are made. The

STERLING HUNKINS   PETER ROSENFELD   JOSEPH TEKULA   DAVID WALTER   STUART SANKEY
    alto   tenor   baritone   small bass   contrabass

only objective evaluation so far comes from A. H. Benade at Case Institute: "I used my 100-W amplifier to run a tape recorder alternately at 60 and 90 cps while recording a good violin with the machine's gearshift set at the three nominal 1-, 3.5- and 7.5-in/sec speeds. This was done in such a way as to make a tape which, when played back at 3.5 in/sec, would give forth sounds at the pitches of the six smaller instruments in the new violin family (small bass and contrabass excluded). There were some interesting problems about the subjective speed of low- compared with high-pitch playing, but the musician was up to it and we managed to guess reasonably well. The playing was done without vibrato. It is a tribute to everyone involved in the design of those fiddles that they really do sound like their scientifically transposed cousin violin."

But as yet we know only part of *why* this theory of resonance placement is working so well. Probing deeper into this "why" is one of the challenges that lie ahead. Still unsolved are the problems of the intricate vibrational patterns within each free plate as compared to those in the assembled instrument; the reasons for the effect of moisture and various finishes on the tone of a violin and the possibility of some day being able to write adequate specifications for a fabricated material that will equal the tone qualities of wood!

∘ ∘ ∘

This work has received support from the John Simon Guggenheim Memorial Foundation, the Martha Baird Rockefeller Fund for Music, the Alice M. Ditson Fund of Columbia University, the Catgut Acoustical Society and private contributions.

References

1. F. A. Saunders, "The mechanical action of violins," J. Acoust. Soc. Am. 9, 81 (1937).
2. C. M. Hutchins, A. S. Hopping, F. A. Saunders, "Subharmonics and plate tap tones in violin acoustics," J. Acoust. Soc. Am. 32, 1443 (1960).
3. J. C. Schelleng, "The violin as a circuit," J. Acoust. Soc. Am. 35, 326 (1963).
4. F. A. Saunders, "Recent work on violins," J. Acoust. Soc. Am. 25, 491 (1953).
5. F. A. Saunders, "The mechanical action of instruments of the violin family," J. Acoust. Soc. Am. 17, 169 (1946).
6. F. A. Saunders, unpublished notebooks.
7. H. Meinel, "Regarding the sound quality of violins and a scientific basis for violin construction," J. Acoust. Soc. Am. 29, 817 (1957).
8. F. Eggers, "Untersuchung von Corpus-Schwingungen am Violoncello,"

Acustica 9, 453 (1959).
9. W. Lottermoser, W. Linhart, "Beitrag zur akustichen Prufung von Geigen und Bratschen," Acustica 7, 281 (1957).
10. C. M. Hutchins, A. S. Hopping, F. A. Saunders, "A study of tap tones," The Strand, August, September (1958).
11. C. M. Hutchins, "The physics of violins," Scientific American 207, no. 5, 78 (1962).
12. R. H. Scanlan, "Vibration modes of coupled plates," J. Acoust. Soc. Am. 35, 1291 (1963).
13. F. A. Saunders, C. M. Hutchins, "On improving violins," Violins and Violinists 13, nos. 7, 8 (1952).
14. F. L. Dautrich, H. Dautrich, "A chapter in the history of the violin family," The Catgut Acoustical Society Newsletter No. 4 (1 Nov. 1965).
15. C. M. Hutchins, The Catgut Acoustical Society Newsletter No. 5 (1 May 1966) and No. 6 (1 Nov. 1966).
16. M. Praetorius, *Syntagma Musicum II: de Organographia* (1619); re-

printed 1964 by Internationale Gesellschaft für Musikwissenschaft, Barenreiter Kassel, Basel, London, New York, page 26.
17. G. Grove, *Grove's Dictionary of Music and Musicians*, 5th ed., St. Martins Press, New York (1954). vol. 8, page 809.
18. J. C. Schelleng, "Power relations in the violin family," paper presented at 71st meeting, Acoustical Society of America, Boston (3 June 1966).
19. C. M. Hutchins, J. C. Schelleng, "A new concert violin," paper presented to the Audio Engineering Society, 12 Oct. 1966 (to be published).
20. C. M. Hutchins, "Comparison of the acoustical and constructional parameters of the conventional 16 to 17-in. viola and the new 20-in. vertical viola," J. Acoust. Soc. Am. 36, 1025 (1964) (abstract only).
21. C. M. Hutchins, "The new contrabass violin," American String Teacher, Spring 1966.

Some nonscientists hold odd views of the nature of science. This article catalogs and analyses the most common fallacies.

17   The Seven Images of Science

Gerald Holton

An article from *Science,* 1960.

Pure Thought and Practical Power

Each person's image of the role of science may differ in detail from that of the next, but all public images are in the main based on one or more of seven positions. The first of these goes back to Plato and portrays science as an activity with double benefits: Science as pure thought helps the mind find truth, and science as power provides tools for effective action. In book 7 of the *Republic,* Socrates tells Glaucon why the young rulers in the Ideal State should study mathematics: "This, then, is knowledge of the kind we are seeking, having a double use, military and philosophical; for the man of war must learn the art of number, or he will not know how to array his troops; and the philosopher also, because he has to rise out of the sea of change and lay hold of true being. . . . This will be the easiest way for the soul to pass from becoming to truth and being."

The main flaw in this image is that it omits a third vital aspect. Science has always had also a mythopoeic function—that is, it generates an important part of our symbolic vocabulary and provides some of the metaphysical bases and philosophical orientations of our ideology. As a consequence the methods of argument of science, its conceptions and its models, have permeated first the intellectual life of the time, then the tenets and usages of everyday life. All philosophies share with science the need to work with concepts such as space, time, quantity, matter, order, law, causality, verification, reality. Our language of ideas, for example, owes a great debt to statics, hydraulics, and the model of the solar system. These have furnished powerful analogies in many fields of study. Guiding ideas—such as conditions of equilibrium, centrifugal and centripetal forces, conservation laws, feedback, invariance, complementarity —enrich the general arsenal of imaginative tools of thought.

A sound image of science must embrace each of the three functions. However, usually only one of the three is recognized. For example, folklore often depicts the life of the scientist either as isolated from life and from beneficent action or, at the other extreme, as dedicated to technological improvements.

Iconoclasm

A second image of long standing is that of the scientist as iconoclast. Indeed, almost every major scientific advance has been interpreted—either triumphantly or with apprehension—as a blow against religion. To some extent science was pushed into this position by the ancient tendency to prove the existence of God by pointing to problems which science could not solve at the time. Newton thought that the regularities and stability of the solar system proved it "could only proceed from the counsel and dominion of an intelligent and powerful Being," and the same attitude governed thought concerning the earth's formation before the theory of geological evolution, concerning the descent of man before the theory of biological evolution, and concerning the origin of our galaxy before modern cosmology. The advance of knowledge therefore made inevitable an apparent conflict between science and religion. It is now clear how large a price had to be paid for a misunderstanding of both science and religion: to base religious beliefs on an estimate of what science cannot do is as foolhardy as it is blasphemous.

The iconoclastic image of science has, however, other components not ascribable to a misconception of its functions. For example, Arnold Toynbee charges science and technology with usurping the place of Christianity as the main source of our new symbols. Neo-orthodox theologians call science the "self-estrangement" of man because it carries him with idolatrous zeal along a dimension where no ultimate—that is, religious—concerns prevail. It is evident that these views fail to recognize the multitude of divergent influences that shape a culture, or a person. And on the other hand there is, of course, a group of scientists, though not a large one, which really does regard science as largely an iconoclastic activity. Ideologically they are, of course, descendants of Lucretius, who wrote on the first pages of *De rerum natura,* "The terror and darkness of mind must be dispelled not by the rays of the sun and glittering shafts of day, but by the aspect and the law of nature: whose first principle we shall begin by thus stating, nothing is ever gotten out of nothing by divine power." In our day this ancient trend has assumed political significance owing to the fact that in Soviet literature scientific teaching and atheistic propaganda are sometimes equated.

Ethical Perversion

The third image of science is that of a force which can invade, possess, pervert, and destroy man. The current stereotype of the soulless, evil scientist is the psychopathic investigator of science fiction or the nuclear destroyer —immoral if he develops the weapons he is asked to produce, traitorous if he refuses. According to this view, scientific morality is inherently negative. It causes the arts to languish, it blights culture. and when applied to human affairs, it leads to regimentation and to the impoverishment of life. Science is the serpent seducing us into eating the fruits of the tree of knowledge—thereby dooming us.

The fear behind this attitude is genuine but not confined to science: it is directed against all thinkers and innovators. Society has always found it hard to deal with creativity, innovation, and new knowledge. And since science assures a particularly rapid, and therefore particularly disturbing, turnover of ideas, it remains a prime target of suspicion.

Factors peculiar to our time intensify this suspicion. The discoveries of "pure" science often lend themselves readily to widespread exploitation through technology. The products of technology—whether they are better vaccines or better weapons—have the characteristics of frequently being very effective, easily made in large quantities, easily distributed, and very appealing. Thus we are in an inescapable dilemma—irresistibly tempted to reach for the fruits of science, yet, deep inside, aware that our metabolism may not be able to cope with this ever-increasing appetite.

Probably the dilemma can no longer be resolved, and this increases the anxiety and confusion concerning science. A current symptom is the popular identification of science with the technology of superweapons. The bomb is taking the place of the microscope, Wernher von Braun, the place of Einstein, as symbols for modern science and scientists. The efforts to convince people that science itself can give man only knowledge about himself and his environment, and occasionally a choice of action, have been largely unavailing. The scientist *as scientist* can take little credit or responsibility either for facts he discovers—for he did not create them—or for the uses others make of his discoveries, for he generally is neither permitted nor specially fitted to make these decisions. They are controlled by considerations of ethics, economics, or politics and therefore are shaped by the values and historical circumstances of the whole society.

There are other evidences of the widespread notion that science itself cannot contribute positively to culture. Toynbee, for example, gives a list of "creative individuals," from Xenophon to Hindenburg and from Dante to Lenin, but does not include a single scientist. I cannot forego the remark that there is a significant equivalent on the level of casual conversation. For when the man in the street—or many an intellectual—hears that you are a physicist or mathematician, he will usually remark with a frank smile, "Oh, I never could understand that subject"; while intending this as a curious compliment, he betrays his intellectual dissociation from scientific fields. It is not

fashionable to confess to a lack of acquaintance with the latest ephemera in literature or the arts, but one may even exhibit a touch of pride in professing ignorance of the structure of the universe or one's own body, of the behavior of matter or one's own mind.

The Sorcerer's Apprentice

The last two views held that man is inherently good and science evil. The next image is based on the opposite assumption—that man cannot be trusted with scientific and technical knowledge. He has survived only because he lacked sufficiently destructive weapons; now he can immolate his world. Science, indirectly responsible for this new power, is here considered ethically neutral. But man, like the sorcerer's apprentice, can neither understand this tool nor control it. Unavoidably he will bring upon himself catastrophe, partly through his natural sinfulness, and partly through his lust for power, of which the pursuit of knowledge is a manifestation. It was in this mood that Pliny deplored the development of projectiles of iron for purposes of war: "This last I regard as the most criminal artifice that has been devised by the human mind; for, as if to bring death upon man with still greater rapidity, we have given wings to iron and taught it to fly. Let us, therefore, acquit Nature of a charge that belongs to man himself."

When science is viewed in this plane —as a temptation for the mischievous savage—it becomes easy to suggest a moratorium on science, a period of abstinence during which humanity somehow will develop adequate spiritual or social resources for coping with the possibilities of inhuman uses of modern technical results. Here I need point out only the two main misunderstandings implied in this recurrent call for a moratorium.

First, science of course is not an occupation, such as working in a store or on an assembly line, that one may pursue or abandon at will. For a creative scientist, it is not a matter of free choice what he shall do. Indeed it is erroneous to think of him as advancing toward knowledge; it is, rather, knowledge which advances towards him, grasps him, and overwhelms him. Even the most superficial glance at the life and work of a Kepler, a Dalton, or a

Pasteur would clarify this point. It would be well if in his education each person were shown by example that the driving power of creativity is as strong and as sacred for the scientist as for the artist.

The second point can be put equally briefly. In order to survive and to progress, mankind surely cannot ever know too much. Salvation can hardly be thought of as the reward for ignorance. Man has been given his mind in order that he may find out where he is, what he is, who he is, and how he may assume the responsibility for himself which is the only obligation incurred in gaining knowledge.

Indeed, it may well turn out that the technological advances in warfare have brought us to the point where society is at last compelled to curb the aggressions that in the past were condoned and even glorified. Organized warfare and genocide have been practiced throughout recorded history, but never until now have even the war lords openly expressed fear of war. In the search for the causes and prevention of aggression among nations, we shall, I am convinced, find scientific investigations to be a main source of understanding.

Ecological Disaster

A change in the average temperature of a pond or in the salinity of an ocean may shift the ecological balance and cause the death of a large number of plants and animals. The fifth prevalent image of science similarly holds that while neither science nor man may be inherently evil, the rise of science happened, as if by accident, to initiate an ecological change that now corrodes the only conceivable basis for a stable society. In the words o Jacques Maritain, the "deadly disease" science set off in society is "the denial of eternal truth and absolute values."

The main events leading to this state are usually presented as follows. The abandonment of geocentric astronomy implied the abandonment of the conception of the earth as the center of creation and of man as its ultimate purpose. Then purposive creation gave way to blind evolution. Space, time, and certainty were shown to have no absolute meaning. All a priori axioms were discovered to be merely arbitrary conveniences. Modern psychology and anthropology led to cultural relativism. Truth itself has been dissolved into probabilistic and indeterministic statements. Drawing upon analogy with the sciences, liberal philosophers have become increasingly relativistic, denying either the necessity or the possibility of postulating immutable verities, and so have undermined the old foundations of moral and social authority on which a stable society must be built.

It should be noted in passing that many applications of recent scientific concepts outside science merely reveal ignorance about science. For example, relativism in nonscientific fields is generally based on farfetched analogies. Relativity theory, of course, does not find that truth depends on the point of view of the observer but, on the contrary, reformulates the laws of physics so that they hold good for every observer, no matter how he moves or where he stands. Its central meaning is that the most valued truths in science are wholly independent of the point of view. Ignorance of science is also the only excuse for adopting rapid changes within science as models for antitraditional attitudes outside science. In reality, no field of thought is more conservative than science. Each change necessarily encompasses previous knowledge. Science grows like a tree, ring by ring. Einstein did not prove the work of Newton wrong; he provided a larger setting within which some contradictions and asymmetries in the earlier physics disappeared.

But the image of science as an ecological disaster can be subjected to a more severe critique. Regardless of science's part in the corrosion of absolute values, have those values really given us always a safe anchor? A priori absolutes abound all over the globe in completely contradictory varieties. Most of the horrors of history have been carried out under the banner of some absolutistic philosophy, from the Aztec mass sacrifices to the auto-da-fé of the Spanish Inquisition, from the massacre of the Huguenots to the Nazi gas chambers. It is far from clear that any society of the past did provide a meaningful and dignified life for more than a small fraction of its members. If, therefore, some of the new philosophies, inspired rightly or wrongly by science, point out that absolutes have a habit of changing in time and of contradicting one another, if they invite a re-examination of the bases of social authority and reject them when those bases prove false (as did the Colonists in this country), then one must not blame a relativistic philosophy for bringing out these faults. They were there all the time.

In the search for a new and sounder basis on which to build a stable world, science will be indispensable. We can hope to match the resources and structure of society to the needs and potentialities of people only if we know more about man. Already science has much to say that is valuable and important about human relationships and problems. From psychiatry to dietetics, from immunology to meteorology, from city planning to agricultural research, by far the largest part of our total scientific and technical effort today is concerned, indirectly or directly, with man —his needs, relationships, health, and comforts. Insofar as absolutes are to help guide mankind safely on the long and dangerous journey ahead, they surely should be at least strong enough to stand scrutiny against the background of developing factual knowledge.

Scientism

While the last four images implied a revulsion from science, scientism may be described as an addiction to science. Among the signs of scientism are the habit of dividing all thought into two categories, up-to-date scientific knowledge and nonsense; the view that the mathematical sciences and the large nuclear laboratory offer the only permissible models for successfully employing the mind or organizing effort; and the identification of science with technology, to which reference was made above.

One main source for this attitude is evidently the persuasive success of recent technical work. Another resides in the fact that we are passing through a period of revolutionary change in the nature of scientific activity—a change triggered by the perfecting and disseminating of the methods of basic research by teams of specialists with widely different training and interests. Twenty years ago the typical scientist worked alone or with a few students and colleagues. Today he usually belongs to a sizable group working under a contract with a substantial annual budget. In the research institute of one university more than 1500 scientists and technicians are grouped around a set of multimillion-dollar machines; the funds come from government agencies whose ultimate aim is national defense.

Everywhere the overlapping interests of basic research, industry, and the military establishment have been merged in a way that satisfies all three. Science has thereby become a large-scale operation with a potential for immediate and world-wide effects. The results are a splendid increase in knowledge, and also side effects that are analogous to those of sudden and rapid urbanization—a strain on communication facilities, the rise of an administrative bureaucracy, the depersonalization of some human relationships.

To a large degree, all this is unavoidable. The new scientific revolution will justify itself by the flow of new knowledge and of material benefits that will no doubt follow. The danger— and this is the point where scientism enters—is that the fascination with the *mechanism* of this successful enterprise may change the scientist himself and society around him. For example, the unorthodox, often withdrawn individual, on whom most great scientific advances have depended in the past, does not fit well into the new system. And society will be increasingly faced with the seductive urging of scientism to adopt generally what is regarded—often erroneously—as the pattern of organization of the new science. The crash program, the breakthrough pursuit, the megaton effect are becoming ruling ideas in complex fields such as education, where they may not be applicable.

Magic

Few nonscientists would suspect a hoax if it were suddenly announced that a stable chemical element lighter than hydrogen had been synthesized, or that a manned observation platform had been established at the surface of the sun. To most people it appears that science knows no inherent limitations. Thus, the seventh image depicts science as magic, and the scientist as wizard, *deus ex machina*, or oracle. The attitude toward the scientist on this plane ranges from terror to sentimental subservience, depending on what motives one ascribes to him.

18   Scientific Cranks

Martin Gardner

An excerpt from his book *Fads and Fallacies in the Name of Science,* 1957.

Cranks vary widely in both knowledge and intelligence. Some are stupid, ignorant, almost illiterate men who confine their activities to sending "crank letters" to prominent scientists. Some produce crudely written pamphlets, usually published by the author himself, with long titles, and pictures of the author on the cover. Still others are brilliant and well-educated, often with an excellent understanding of the branch of science in which they are speculating. Their books can be highly deceptive imitations of the genuine article—well-written and impressively learned. In spite of these wide variations, however, most pseudo-scientists have a number of characteristics in common.

First and most important of these traits is that cranks work in almost total isolation from their colleagues. Not isolation in the geographical sense, but in the sense of having no fruitful contacts with fellow researchers. In the Renaissance, this isolation was not necessarily a sign of the crank. Science was poorly organized. There were no journals or societies. Communication among workers in a field was often very difficult. Moreover, there frequently were enormous social pressures operating against such communication. In the classic case of Galileo, the Inquisition forced him into isolation because the Church felt his views were undermining religious faith. Even as late as Darwin's time, the pressure of religious conservatism was so great that Darwin and a handful of admirers stood almost alone against the opinions of more respectable biologists.

Today, these social conditions no longer obtain. The battle of science to free itself from religious control has been almost completely won. Church groups still oppose certain doctrines in biology and psychology, but even this opposition no longer dominates scientific bodies or journals. Efficient networks of communication within each science have been established. A vast cooperative process of testing new theories is constantly going on—a process amazingly free (except, of course, in totalitarian nations) from control by a higher "orthodoxy." In this modern framework, in which scientific progress has become dependent on the constant give and take of data, it is impossible for a working scientist to be isolated.

The modern crank insists that his isolation is not desired on his part. It is due, he claims, to the prejudice of established scientific groups against new ideas. Nothing could be further from the truth. Scientific journals today are filled with bizarre theories. Often the quickest road to fame is to overturn a firmly-held belief. Einstein's work on relativity is the outstanding example. Although it met with considerable opposition at first, it was on the whole an intelligent opposition. With few exceptions, none of Einstein's reputable opponents dismissed him as a crackpot. They could not so dismiss him because for years he contributed brilliant articles to the journals and had won wide recognition as a theoretical physicist. In a surprisingly short time, his relativity theories won almost universal acceptance, and one of the greatest revolutions in the history of science quietly took place.

It would be foolish, of course, to deny that history contains many sad examples of novel scientific views which did not receive an unbiased hearing, and which later proved to be true. The pseudo-scientist never tires reminding his readers of these cases. The opposition of traditional psychology to the study of hypnotic phenomena (accentuated by the fact that Mesmer was both a crank and a charlatan) is an outstanding instance. In the field of medicine, the germ theory of Pasteur, the use of anesthetics, and Dr. Semmelweiss' insistence that doctors sterilize their hands before attending childbirth are other well known examples of theories which met with strong professional prejudice.

Probably the most notorious instance of scientific stubbornness was the refusal of eighteenth century astronomers to believe that stones actually fell from the sky. Reaction against medieval superstitions and old wives' tales was still so strong that whenever a meteor fell, astronomers insisted it had either been picked up somewhere and carried by the wind, or that the persons who claimed to see it fall were lying. Even the great French *Académie des Sciences* ridiculed this folk belief, in spite of a number of early studies of meteoric phenomena. Not until April 26, 1803, when several thousand small meteors fell on the town of L'Aigle, France, did the astronomers decide to take falling rocks seriously.

Many other examples of scientific traditionalism might be cited, as well as cases of important contributions made by persons of a crank variety. The discovery of the law of conservation of energy by Robert Mayer, a psychotic German physician, is a classic instance. Occasionally a layman, completely outside of science, will make an astonishingly prophetic guess—like Swift's prediction about the moons of Mars (to be discussed later), or Samuel Johnson's belief (expressed in a letter, in 1781, more than eighty years before the discovery of germs) that microbes were the cause of dysentery.

One must be extremely cautious, however, before comparing the work of some contemporary eccentric with any of these earlier examples, so frequently cited in crank writings. In medicine, we must remember, it is only in the last fifty years or so that the art of healing has become anything resembling a rigorous scientific discipline. One can go back to periods in which medicine was in its infancy, hopelessly mixed with superstition, and find endless cases of scientists with unpopular views that later proved correct. The same holds true of other sciences. But the picture today is vastly different. The prevailing spirit among scientists, outside of totalitarian countries, is one of eagerness for fresh ideas. In the great search for a cancer cure now going on, not the slightest stone, however curious its shape, is being left unturned. If anything, scientific journals err on the side of permitting *questionable* theses to be published, so they may be discussed and checked in the hope of finding something of value. A few years ago a student at the Institute for Advanced Studies in Princeton was asked how his seminar had been that day. He was quoted in a news magazine as exclaiming, "Wonderful! Everything we knew about physics last week isn't true!"

Here and there, of course—especially among older scientists who, like everyone else, have a natural tendency to become set in their opinions—one may occasionally meet with irrational prejudice against a new point of view. You cannot blame a scientist for unconsciously resisting a theory which may, in some cases, render his entire life's work obsolete. Even the great Galileo refused to accept Kepler's theory, long after the evidence was quite strong, that planets move in ellipses. Fortunately there are always, in the words of Alfred Noyes, "The young, swift-footed, waiting for the fire," who can form the vanguard of scientific revolutions.

It must also be admitted that in certain areas of science, where empirical data are still hazy, a point of view may acquire a kind of cult following and harden into rigid dogma. Modifications of Einstein's theory, for example, sometimes meet a resistance similar to that which met the original theory. And no doubt the reader will have at least one acquaintance for whom a particular brand of psychoanalysis has become virtually a religion, and who waxes highly indignant if its postulates are questioned by adherents of a rival brand.

Actually, a certain degree of dogma—of pig-headed orthodoxy— is both necessary and desirable for the health of science. It forces the scientist with a novel view to mass considerable evidence before his theory can be seriously entertained. If this situation did not exist, science would be reduced to shambles by having to examine every new-fangled notion that came along. Clearly, working scientists have more important tasks. If someone announces that the moon is made of green cheese, the professional astronomer cannot be expected to climb down from his telescope and write a detailed refutation. "A fairly complete textbook of physics would be only part of the answer to Velikovsky," writes Prof. Laurence J. Lafleur, in his excellent article on "Cranks and Scientists" (*Scientific Monthly,* Nov., 1951), "and it is therefore not surprising that the scientist does not find the undertaking worth while."

The modern pseudo-scientist—to return to the point from which we have digressed—stands entirely outside the closely integrated channels through which new ideas are introduced and evaluated. He works in isolation. He does not send his findings to the recognized journals, or if he does, they are rejected for reasons which in the vast majority of cases are excellent. In most cases the crank is not well enough informed to write a paper with even a surface resemblance to a significant study. As a consequence, he finds himself excluded from the journals and societies, and almost universally ignored by the competent workers in his field. In fact, the reputable scientist does not even know of the crank's existence unless his work is given widespread publicity through non-academic channels, or unless the scientist makes a hobby of collecting crank literature. The eccentric is forced, therefore, to tread a lonely way. He speaks before organizations he himself has founded, contributes to journals he himself may edit, and—until recently—publishes books only when he or his followers can raise sufficient funds to have them printed privately.

A second characteristic of the pseudo-scientist, which greatly strengthens his isolation, is a tendency toward paranoia. This is a mental condition (to quote a recent textbook) "marked by chronic, systematized, gradually developing delusions, without hallucinations, and with little tendency toward deterioration, remission, or recovery." There is wide disagreement among psychiatrists about the causes of paranoia. Even if this were not so, it obviously is not within the scope of this book to discuss the possible origins of paranoid traits in individual cases. It is easy to understand, however, that a strong sense of personal greatness must be involved whenever a crank stands in solitary, bitter opposition to every recognized authority in his field.

If the self-styled scientist is rationalizing strong religious convictions, as often is the case, his paranoid drives may be reduced to a minimum. The desire to bolster religious beliefs with science can be a powerful motive. For example, in our examination of George McCready Price, the greatest of modern opponents of evolution, we shall see that his devout faith in Seventh Day Adventism is a sufficient explanation for his curious geological views. But even in such cases, an element of paranoia is nearly always present. Otherwise the pseudo-scientist would lack the stamina to fight a vigorous, single-handed battle against such overwhelming odds. If the crank is insincere—

interested only in making money, playing a hoax, or both—then obviously paranoia need not enter his make-up. However, very few cases of this sort will be considered.

There are five ways in which the sincere pseudo-scientist's paranoid tendencies are likely to be exhibited.

(1) He considers himself a genius.

(2) He regards his colleagues, without exception, as ignorant blockheads. Everyone is out of step except himself. Frequently he insults his opponents by accusing them of stupidity, dishonesty, or other base motives. If they ignore him, he takes this to mean his arguments are unanswerable. If they retaliate in kind, this strengthens his delusion that he is battling scoundrels.

Consider the following quotation: "To me truth is precious. . . . I should rather be right and stand alone than to run with the multitude and be wrong. . . . The holding of the views herein set forth has already won for me the scorn and contempt and ridicule of some of my fellowmen. I am looked upon as being odd, strange, peculiar. . . . But truth is truth and though all the world reject it and turn against me, I will cling to truth still."

These sentences are from the preface of a booklet, published in 1931, by Charles Silvester de Ford, of Fairfield, Washington, in which he proves the earth is flat. Sooner or later, almost every pseudo-scientist expresses similar sentiments.

(3) He believes himself unjustly persecuted and discriminated against. The recognized societies refuse to let him lecture. The journals reject his papers and either ignore his books or assign them to "enemies" for review. It is all part of a dastardly plot. It never occurs to the crank that this opposition may be due to error in his work. It springs solely, he is convinced, from blind prejudice on the part of the established hierarchy—the high priests of science who fear to have their orthodoxy overthrown.

Vicious slanders and unprovoked attacks, he usually insists, are constantly being made against him. He likens himself to Bruno, Galileo, Copernicus, Pasteur, and other great men who were unjustly persecuted for their heresies. If he has had no formal training in the field in which he works, he will attribute this persecution to a scientific masonry, unwilling to admit into its inner sanctums anyone who has not gone through the proper initiation rituals. He repeatedly calls your attention to important scientific discoveries made by laymen.

(4) He has strong compulsions to focus his attacks on the greatest scientists and the best-established theories. When Newton was the outstanding name in physics, eccentric works in that science were violently anti-Newton. Today, with Einstein the father-symbol of authority, a crank theory of physics is likely to attack Einstein in the name of Newton. This same defiance can be seen in a tendency to

assert the diametrical opposite of well-established beliefs. Mathematicians prove the angle cannot be trisected. So the crank trisects it. A perpetual motion machine cannot be built. He builds one. There are many eccentric theories in which the "pull" of gravity is replaced by a "push." Germs do not cause disease, some modern cranks insist. Disease produces the germs. Glasses do not help the eyes, said Dr. Bates. They make them worse. In our next chapter we shall learn how Cyrus Teed literally turned the entire cosmos inside-out, compressing it within the confines of a hollow earth, inhabited only on the inside.

(5) He often has a tendency to write in a complex jargon, in many cases making use of terms and phrases he himself has coined. Schizophrenics sometimes talk in what psychiatrists call "neologisms" —words which have meaning to the patient, but sound like Jabberwocky to everyone else. Many of the classics of crackpot science exhibit a neologistic tendency.

When the crank's I.Q. is low, as in the case of the late Wilbur Glenn Voliva who thought the earth shaped like a pancake, he rarely achieves much of a following. But if he is a brilliant thinker, he is capable of developing incredibly complex theories. He will be able to defend them in books of vast erudition, with profound observations, and often liberal portions of sound science. His rhetoric may be enormously persuasive. All the parts of his world usually fit together beautifully, like a jig-saw puzzle. It is impossible to get the best of him in any type of argument. He has anticipated all your objections. He counters them with unexpected answers of great ingenuity. Even on the subject of the shape of the earth, a layman may find himself powerless in a debate with a flat-earther. George Bernard Shaw, in *Everybody's Political What's What?*, gives an hilarious description of a meeting at which a flat-earth speaker completely silenced all opponents who raised objections from the floor. "Opposition such as no atheist could have provoked assailed him"; writes Shaw, "and he, having heard their arguments hundreds of times, played skittles with them, lashing the meeting into a spluttering fury as he answered easily what it considered unanswerable."

In the chapters to follow, we shall take a close look at the leading pseudo-scientists of recent years, with special attention to native specimens. Some British books will be discussed, and a few Continental eccentric theories, but the bulk of crank literature in foreign tongues will not be touched upon. Very little of it has been translated into English, and it is extremely difficult to get access to the original works. In addition, it is usually so unrelated to the American scene that it loses interest in comparison with the work of cranks closer home.

The laws of mechanics apply, of course, equally to all matter, and therefore to the athlete, to the grasshopper, and to the physics professor too.

---

19 Physics and the Vertical Jump

Elmer L. Offenbacher

An article from the *American Journal of Physics*, 1970.

The physics of vertical jumping is described as an interesting and "relevant" illustration for motivating students in a general physics course to master the kinematics and dynamics of one dimensional motion. The equation for the height of the jump is derived (1) from the kinematic equations and Newton's laws of motion and (2) from the conservation of energy principle applied to the potential and kinetic energies at two positions of the jump. The temporal behavior of the reaction force and the center of gravity position during a typical jump are discussed. Mastery of the physical principles of the jump may promote understanding of certain biological phenomena, aspects of physical education, and even of documents on ancient history.

I. INTRODUCTION

When the New York Mets recently won the 1969 World Series in baseball,[1] the New York Times carried a front page picture of one of the players jumping for joy into the arms of another. Jumping for joy might occur even in a physics class if a student should suddenly realize that he understands something new. The something new can be on quite an old subject. This paper will present some aspects of the ancient subject of jumping, the broad jump, and the high jump.[2]

The physics of the *vertical jump*, in particular, is sufficiently simple in its basic elements that it can be mastered by most students in an introductory physics course. At the same time, it has the appealing feature for our hippie-like alienated college student of being *relevant* to so many modern experiences. Neil Armstrong's ability to jump up high on the moon,[3] or Bob Beamon's record breaking broad jump in Mexico,[4] or just plain off-the-record jumping on a dance floor or basketball court are more exciting illustrations of the pull of gravity to the average student—and perhaps to some professors too—than are Galileo's bronze balls rolling down inclined planes.[5] (No slight to Galileo is intended!)

Should these examples not produce enough class participation (or even if they do), the instructor can liven things up by on the spot jumping experiments. For example, he can suspend from the ceiling some valuable coin (a "copper sandwich" quarter will do too) which is just an inch or two above the jumping reach of a six footer (about nine feet from the floor). The instructor then might announce that the coin will be given to whoever can jump up and reach it. To the surprise of most of the class, the six footer can't quite make it. For the participation of the shorter members of the class, one can suspend other coins at lower levels and allow students in certain height ranges to jump for specific coins.[6]

The problem of class involvement in a recitation section of an introductory noncalculus physics course was the stimulus which lead the author to research the "science" of jumping; his findings may perhaps provide other teachers with a stimulant (legal and harmless) for their class discussions.[7]

A description of the physics of vertical jumping can be directed towards one or more of several goals such as (a) application of one dimensional kinematic equations of motion, (b) illustration of Newton's third law on reaction forces,[8] (c) study of *nonuniformly* accelerated one dimensional motion, (d) motivation for learning the derivation r kinematical equations, and (e) application of physical principles in other disciplines such as zoology, physical education, and physiology.

For simplicity, the presentation which follows will be restricted primarily to the *standing vertical jump*. However, some features can easily be extended to other kinds of jumping such as the standing broad jump or the swimmer's dive. The latter examples illustrate the application of the kinematic equations in two dimensions.

II. THE PHYSICS OF JUMPING: CLASS PRESENTATION

One can initiate the class discussion on jumping by such questions as: How high can you jump? Could you do better if you were in a high flying airplane, if your legs were longer, if you were in

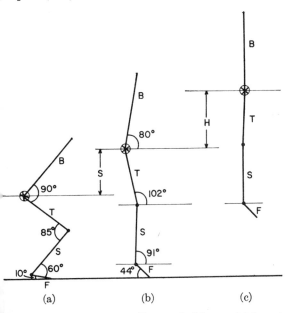

FIG. 1. Positions of the standing vertical jump: (a) lowest crouched position, (b) position before losing contact with the ground, (c) highest vertical position. F=foot, S=shin, T=thigh, and B=back. ⊗ marks the position of the center of gravity.

Philadelphia or in Mexico City, if you wore sneakers or jumped with barefeet? How good is man as a jumper compared to a kangaroo or a grasshopper? In what way does an individual's physical condition affect the maximum height of his jump?

The order and nature of the presentation can be varied according to the instructor's imagination.

If the class is "willing" to be taught a derivation, then one can start by deriving

$$d = v_0 t + \tfrac{1}{2} a t^2. \qquad (1)$$

It is useful to impress upon the students the fact that this kinematical equation for uniform acceleration can be derived purely from the definitions of average velocity and acceleration.[9] Such a derivation can be easily mastered by virtually every student.

Derivation of the Height Equation from the Kinematic Equations and Newton's Third Law

The definition of uniform acceleration can be written as

$$v_f = v_0 + at \qquad (2)$$

where v_f is the final velocity, v_0 is the original velocity, a is the uniform acceleration, and t is the interval over which the velocity change occurred. Eliminating the time between Eqs. (1) and (2), one obtains the well-known relation between v_f, v_0, and the distance d over which uniform acceleration takes place:

$$v_f^2 = v_0^2 + 2ad \qquad (3)$$

The total distance over which the displacement of the center of gravity takes place during the jump may be divided into two segments (see Fig. 1), the stretching segment S and the free flight path H. One can now apply Eq. (3) over the two different segments as follows. For the stretching part {which extends from the beginning of the crouched position to the erect position before contact with the ground is lost [Figs. 1(a) and 1(b)]} the acceleration, a, is given by the *average net* upward force on the jumper, F_n, divided by the mass of the jumper, m. As $v_0 = 0$, substitution in Eq. (3) gives

$$v_{j0}^2 = (2F_n/m)S, \qquad (4a)$$

where

$$F_n = F_r - mg,$$

F_r is the average reaction force of the ground on the jumper during the upward displacement S. We have labeled the final velocity at the end of segments as v_{j0}, the jumping off velocity.

For the free flight path, however, the final

FIG. 2. Grasshopper's jump. Just before a takeoff all the joints of the hindlimbs of a grasshopper are tightly folded up at the sides of the body. As soon as the jump begins these joints extend. The limbs extend to their maximum extent in about 1/30 sec. (From J. Gray, Ref. 10.)

velocity at the highest position is zero, the acceleration is $-g$, and $v_0 = v_{j0}$. One then obtains H, the displacement of the center of gravity from the erect position to the highest point, [Figs. (1b) and 1(c)] from the equation

$$0 = v_{j0}{}^2 - 2gH. \tag{4b}$$

Or, combining (4a) and (4b) one finally obtains

$$H = F_n S / mg. \tag{5}$$

Derivation Based on Conservation of Energy

An alternative way of deriving this result using the conservation of energy principle is as follows: Take the crouched position as the zero reference potential. The total amount of work done on the jumper by the floor during the push off period is equal to the potential energy change, mgS, plus the kinetic energy imparted at position S which is

$$\int_0^S F_n dS.$$

At the top of the jump the kinetic energy is again zero and the potential energy is $mg(H+S)$. Therefore, from the conservation of energy principle

$$mg(H+S) = mgS + \int_0^S F_n dS.$$

When solved for H this gives an equation equivalent to (5)

$$H = \int_0^S F_n dS \Big/ mg. \tag{6}$$

Note that $F_n S$ in Eq. (5) is replaced by the integral

$$\int_0^S F_n dS.$$

This makes Eq. (6) valid for nonuniform acceleration, whereas use of Eq. (3) in the previous derivation involves the assumption of uniform acceleration.

In a typical jump a man weighing 140 lb producing an average reaction force during take off of about 300 lb and able to stretch over a distance S of 1.4 ft will lift his center of gravity 1.6 ft:

$$H = \left(\frac{300 - 140}{140}\right) \times 1.4 = 1.6 \text{ ft.}$$

With the help of Eq. (5) the student should now be able to answer many of the questions posed earlier such as the effect of gravity or of the length of one's legs. Consideration of Eq. (5) might also give the student some clue about the remarkable

256

jumping ability of the grasshopper. A series of positions during a grasshopper's jump are shown in Fig. 2.[10] The pictures were taken at intervals of 1/120 sec. Particularly noteworthy are (1) the rapid take off for his jump (about 1/30 sec compared to the human take off time of more than half a second) and (2) the long stretch, S, permitted because of his long hind legs and their particular construction. (See Sec. IV for further details). Indeed, these pictures might instill the student high jump athlete (the one who may have succeeded in getting the valuable coin) with a bit of humility. Whereas for a superior athlete a jump up to $\frac{1}{3}$ his height is a creditable performance, an average grasshopper can jump well over ten times his own height and even a 5-ft kangaroo can jump up to 8 ft above the ground!

III. GERRISH'S STANDING VERTICAL JUMP

In Fig. 3(a) is shown the time record of the center of gravity *position* and the ground's reaction force F_r in a typical vertical jump of Paul H. Gerrish, the author of a 1934 Ph.D thesis on the subject of jumping.[11] It is interesting to note that during the first 0.42 sec of the jump the reaction force is less than the static weight,[12] and that the downward velocity reaches a maximum of 3.8 ft/sec. After 0.61 sec, the velocity is zero and the drop of the center of gravity is about 1.2 ft. The upward acceleration has a duration of 0.24 sec; during that period the reaction force varies from about twice his weight to about 2.4 times his weight. The "gravity controlled" part of his jump (from lift off to the highest point) takes about 0.3 sec while the total time for the entire jump is less than 2 sec.

Apparatus

Gerrish designed his own force meter.[13] This was a device which minimized the vibration and inertia forces and which transmitted the force of the jump on a platform via hydrostatic pressure to an Ashton single spring Bourbon-type pressure gauge. He used a calibrated 16-mm movie camera with a speed of 53.1 frames per second for timing the sequence of positions. He obtained the appropriate height in each frame by aligning, with the aid of 22 (or 44) fold magnification, a refer-

ence mark close to the center of gravity of his body (over the anterior superior spine of the right ilium) with the divisions of a surveyor's measuring rod.

Statistical Results for Other Jumpers

In Gerrish's analysis of 270 jumps of 45 Columbia University men he found that the tallest or heaviest jumpers did not always demonstrate greater maximum forces, velocities, powers, or height displacements for the jump than the shortest or lightest jumpers, respectively.[14] He also noted that maximum height displacement varied within the rather narrow range of 1 and 2 ft and that the subjects demonstrated a range of *minimum* forces from 15%–74% of their static weight, and a range of *maximum* forces from 210%–375% of this weight.

Analysis of Jump

An interesting aspect of the jump is the energy and power requirement for jumping. From the raw data of Fig. 3(a) one can compute the velocity curve and then construct a power curve by multiplying the latter with the appropriate ordinates of the force curve. These curves are shown in Fig. 3(b). The reader may find it interesting to analyze these curves in detail. It should be noted that the force and height curves are consistent with each other, thus providing evidence for the validity of the measurements in Fig. 3(a). This consistency was checked in two ways. (1) The impulse imparted to the jumper at the end of the stretch P_{j0} can be calculated from the integral

$$\int_{T_1}^{T_3} F_n dt.$$

This value agrees to within 0.4% with the momentum obtained from the free flight deceleration to maximum height, $P_{j0} = mv_{j0} = mg(T_4 - T_3)$. (2) The force curve can be integrated twice with respect to time and the resultant curve turns out to agree well with the height curve.

The achievement in the vertical jump is directly related to the power developed during the jump. This in turn depends on the steepness of the velocity curve and the ability to maintain close

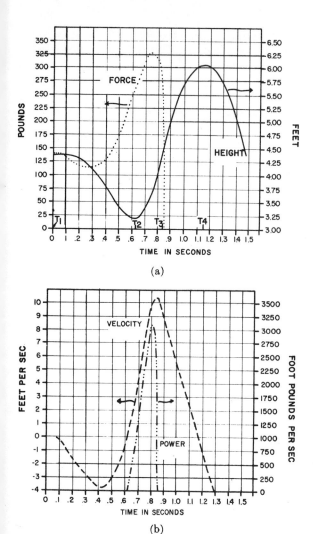

FIG. 3. (a) The temporal sequence of the floor's reaction (FORCE) and the center of gravity position (HEIGHT) during a typical vertical jump beginning with the standing position. (b) The velocity of the center of gravity (VELOCITY) and the applied (POWER) [the product of FORCE of Fig. 3(a) and VELOCITY of Fig. 3(b)].

to the maximum force during the 0.2 sec of the stretching segment[15] [see Fig. 3(b)].

IV. JUMPING AND OTHER DISCIPLINES

The student's motivation for learning a new subject is usually enhanced if he is made to realize its connection with other studies he is undertaking simultaneously or in which he has some innate interest. To cite a few examples of how an understanding of the physics of jumping can be helpful

in other fields of study, let us turn to an application in biology (the jump of the grasshopper) and to two applications in physical education (Olympic records and the Sargent jump).

Biological Application

The outstanding animal jumpers include, in addition to the kangaroo and grasshopper, the frog and the flea. Although these animals perform much better than man when their jumps are measured in terms of their body length,[16] the ratio of their broad jump to high jump lengths is between 3 and 4 which is similar to man's performance. Actually, the fact that animals can jump higher in terms of their own dimensions is not surprising as can be shown by the following simple scaling argument. If it is assumed that the strength of an animal to exert a force F is proportional to the cross sectional area of his muscular tissue A then F is proportional to L^2, where L specifies its linear dimension. However, the mass m for constant density is proportional to L^3. Therefore, the acceleration, being equal to F/m, is proportional to L^{-1}. As the stretch distance S is proportional to L, one sees from Eq. (4a) that v_{j0} is *unaffected* by a down scaling. Therefore, the relatively large jumping achievements of the smaller insects are not really too surprising because if v_{j0} is unaffected, so is H [see Eq. (4b)].

In a 1958 article in Scientific American, a grasshopper's physiology, responsible for its skill in jumping, is described. One of its secrets lies in the construction of its hind legs. These legs differ from those of most other insects in that the angle between the femur (thigh) and the tibia (shin) is not obtuse but acute. This permits a bigger value for S and a longer period of possible acceleration as was mentioned before. Another feature is that its extensor muscle (which straightens the leg) is larger than its flexor muscle (which bends it). It can lift off from the ground a weight ten times its own and develops, during this feat, a tension equal to 250 times its own weight.

Jumping and Athletics

While jumping is a component of many sports (for example, basketball, diving, skiing), it has for many centuries captured men's imagination in its own right. Indeed, Beamon's record-breaking broad jump of 29 ft 2½ in. bettering the previous world record by almost two feet (1 ft 9¾ in.) was the sensation of the 1968 Mexico Olympics.[4]

Olympic Records and the Acceleration of Gravity

In comparing record performances, one should, in all fairness, take account of variations in g that exist between two localities.[18] From Eq. (5) one can calculate the difference in height, ΔH, which results from the difference in the g values between two localities. Namely, the fractional change in H is equal to the negative of the fractional change in g: $\Delta H/H = -\Delta g/g$. As the maximum variation of g on the surface of the earth is about ½%, in a seven foot jump ΔH expressed in inches may be as much as 0.42 in. $(7 \times 12 \times 0.005)$. As high jumps and broad jumps are customarily recorded to ⅛-th of an inch or even 1/16-th of an inch, a fair comparison

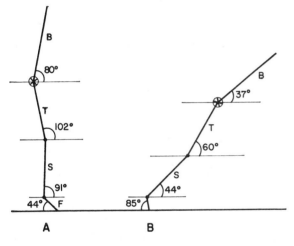

Fig. 4. Comparison of the takeoff position in the standing high jump, A, and the standing broad jump of a skilled college woman. (From J. M. Cooper and R. B. Glassow, Ref. 22.)

may very well reverse the standings of the record holders. An examination of the *broad* jump winners at the 1948 London Olympics (Latitude 51°30′N) and the 1956 Melbourne Olympics (Latitude 37°52′S) shows indeed that W. Steele's (U.S.) performance in London of 25 ft 8 1/16 in. was better than G. Bell's (U.S.) jump of 25 ft 8¼ in. in Melbourne when their jumps are compared at the same g. The increase in g of 1.09 cm/sec² from Melbourne to London accounts for a decrease in jump length of 0.34 in.,[19] whereas their actual recorded difference is only 0.19 in. This "injustice" in reality didn't matter too much because both records were below the 26 ft 5 5/16 in. record established by Jesse Owens in the 1936 Olympics in Berlin. This wasn't broken until the 1960 Olympics, which in turn was bettered phenomenally two years ago by Beamon.

The Sargent Jump
(or jumping as a test of athletic ability)

The standing vertical jump has been used for close to half a century by persons interested in tests and measurements in physical education. In searching for a physical ability test which would correlate with an individual's performance in track and field events, it was found that a particular type of vertical jump, known as the Sargent jump,[20] produced a high correlation with such events as the six second run, running high jump, standing broad jump, and the shot put. The instructions for the adminstration of the Sargent jump read as follows:

> the jumper is to swing his arms downward and backward inclinging the body slightly forward and bending the knees to about 90° and raising the heels. He is to pause a "moment" in this position and then to jump vertically upward as high as possible, swinging his arms vigorously forward and upward to a vertical position. Just before the highest point of the jump he is to swing his arms forward and downward to his side. The end of the downward swing should be timed so as to coincide with the reaching of the highest point of the jump. The legs should be stretched downward and the head should be stretched upward without tilting the chin.[21]

Gerrish's jump was similar to the Sargent jump except for the arm movements. In his thesis, he makes the interesting observation that the location of the center of gravity did not vary by more than ½ in. for various body positions (with legs bent, trunk inclined forward, etc.) assumed during his jump. Apparently, the purpose of the downward swing of the arms in the Sargent jump is to displace the center of gravity downward with respect to the body so as to increase the height reached by the top of the head.

Broad jumping

Broad jumping is closely related to the high jump except that the initial velocity is at an angle less than 90° with the horizontal. Ideally, if the body were to be considered as a free projectile, for maximum range the take off velocity should be directed at 45° with the horizontal (see equation in Ref. 19). The actual take off directions of broad jumpers turn out to be around 30°.

The take off position in the *standing high jump* and the *standing broad jump* of a skilled college woman is shown in Fig. 4.[22] Note that the difference in inclination of body segments is mainly due to the difference in foot inclination. In the broad jump additional distance can be gained by shifting the center of gravity backwards through the motion of the arms, especially if the broad jumper grasps weights in each hand. Recent experiments have shown that the length of the jump could be increased by 15–20 cm if the jumper holds 5-lb weights in each hand.[23] These experiments were conducted in a historical–philological study to understand some "legends" of broad jumping feats of Phayllos of Kroton and Chionis of Sparta. This study arrives at the conclusion that if the pentathlon events of these two athletes consisted of five partial jumps (i.e., five standing broad jumps with a pause in between each jump), then the record distances of 55 and 52 ft, respectively attributed to the above athletic heroes are believable; yet they represent superior performances worthy of legendary transmission.

V. SUMMARY AND SUGGESTIONS FOR JUMPING FARTHER

It is suggested in this paper that jumping "exercises" could provide lively, student-involving, real physical situations to teach some of the beginning fundamentals of mechanics. Realistic discussion of the factors affecting the "altitude" of a jump can be conducted with the help of Fig. 3 which describes the temporal behavior of the reaction forces and center of gravity positions in a typical jump. Although this provides only sample curves for a specific type of jump, most likely the general features are similar in many other kinds of jumps such as the broad jump or the chalk and

Sargent jumps. The phase lag of the force curve behind the position curve and the initial dip in the force curve are common features of all of these jumps.

The application of the laws of mechanics to biology and athletics will motivate some students to make the special effort required to understand such concepts as Newton's third law, the relation-

Fig. 5. J. Robert Oppenheimer's jump as recorded in Halsman's *Jump Book* (Simon and Schuster, New York, 1959).

ship of velocity to position in nonuniform accelera-tion, the physical concept of power and momen-tum, the effect of gravity and its variation with position, even the meaning of conservation of energy when biological systems are involved. Furthermore, to the interested and capable student, it might provide the stimulus for con-ducting some fairly simple experiments which will provide useful information to the coach or athletic director as well as possibly to the psychologist and physiologist. These experiments may include different kinds of jumps (i.e., jumping off with one leg, the broad jump, or the Sargent jump) or varying the footwear used, the jumping surface or the rest period between jumps. It should also be possible with today's advances in photographic techniques and data analysis to improve and enlarge on Gerrish's work to the point where the jumping process could be analyzed reliably in varied situations.

In searching for references on the physics of jumping I came across an amusing book entitled *The Jump Book* (Simon and Schuster, New York, 1959) by the prize winning Life photographer Philippe Halsman, self-styled founder of the "science" of Jumpology. In describing and categorizing the jumps of the famous people who his synchronized camera caught up in the air, he jovially suggests that jumping could be used as a psychological test (*a la* Rorschach), and its analysis could constitute a new field of psychological in-vestigation which he named Jumpology.

Although the persons in these photographs were evidently not instructed to jump for height, some of them did seem to reach for that goal. One of them was J. Robert Oppenheimer (Fig. 5). Who knows whether having students jump up in the physics laboratory might instantaneously identify a potentially great scientist. One might just com-pare the student's jump with the one by J. Robert Oppenheimer.

[1] The New York Mets won the 1969 World Series against the Baltimore Orioles after a phenomenal rise from last place to take the Eastern Division title and the National League pennant.

[2] A certain kind of broad jump was one of the five track and field events of the annual Tailteann games held at Tailtu, County Meath, Ireland as early as 1829 B.C. It was also one of the features of the Pentathlon in the ancient Olympic games (Encyclopedia Brittanica, 1967 Edition, Vol. 13, p. 132).

[3] New York Times, July 21, p. 1, Col. 3 (1969).

[4] New York Times, Oct. 27, Sect. 5, p. 3, Col. 6 (1968); World Almanac, p. 878 (1969).

[5] Galileo's *Two New Sciences* (1638).

[6] The average vertical jumping height with ordinary shoes and in shirt sleeves is about 19 inches. This figure is based on a study made by Franklin Henry [Res. Quart. **13**, 16 (1942)] of 61 male students aged 19–24 years at the Berkely campus of the University of California.

[7] H. R. Crane suggested in a recent article in this Journal [**36**, 1137 (1968)] that relevant examples and exercises be incorporated into noncalculus physics course. An exercise involving the physics of jumping can be found in, S. Borowitz and A. Beiser, *Essentials of Physics* [(Addison–Wesley Publ. Corp., Reading, Mass., 1966), Chap. 5, Problem 7.] Even though this is a calculus level text, students usually are not able to solve this problem without the use of the energy conservation principle, which is described only later on in the text in Chap. 7. Also see F. W. Sears and M. W. Zemansky, *University Physics* (1964) Problem 6-16.

[8] The third law also explains the physics of walking. For a note on the physics of walking see R. M. Sutton, Amer. J. Phys. **23**, 490 (1955).

[9] J. G. Potter, Amer. J. Phys. **35**, 676 (1967).

[10] J. Gray, *How Animals Move* (Cambridge University Press, London, 1953), opposite p. 70.

[11] P. H. Gerrish, *A Dynamical Analysis of the Standing Vertical Jump*, Ph.D. thesis Teachers College, Columbia University, 1934.

[12] In all 270 tests of 45 other jumpers, he found this time always to be less than 0.5 sec.

[13] Reference 11, p. 7.

[14] In the 1960 Rome Olympics, the much shorter Russian Shav Lakadze won the high jump gold medal whereas the tall world record holder at that time, John Thomas, barely got the bronze medal. [*Olympic Games 1960*, H. Lechenperg, Ed. (A. S. Barnes & Co., 1960), p. 198.] Also see H. Krakower, Res. Quart. **12**, 218 (1941).

[15] See article by R. M. Sutton [Amer. J. Phys. **23**, 490 (1955)] for a discussion of the forces developed in the foot.

[16] Reference 10, p. 69.

[17] G. Hogle, Scientific American **198**, 30 (1958).

[18] This was pointed out by P. Kirkpatrick, Scientific American **11**, 226 (1937); Amer. J. Phys. **12**, 7 (1944).

[19] The range formula applicable to broad jumping, i.e., $R = V_0^2 \sin 2\alpha/g$, where α is the angle of the jumping off direction with the horizontal also gives $\Delta R/R = -\Delta g/g$. Therefore, $\Delta R = 25.7 \times 12$ (in.) $\times 1.09/978 = 0.34$ in.

[20] D. A. Sargent, Amer. Phys. Ed. Rev. **26**, 188 (1921).

[21] D. Van Dalen, Res. Quart. **11**, 112 (1940). Also see footnote cited in Ref. 6.

[22] J. M. Cooper and R. B. Glassow, *Kinesiology* (C. V. Mosby Co., St. Louis, Missouri, 1963).

[23] *Joachim Ebert*: Zum Pentathlon Der Antike Unter-suchungen uber das System der Siegerermittlung und die Ausführung des Halterensprunges, Abhandlung der Sächsichen Akademie der Wissenschaft zur Leipzig—Philologisch-Historische Klasse Band 56 Heft 1, Akademie Verlag, Berlin (1963).

LEO L. BERANEK

Leo L. Beranek is director of Bolt Beranek and Newman Inc., a consulting company in communications physics in Cambridge, Massachusetts. He has been associated with MIT since 1946, and was the director of the Electro-Acoustics Laboratory at Harvard during World War II. He is president of Boston Broadcasters, Inc. He has done work in architectural acoustics (such as designing auditoriums), acoustic measurements, and noise control.

JACOB BRONOWSKI

Jacob Bronowski, who received his Ph.D. from Cambridge University in 1933, is now a Fellow of the Salk Institute of Biological Studies in California. He has served as Director of General Process Development for the National Coal Board of England, as the Science Deputy to the British Chiefs of Staff, and as head of the Projects Division of UNESCO. In 1953 he was Carnegie Visiting Professor at the Massachusetts Institute of Technology.

ALEXANDER CALANDRA

Alexander Calandra, Associate Professor of Physics at Washington University, St. Louis, since 1950, was born in New York in 1911. He received his B.S. from Brooklyn College and his Ph.D. in statistics from New York University. He has been a consultant to the American Council for Education and for the St. Louis Public Schools, has taught on television, and has been the regional counselor of the American Institute of Physics for Missouri.

ARTHUR C. CLARKE

Arthur C. Clarke, British scientist and writer, is a Fellow of the Royal Astronomical Society. During World War II he served as technical officer in charge of the first aircraft ground-controlled approach project. He has won the Kalinga Prize, given by UNESCO for the popularization of science. The feasibility of many of the current space developments was perceived and outlined by Clarke in the 1930's. His science fiction novels include Childhoods End and The City and the Stars.

ROBERT MYRON COATES

Robert Myron Coates, author of many books and articles, was born in New Haven, Connecticut, in 1897 and attended Yale University. He is a member of the National Institute of Arts and Letters and has been an art critic for The New Yorker magazine. His books include The Eater of Darkness, The Outlaw Years, The Bitter Season, and The View From Here.

E. J. DIJKSTERHUIS

E. J. Dijksterhuis was born at Tilburg, Holland, in 1892, and later became a professor at the University of Leyden. Although he majored in mathematics and physics, his school examinations forced him to take Latin and Greek, which awakened his interest in the early classics of science. He published important studies on the history of mechanics, on Euclid, on Simon Steven and on Archimedes. Dijksterhuis died in 1965.

ALBERT EINSTEIN

Albert Einstein, considered to be the most creative physical scientist since Newton, was nevertheless a humble and sometimes rather shy man. He was born in Ulm, Germany, in 1879. He seemed to learn so slowly that his parents feared that he might be retarded. After graduating from the Polytechnic Institute in Zurich, he became a junior official at the Patent Office at Berne. At the age of twenty-six, and quite unknown, he published three revolutionary papers in theoretical physics in 1905. The first paper extended Max Planck's ideas of quantization of energy, and established the quantum theory of radiation. For this work he received the Nobel Prize for 1921. The second paper gave a mathematical theory of Brownian motion, yielding a calculation of the size of a molecule. His third paper founded the special theory of relativity. Einstein's later work centered on the general theory of relativity. His work has a profound influence not only on physics, but also on philosophy. An eloquent and widely beloved man, Einstein took an active part in liberal and anti-war movements. Fleeing Nazi Germany, he settled in the United States in 1933 at the Institute for Advanced Study in Princeton. He died in 1955.

RICHARD PHILLIPS FEYNMAN

Richard Feynman was born in New York in 1918, and graduated from the Massachusetts Institute of Technology in 1939. He received his doctorate in theoretical physics from Princeton in 1942, and worked at Los Alamos during the Second World War. From 1945 to 1951 he taught at Cornell, and since 1951 has been Tolman Professor of Physics at the California Institute of Technology. Professor Feynman received the Albert Einstein Award in 1954, and in 1965 was named a Foreign Member of the Royal Society. In 1966 he was awarded the Nobel Prize in Physics, which he shared with Shinichero Tomonaga and Julian Schwinger, for work in quantum field theory.

R. J. FORBES

R.J. Forbes, professor at the University of Amsterdam, was born in Breda, Holland, in 1900.

After studying chemical engineering, he worked for the Royal Dutch Shell Group in their laboratories and in refineries in the East Indies. Interested in archaeology and museum collections, he has published works on the history of such fields as metallurgy, alchemy, petroleum, road-building, technology, and distillation.

KENNETH W. FORD

Kenneth W. Ford was born in 1917 at West Palm Beach, Florida. He did his undergraduate work at Harvard College. His graduate work at Princeton University was interrupted by two years at Los Alamos and at Project Manhattan in Princeton. He worked on a theory of heavy elementary particles at the Imperial College in London, and at the Max Planck Institute in Göttingen, Germany. Before joining the faculty at the University of California, Irvine, as chairman of the Department of Physics, Mr. Ford was Professor of Physics at Brandeis University.

GEORGE GAMOW

George Gamow, a theoretical physicist from Russia, received his Ph.D. in physics at the University of Leningrad. At Leningrad he became professor after being a Carlsberg fellow and a university fellow at the University of Copenhagen and a Rockefeller fellow at Cambridge University. He came to the United States in 1933 to teach at the George Washington University and later at the University of Colorado. His popularization of physics are much admired.

MARTIN GARDNER

Martin Gardner, well-known editor of the "Mathematical Games" department of the Scientific American, was born in Tulsa, Oklahoma, in 1914. He received a B.A. in philosophy from the University of Chicago in 1939, worked as a publicity writer for the University, and then wrote for the Tulsa Tribune. During World War II he served in the Navy. Martin Gardner has written humorous short stories as well as serious articles for such journals as Scripta Mathematica and Philosophy of Science, and is the best-selling author of The Annotated Alice, Relativity for the Million, Math, Magic, and Mystery, as well as two volumes of the Scientific American Book of Mathematical Puzzles and Diversions.

GERALD HOLTON

Gerald Holton received his early education in Vienna, at Oxford, and at Wesleyan University, Connecticut. He has been at Harvard University since receiving his Ph.D. degree in physics there in 1948; he is Professor of Physics, teaching courses in physics as well as in the history of science. He was the founding editor of the quarterly Daedalus. Professor Holton's experimental research is on the properties of matter under high pressure. He is co-director of Harvard Project Physics.

CARLEEN MALEY HUTCHINS

Carleen Hutchins was born in Springfield, Massachusetts, in 1911. She received her A.B. from Cornell University and her M.A. from New York University. She has been designing and constructing stringed instruments for years. Her first step was in 1942 when "I bought an inexpensive weak-toned viola because my musical friends complained that the trumpet I had played was too loud in chamber music, as well as out of tune with the strings — and besides they needed a viola." In 1947, while on a leave of absence from the Brearley School in New York, she started making her first viola — it took two years. She has made over fifty, selling some to finance more research. In 1949 she retired from teaching and then collaborated with Frederick A. Saunders at Harvard in the study of the acoustics of the instruments of the violin family. She has had two Guggenheim fellowships to pursue this study.

LEOPOLD INFELD

Leopold Infeld, a co-worker with Albert Einstein in general relativity theory, was born in 1898 in Poland. After studying at the Cracow and Berlin Universities, he became a Rockefeller Fellow at Cambridge where he worked with Max Born in electromagnetic theory, and then a member of the Institute for Advanced Study at Princeton. For eleven years he was Professor of Applied Mathematics at the University of Toronto. He then returned to Poland and became Professor of Physics at the University of Warsaw and until his death on 16 January 1968 he was director of the Theoretical Physics Institute at the University. A member of the presidium of the Polish Academy of Science, Infeld conducted research in theoretical physics, especially relativity and quantum theories. Infeld was the author of The New Field Theory, The World in Modern Science, Quest, Albert Einstein, and with Einstein The Evolution of Physics.

JAMES CLERK MAXWELL

See J. R. Newman's articles in Readers 3 and 4.

ROBERT B. MOORE

Robert B. Moore was born in Windsor, Newfoundland in 1935. He attended McGill University in Canada as an undergraduate, continued for his Ph.D. in physics, and remained there as a professor. He is a nuclear physicist, specializing in nuclear spectroscopy.

Authors and Artists

JAMES ROY NEWMAN

James R. Newman, lawyer and mathematician, was born in New York City in 1907. He received his A.B. from the College of the City of New York and LL.B. from Columbia. Admitted to the New York bar in 1929, he practiced there for twelve years. During World War II he served as chief intelligence officer, U.S. Embassy, London, and in 1945 as special assistant to the Senate Committee on Atomic Energy. From 1956–57 he was senior editor of The New Republic, and since 1948 had been a member of the board of editors for Scientific American where he was responsible for the book review section. At the same time he was a visiting lecturer at the Yale Law School. J.R. Newman is the author of What is Science?, Science and Sensibility, and editor of Common Sense of the Exact Sciences. The World of Mathematics, and the Harper Encyclopedia of Science. He died in 1966.

ELMER L. OFFENBACHER

Elmer L. Offenbacher, born in Germany in 1923, was educated at Brooklyn College and University of Pennsylvania, and is professor of physics at Temple University in Philadelphia. His primary research field is solid state physics.

ERIC MALCOLM ROGERS

Eric Malcolm Rogers, Professor of Physics at Princeton University, was born in Bickley, England, in 1902. He received his education at Cambridge and later was a demonstrator at the Cavendish Laboratory. Since 1963 he has been the organizer in physics for the Nuffield Foundation Science Teaching Project. He is the author of the textbook, Physics for the Inquiring Mind.

RICHARD STEVENSON

Richard Stevenson was born in Windsor, Ontario in 1931. He obtained a degree in mechanical engineering from MIT in 1957, and is now associate professor of physics at McGill University in Canada. He does research on the magnetic properties of solids and high pressure physics.

PETER GUTHRIE TAIT

Peter Guthrie Tait, collaborator of William Thomson (Lord Kelvin) in thermodynamics, was born at Dalkeith, Scotland, in 1831. He was educated at the Academy of Edinburgh (where James Clerk Maxwell was also a student), and at Peterhouse, Cambridge. He remained at Cambridge as a lecturer before becoming Professor of Mathematics at Queen's College, Belfast. There he did research on the density of ozone and the action of the electric discharge of oxygen and other gases. From 1860 until his death in 1901 he served as Professor of Natural Philosophy at Edinburgh. In 1864 he published his first important paper on thermodynamics and thermoelectricity and thermal conductivity. With Lord Kelvin he published the textbook Elements of Natural Philosophy in 1867.

BARON KELVIN, WILLIAM THOMSON

Baron Kelvin, William Thomson, British scientist and inventor, was born in Belfast, Ireland, in 1824. At the age of eleven he entered the University of Glasgow where his father was professor of mathematics. In 1841 he went to Peterhouse, at Cambridge University. In 1848 Thomson proposed a temperature scale independent of the properties of any particular substance, and in 1851 he presented to the Royal Society of Edinburgh a paper reconciling the work on heat of Sadi Carnot with the conclusions of Count von Rumford, Sir Humphrey Davy, J.R. von Mayer and J.P. Joule. In it he stated the Second Law of Thermodynamics. Lord Kelvin worked on such practical applications as the theory of submarine cable telegraphy and invented the mirror galvanometer. In 1866 he was knighted, 1892 raised to peerage, and in 1890 elected president of the Royal Society. He died in 1907.

LEONARDO DA VINCI

Leonardo da Vinci, the exemplor of "l'uomo universale," the Renaissance ideal, was born in 1452 near Vinci in Tuscany, Italy. Without a humanistic education, he was apprenticed at an early age to the painter-sculptor Andrea del Verrocchio. The first 10 years of Leonardo's career were devoted to painting, culminating in the "Adoration of the Magi." Defensive to criticisms on his being "unlettered," Leonardo emphasized his ability as inventor and engineer, becoming a fortification expert for the militarist Cesare Borgia. By 1503 he was working as an artist in almost every field. "Mona Lisa" and "The Last Supper" are among the world's most famous paintings. Besides his engineering feats such as portable bridges, machine guns, tanks, and steam cannons, Leonardo contrived highly imaginative blueprints such as the protoheliocopter and a flying machine. His prolific life terminated in the Castle of Cloux near Amboise on May 2, 1519.

HARVEY ELLIOTT WHITE

Harvey Elliott White, Professor of Physics at the University of California, Berkeley, was born in Parkersburg, West Virginia in 1902. He attended Occidental College and Cornell University where he received his Ph.D. in 1929. In 1929–30 he was an Institute Research Fellow at the Physics and Technology Institute in Germany. His special interests are atomic spectra and ultraviolet and infrared optics.